CONTENTS

DESIGN OF OFFSHORE STRUCTURES

SHIP OPERATIONS

LOADINGS AND STRUCTURES

PAPER NO.1.

WHAT IS ABNORMAL? - DEFINING THE UNDEFINABLE

by J A Crawford, A W Gilfillan and R A Benson, YARD Ltd, UK

Paper presented at the

International Conference

**DESIGN AND OPERATION FOR
ABNORMAL CONDITIONS**

21 22 OCTOBER 1997 GLASGOW

WHAT IS ABNORMAL - DEFINING THE UNDEFINABLE

A W Gilfillan, FRINA, J A Crawford, MRINA and R M Benson, MRINA
YARD Ltd

SUMMARY

Hindsight is a wonderful thing. It provides the basis for changes to rules and regulations, and a measure for defining what is normal and abnormal. However what is abnormal for one design may be the norm for another. How are designers to decide what degree of abnormality needs to be taken into account for a particular design and how can account be taken of a change in operation (area or practice) in later years of the vessels service life ?

The paper discusses these problems from a designer's point of view with respect to the major hazards of flooding, fire, structural failure, collision and grounding and also with respect to environmental issues.

AUTHORS' BIOGRAPHIES

Mr Allan Gilfillan is Ship Projects Director and Chief Naval Architect for YARD Ltd. He has been with the company for twenty-six years having joined them from John Brown & Co., latterly Upper Clyde Shipbuilders. He has been involved in a wide range of projects in the naval, commercial shipping and offshore sectors. He is both a member of the Institution's Council and Chairman of the Safety Committee.

Mr Jim Crawford is Ship Design Manager within the Ship Projects Group of YARD. He has been with the company for thirteen years following the demise of Scott Lithgow under British Shipbuilders. He has been involved in the design of virtually every ship type afloat.

Mr Richard Benson is the Senior Structural Specialist within YARD's Naval Architecture Section. He has been with the company fifteen years after leaving Cammell Laird Shipbuilders. He has been involved in numerous structural design and analysis projects based on both classification society and naval design codes.

1. INTRODUCTION

Hindsight provides the basis for changes to rules and regulations, and a measure for defining what is normal and abnormal. As time progresses rules and regulations change to reflect the accumulated knowledge within the domain; the domain knowledge and practices at the end of a ships life are quite different from those when the ship was originally designed. What is considered unsafe now was accepted practice a number of years ago. Typical examples in recent experience include fire safety and Ro-Ro stability.

The improvement in a standard of safety over time is generally a stepped function as shown in Fig. 1. At the time the ship was designed, the pertaining standard would normally be achieved with a margin to take into account known changes to be implemented during the build period. In the example shown in Fig. 1, the standard is improved in stages until in the present situation the vessel fails to meet the revised standard

and some modification is required to bring it into compliance. It is also anticipated that further enhancements might be introduced at some later date, shown dotted. The dilemma for the naval architect at the design stage is to decide what prudent margin should be allowed in the design, and the same dilemma applies to the owner in deciding what changes need to be done to bring the vessel up to a current standard. The Authors' 1991 paper (Ref. 1) discussed this dilemma and advocated the introduction of the safety case concept into the shipping industry. The purpose of this paper is to see whether the way ahead is any clearer now than it was in 1991.

2. THE APPROACH TO SAFETY

In the intervening years the Safety Case concept has been discussed within the marine industry and is being investigated by IMO and MSA as a means of evaluating the efficacy of new legislation. The UK Ministry of Defence has adopted the concept for all new ships as defined in JSP430 (Ref. 2) and the authors' company has been instrumental in delivering the first new ship - HMS SCOTT - to the Royal Navy to the new safety standard (Ref. 3). The principles used in evaluating hazards provide the naval architect with a logical method to decide the extent to which a particular standard of safety should be exceeded, and the boundary between normal and abnormal loads.

In the Safety Case approach, hazards are assessed on the basis of the severity of their consequence and the predicted frequency of occurrence. Fig. 2 illustrates the approach. Clearly there is an envelope of severity and probability covered by Classification Rules and IMO and MSA Regulations. There are then those events which although serious in consequence are sufficiently rare or unusual to be beyond the reasonable scope of responsibility of the designer, for example, the loss of the trawler ANTARES after getting its nets caught on the submarine HMS TRENCHANT (Ref. 4). There is then a middle ground for which the designer has a responsibility to ensure that there is an adequate margin of safety over the "rule minimum".

There has been a steady growth of new regulations over recent years and improved enforcement, certainly within Europe. Following the HERALD OF FREE ENTERPRISE and ESTONIA disasters, major new regulations covering the safety of Ro-Ro ships have been introduced at an unprecedented speed in response to public demand for action. It remains to be seen how robust this legislation will prove in practice with owners and builders seeking flexibility in interpretation within the principles enshrined in the regulations. The marine industry has in the past been master at developing designs which explore loopholes in badly worded rules and legislators need to be alert to this danger especially in rules introduced quickly.

Another problem facing designers with the introduction of new legislation is different interpretation amongst the various bodies responsible for its implementation or, more often, inadequate guidance given to local surveyors about what is and is not allowed. This is a particular problem where new legislation is applied retrospectively to a partially completed newbuilding and can result in delay and dislocation not only to the subject vessel but to the whole shipbuilding programme.

There is no doubt that human factors contribute significantly to accidents, but in many cases the human error triggers a combination of factors which have been incubating for several years. Some of these factors are built in at the design stage and others during construction through the use of wrong materials, or inadequate dimensional control. The designer has therefore to look forward and build in as many failsafe features into his design as possible as well as making it production kindly. One approach is to consult operators and maintainers in informal discussion or more formally through Hazops. References 3 and 5 describe this later approach as applied to HMS SCOTT and STENA EXPLORER respectively.

All rules and regulations produced by classification societies and regulatory bodies are based on a set of loading assumptions, determined by factors such as sea state, wind force, maximum hydrostatic or hydro-dynamic load, extent of flooding, intensity of fire, and even the physical fitness of crew and passengers. In several instances the thinking behind new legislation is described in papers to RINA and other learned societies and conferences. It would be sensible for new legislation to refer to these papers as they provide background information for defining what the legislators believe to be a normal load. A loading regime beyond this is abnormal and an appropriate health warning is needed to highlight to the designer his responsibility to investigate the means of dealing with abnormal loads. The phrase "will be specially considered" is used by rule makers as a let out and needs better definition of "when, by whom and on the basis of what information".

Thus in regulatory terms, abnormal loads are those in excess of what has been assumed in developing the legislation. But how abnormal are they in practice, and what can the naval architect and marine engineer do to take some account of abnormal loads in their design, particularly when the boundary between normal and abnormal is so ill defined in many instances?

3.   STABILITY

The rules covering intact and damage stability have been enhanced steadily over the years to handle abnormal loads, most recently to introduce tighter regulations for Ro-Ro ferries.

3.1   INTACT STABILITY

The abnormal loads affecting stability include wind, ice and loose water, whether from flooding, fire-fighting or free surface effects in tanks. The recently introduced Code for High Speed Vessels introduces a concept of linking stability and life saving appliances with the time taken to get assistance to the vessel in the event of an accident. A logical extension of this principle must be the need for enhanced standards for vessels operating in remote sea areas.

The authors' company was involved in the design of the *Thetis* class of Fishery Protection Vessels for Greenland in which enhanced stability was required to allow for the wind loading arising from catabatic winds of 150 knots, which are regularly encountered in the Greenland fjords (Ref. 6).

The other abnormal load encountered in the higher latitudes is ice accretion, and this is a particular problem for small boats such as trawlers where the added weight of ice can build up to significant proportion of displacement. Since the northern fishing grounds have become closed to the British fishing fleet, this problem is seen less in the UK, but cannot be ignored for any vessel designed to operate in cold climates. In the case of the *Thetis* class the vessel was designed with closed in mooring decks fore and aft to eliminate ice accretion on deck fittings and with trace heating on plane surfaces such as decks, superstructure and masts.

One other abnormal load over which the designer has no control is overloading and or movement of cargo or, more tragically in a number of well publicised recent accidents, of passengers on ferries.

Free surface effects can arise from abnormal loads such as accumulated fire-fighting water or from inherent design features such as cross-flooding devices or very wide tanks on oil tankers. To illustrate the last point, YARD were called in by the owner of a double skin tanker which during manoeuvring trials had taken up an angle of loll, which could only be corrected by turning in the opposite direction. It transpired that the owners had wished the trial to be carried out at the ship's load draft, and the trials condition included two slack cargo holds, virtually the full breadth of the ship. Further investigation found that two sets of loading conditions had been submitted to the classification society, one to demonstrate adequate stability and the other showing

2

satisfactory longitudinal strength. Moreover damage stability was given too much emphasis at the expense of intact stability, which ignored some very basic principles. Unfortunately the intact stability and longitudinal strength conditions were mutually incompatible and this had been missed as each book had been approved by different departments within the classification society. The reasons are historical, but logic dictates that some form of unified approval is desirable and indeed class rules do now allow for this. It is still the case, however, that for UK registered ships, that MSA approve stability but not longitudinal strength.

3.2 COLLISION, GROUNDING AND DAMAGE STABILITY

Abnormal loads arising from collision and grounding result in internal flooding and/or local deformation of structure and loss of strength and occasionally catastrophic failure of the hull girder, as well as flooding of compartments and loss of stability. The rules covering stability and subdivision have been enhanced in recent years to reflect concerns over safety and environmental pollution.

For Ro-Ro ferries, water on the vehicle deck was seen as an abnormal load until the current rules arising out of the Stockholm Agreement required designers to take account of a depth of water on the vehicle deck proportional to freeboard and to the significant wave height encountered in the area of operation. This, and the virtual elimination of the single compartment standard of subdivision are a great step forward, but there remain inconsistencies in the rule requirements. Other recent legislation introduced damage stability requirements for cargo ships over 100 metres and for oil tankers, with the latter being linked to environmental limitations on cargo outflow.

Damage stability calculations are undertaken to demonstrate compliance with the rules. The calculation seeks to determine the equilibrium between total weight and buoyancy in the damaged condition, and the resulting drafts and residual stability are calculated and assessed against established acceptance criteria. The effect of wind and waves are assumed to be taken account of in the margins subsumed in the criteria. The calculations are usually not taken beyond those required to demonstrate compliance with the regulations.

For passenger ships there is be good reason to take the calculations further to define the limiting conditions under which evacuation can take place. This point was made by Hackett and Bedford in their excellent paper on the SS TITANIC (Ref. 7) which confirmed the original hand calculations were at least as comprehensive and accurate as today's methods using computers - our conclusion is that naval architects have yet to take advantage of the power of the computer to explore the boundaries of survivability.

The probability of a vessel surviving a collision is dependent on the location and extent of the damage.

Analysis has been carried out on the distribution of location and extent of damage and embodied into alternative probabilistic approaches to damage stability regulations. The original IMO resolution A265 was years ahead of its time in its demands on computing power, but the logic of the probabilistic method cannot be refuted and its wider adoption is to be welcomed.

As stated above, flooding after a collision or grounding results in abnormal loads on both primary and local structure, but there is no requirement to calculate longitudinal strength in the damaged condition, no doubt due to the same historical split of responsibility as for intact conditions. There is no reason why longitudinal strength calculations cannot be carried out for damaged conditions, initially based on no reduction in the hull girder modulus. It should then be possible to calculate the remaining margin of safety on the hull for the most likely damage scenarios and then consider whether additional material should be introduced to increase survivability.

Flooding can lead to internal structure such as bulkheads being subjected to higher hydrostatic heads than they are traditionally designed to withstand. The recent IACS requirement to strengthen transverse watertight bulkheads of bulk carriers to withstand hydrostatic loads comes some 30 years after the introduction of the B-60 and B-100 freeboard, in which increased draught is assigned to vessels able to withstand one and two compartment flooding respectively. This delay illustrates the continuing trend of regulatory authorities and classification societies to be out of step in the development of rules and regulations.

Grounding imposes severe stresses on the hull girder especially if it occurs at significant speed, leading in some cases to buckling of the hull girder. The author's company was involved in an investigation into a tanker which had driven over an uncharted ridge in the Galveston River resulting in the hull buckling. It was alleged that the loads on the hull were less that those resulting from the worst wave which the vessel could be expected to meet in its service life, and the shipbuilder was being sued for supplying a vessel that was not "fit for purpose". We were able to show that the loads imposed were abnormal and so that part of the case against the shipbuilder failed.

Grounding is generally caused by poor seamanship or inaccurate charts, or more often as a consequence of a mechanical breakdown, and it is unreasonable to expect designers to take full account of grounding loads as part of his normal structural design process.

4. STRUCTURAL FAILURE

The need to consider abnormal loads might be thought to be limited to innovative types of vessels or an unusual service. Our experience is that most ships of whatever type experience abnormal loads and some extensions beyond the rule baseline needs to be considered. It is also our experience that irregular inspection, poor maintenance and poor structural detailing are the main causes of structural failure.

The design of bulk carriers can, with the benefit of hindsight, be used as an example in order to draw lessons for the future design process. The structural problems suffered by bulk carriers have been well documented in recent years (Ref. 8, for example). These have resulted in the loss of vessels and in loss of life and have precipitated changes to the Classification Society rules in a number of areas.

It has been found that the side shell structure in the holds of bulk carriers can suffer failure, in some cases leading to the loss of the ship. The reason for these failures is the weakening of the frames and lower brackets due to corrosion and mechanical damage. Corrosion may be partly due to neglect, but can also be exacerbated by chemical action from the type of cargo carried. The loss of thickness is also irregular with possible "grooving" of lower brackets producing lines of weakness. This local increase in stress leads to further corrosion and thickness loss. Mechanical damage from the use of diggers, or other cargo handling equipment in the hold itself, further reduces side frame strength.

There are problems in identifying these effects since general corrosion loss can only be verified by measurement and, in any case, the sheer impracticability of gaining access to the structure and the extent of it make regular inspection impossible.

On a global strength level it has been found that the loading rates at bulk cargo terminals can be so high as to pose a potential longitudinal strength problem for the bulk carrier. Indeed the loading rates are so high that it is possible to overload a hold before any action can be taken. The crew may not be aware in any case of the potential seriousness of this effect.

As mentioned previously, there is no requirement for longitudinal strength calculations for the vessel with a flooded hold and the strength of transverse bulkheads in such conditions may not sufficient. It can be seen therefore that a relatively minor failure of the side shell can lead to loss of the ship. The lessons for the designer, therefore, are that he should have a knowledge of:

- **Operation:**

    How the ships are to be operated in practice.

    How they are loaded.

    Time constraints on crew.

- **Cargoes:**

    Physical and chemical composition.

    Methods of handling.

    Behaviour when loaded in hold.

- **Materials:**

    Corrosion.

    Strength.

- **Survey:**

    Inspection methods.

    Scope.

The wide ranging nature of the subjects listed above require either a "designer superman" or a different approach using risk based procedures. Although these aspects may affect the structural design of the vessel in terms of requiring increased scantlings or different structural arrangements, most are not within the usual scope of knowledge of the structural designer.

Ideally, therefore, a review process is required which includes contributions from the various disciplines discussed above, providing a traceable record of what the designer had assumed. This could take the form of a Hazop procedure but needs to take place early in the design process.

The deficiencies in bulk carrier design have been addressed by changes to classification society rules but, inevitably this takes place after the problems have arisen and after the time necessary to investigate and solve them.

It is noticeable that several aspects affecting the structural design are "indefinable" in structural terms. That is, they cannot be expressed as a higher design load or as a reduction in strength. Factors such as extreme waves have also to be addressed and require a joint effort by hydro-dynamicists, structural designers and operators. The operational aspects may be indefinable in structural terms but are foreseeable with input from the right sources. The trick, as always, is knowing the right question to ask.

The magnitude of a load is implicitly associated with a probability of occurrence. This probability is known for the primary loading of longitudinal bending due to waves, but is not generally stated for other local loading on the hull structure. Loading is often buried within the rule formulae. As part of the general approach to overall design for safety, it would be desirable for the classification societies to give information on the derivation of loading and its associated probability of occurrence, or even to define the conditions beyond which the formulae should not be used.

A hindsight review of bulk carriers provides a good example of the problem facing the designer in evaluating abnormal loads for ships in general. The approach discussed is applicable to most types of ship.

5.   FIRE

Over the last few years, much attention has been given to the means of preventing, detecting and extinguishing fires on board ships. It appears that older vessels and vessels carrying hazardous cargoes are those at most risk from a fire at sea, and that human error or poor maintenance are generally more to blame than inherent design faults.

Fire itself is an abnormal load on the ship, but in reality there is not a lot that the designer can do other than minimise the likelihood of a fire starting by following procedures which are well documented and regulated. These include the choice of fire retarding and low smoke materials, the isolation of fuel pipes from hot spots, the incorporation of addressable alarm systems, and the installation of appropriate extinguishing systems to deal with each potential hazard, including possibly duplicate systems provided they are compatible. It is, however, still the case that too much PVC based material remains in regular use in commercial shipbuilding.

6.   EVACUATION

A major fire or ingress of water into the hull can lead to the need to abandon ship and special attention is required to be given to the evacuation and lifesaving appliances for passenger ships in particular. Whilst the movement of large numbers of people can result in abnormal loads, the real problem is the means of evacuating people safely. Large numbers of people under stress have to find their way up perhaps 7 or 8 deck levels through a limited number of exits. The parallels with other forms of evacuation indicate that lives are frequently lost due to confusion despite signs and despite the relative simplicity of evacuation from hotels - generally downwards and aircraft - generally horizontally. The location of ship's lifesaving equipment and evacuation is generally at a single high level and dependent on people applying procedures that, with little practical or realistic exercise of them, will result in a uniform distribution of evacuees in a way that will ensure all leave such a vessel safely. Improved evacuation is perhaps the greatest challenge facing today's designers.

7.   ENVIRONMENTAL ISSUES

The growing awareness of environmental issues presents the designer with the greatest challenge in forecasting what features should be introduced to provide adequate environmental protection throughout the ship's life. The abnormal environmental loads on the ship have been described earlier, but the growing concern is for the abnormal loads imposed by mankind and all his devices, including ships, on the environment.

Much has happened over the last few years to address the problem, for example the introduction of double hull tanker, crude oil washing and other means of reducing pollution of the oceans. Over the last 20 years, operational oil pollution has fallen by 85% and accidental oil pollution has fallen by 50%. Intertanko, from whose brochure the above figures were quoted, aims to eliminate operational pollution and substantially reduce accidental pollution over the next 20 years. To put the problem into perspective, shipping only accounts for about 11% of the pollution of the sea.

Attention has now turned to cutting atmospheric pollution, with the introduction of the Montreal Protocol banning CFCs including Halon, which was a popular fire extinguisher and safer to use than CO_2. Thus the means of dealing with one abnormal load - fire - is itself seen to be an abnormal load on the atmosphere. Attention is now focused on reducing Nitrous and Sulphur content from machinery exhausts, and the designer has to decide whether to allow space in the uptakes for catalytic converters. The Navy has already taken the decision to do so and new designs are required to have both the space for the future fit of equipment and the space for the storage and mixing of urea. Further guidance is required from the engine manufacturers on whether a bypass or in line arrangement is required. The authors view is that a change in regulations is likely and it is easier to allow space early rather than to be faced with a space demanding retrofit at a later stage.

The designer and manufacturer also has a duty to give clear instructions on how the ship and its equipment is to be operated to avoid abnormal pollution of the sea and the atmosphere.

8.   DISCUSSION

In this age of IT when there seems to be a computerised tool available for every facet of engineering design it is tempting to leap to the conclusion that nothing is beyond the range of investigation and confirmation. If failures occur the fault is assumed to lie with economic and practical constraints placed on the designer or the operator/maintainer. These attitudes have been accorded a dangerous respectability through the ALARP (As Low As Reasonably Practicable) principle that is a crucial part of the Safety Case approach to minimising risk. Used wisely, ALARP actually allows experience and judgement to temper analysis in a recorded process.

It is certainly true that if a history of the naval architects' craft was part of the students' curriculum it would be apparent that many major accidents reflect, in some degree, a failure of the imagination; a failure that is either embedded in the rules that regulate the craft or in how they are interpreted by regulators, designers and operators. It would be equally apparent that in every age the risks we run, the value we place on life and on our environment are driven more by the social and economic mores of the time and place than by the technical limits that available knowledge and materials apply.

We have accorded ourselves a self satisfied measure of praise that each winter gale no longer costs dozens or hundreds of lives around our coastline and that ships in our deep sea trades are no longer routinely posted as missing. The infrequent loss of a SPIRIT OF FREE ENTERPRISE or a DERBYSHIRE only shakes our complacency for a time whose duration is directly related to the amount of continuing interest it arouses in newspapers or TV. We take little interest in the loss of fishermen in a Bay of Bengal storm or of an overcrowded ferry in the Far East or South America in collision with an undermanned cargo ship except to regret that the reach of MSA does not extend to these distant nations. Despite such setbacks we applaud each incremental approach to design and regulation that provides a level of safety denied to earlier generations. We consider ourselves as resident in the best of all possible worlds where so long as we maintain the standards achieved to date, with occasional tweaks to take account of developments, then all will be more or less well.

Critics will doubtless attack the foregoing comments as simplistic and inaccurate, citing the continuing efforts of governments and authorities to maintain and advance safety standards. We have one simple question that requires an answer from any who suppose that the best that can be done is being done - Are the new Ro-Ro stability rules sufficiently robust to prevent another HERALD OF FREE ENTERPRISE or ESTONIA disaster? - only time will tell.

If, as already suggested, the training of naval architects included a technical rather than a romantic history of the ship, it would be apparent that the past 50 years have seen advances in ship technology which exceed those in any earlier time, not excluding the evolution of the rudder and the replacement of wind power by mechanical power. Despite the ubiquity of air travel there are more passengers at sea now, in ferries and cruise liners, than at any other time in history. There are vastly greater quantities of raw materials and products, much of it toxic or hazardous, being transported by sea than at the height of the UK's industrial strength. The materials of which ships are constructed and the means by which they are propelled, once relatively benign to the environment if hard on their crews, now range between mild and appalling in their potential hazards to health and life.

Critics of this pessimism might concede that frightening risks have been taken since the last war, but as problems have been identified then action has been taken to bring them under control. The essential difficulty from a designer's point of view is that action has been almost always reactive and in some cases the solutions are no longer capable of containing the problem. Pandora's box can be closed but its contents cannot be restored. The corroding hulks in the Kola Inlet cannot have their radioactivity neutralised; the industrial

economies of the world cannot be sustained unless millions of tonnes of crude oils and chemicals are transported daily through crowded shipping lanes in ships of which the more unscrupulous owners seek to avoid the cost of maintaining skilled crews and basic safety standards.

The pressures faced by the designer to navigate between the Scylla of client intent and the Charybdis of regulatory tolerance are acute enough when standard ship types are being aligned to current regulations. They increase significantly when familiar ship types are stretched to the limits of current technology or regulatory provision. Pressures can become over-whelming when novel types are proposed as a means of filling a market niche or of evading some restriction in regulations.

As ever, it is easier to identify problems than to offer solutions. In an ideal world solutions would come from a combination of governments, regulatory bodies, owners, shipbuilders and workers acting co-operatively and altruistically to achieve and apply standards directed at the greater good of all, irrespective of commercial considerations. In practice these elements have never behaved in such an ideal manner, either collectively or individually. There have only been varying degrees of adherence to these aims. UK governments and the MSA might consider that they have behaved better than most but they have been guilty of delay and evasion too often such that many IMO resolutions have languished without ratification for longer periods than necessary lest some other nation might take commercial advantage.

Owners and shipbuilders might argue that getting out of step with their competitors puts their viability and the jobs of their workers at risk. Government action to restrict the access of unsatisfactory traders to UK ports and facilities or sanctions against governments that permit unfair competition could redress some of this imbalance. It might be thought that the workers are the most disadvantaged element here and while this is generally true, there have been too many instances of workers tolerating or co-operating in unsafe practices, provided the monetary compensation was high enough.

The true safeguard for standards is genuine independence for IMO and MSA from government interference but it is unlikely that this will ever be fully achieved. At the designer level, support is required for an independent Safety Case. The weakness of the Safety Case, aside from the mistaken assumption that the ALARP principle can guarantee an objective approach to standards, is that it can only be created effectively by those who are as close to the content and detail of the design as the designers. Its strength is that it encourages a broad view of the risks that might occur in service using common sense and experience to complement analysis. The designer is not, however, the most appropriate person to create an independent Safety Case; a competent designer will take account of safety features but it is difficult for him to avoid bias towards identified solutions.

9. CONCLUSIONS

The discussion of what is and is not an abnormal load has inevitably drawn us into consideration of what and who defines the boundary in legislative terms, as much as a review of the designers' own professional responsibilities. The following broad conclusions can be reached.

1) The boundary between abnormal and normal is blurred and not easily defined.

2) Part of this blurring is due to inadequate co-ordination between those responsible for international regulations and classification rules. A fundamental realignment is required to converge the interests of the insurance industry and inter-national governments. Both are interested in the safe and efficient movement of ships, and

3) As consequence of 1 and 2 above, the designer cannot rely on rules and regulations to define what is normal and what is not. He must use his own professional judgement to decide what is appropriate for each circumstance, and then record his decision with the reasons.

4) In making his decision the designer must have a full understanding not only of the technical possibilities, but how and where the ship is to operate and how it is to be maintained. A traceable record of all such decisions and the reasoning behind them should be established.

5) The authors' own experience is that this can best be brought together in a formalised method which evaluates the risks and the means of mitigation. The Hazop process is one means of achieving this within a Safety Management Regime and has been found to flush out issues which had been overlooked by the designer and could have caused problems in service.

6) The work of IMO and MSA in developing regula-tions using a safety assessment approach is to be welcomed, but it is only a start. A formalised Safety Management approach offers a good means of managing abnormal loads and conditions and human factors throughout the life of the ship.

ACKNOWLEDGEMENTS

The authors are grateful to their employers YARD for permission to publish this paper, and to their colleagues for assistance in its preparation. The authors take full responsibilities for the views expressed.

REFERENCES

1. CRAWFORD J A, GILFILLAN A W, MACKIE G C: 'The Designer's Dilemma', International Conference on Ro-Ro Safety and Vulnerability, the Way Ahead, RINA, London, April 1991

2. 'JSP 430 Ship Safety management Handbook Volume 1 Issue 1 Policy and Guidance on MOD Ship and Equipment Safety Management', Ministry of Defence 1996

3. LAMB I D, RUDGELY G: 'A Risk Based Approach to Safety', Marine Risk Assessment - A better way to manage your business, IMARE April 1997

4. 'Report of the Chief Inspector of Marine Accidents into the collision between the Fishing Vessel ANTARES and HMS TRENCHANT with the loss of four lives on 22nd November 1990' , HMSO(MAIB) ISBN) 0-11-551128-8, 1992

5. KUO C, PRYKE N, SODAHL B, HOUISON CRAUFURD S: 'A safety Case for Stena Lines's High Speed Ferry HSS1500', RINA Spring Meeting April 1991

6. WATSON D G M & FRIIS A M: 'A new Danish Fishery Inspection Ship Type', Trans RINA 1991'

7. HACKETT C & BEDFORD J G: 'The Sinking of SS Titanic - Investigation by Modern Techniques', Joint Meeting between RINA and IESS December 1996.

8. FERGUSON J M: 'Safety of Bulk Carriers', Trans IESS 1992.

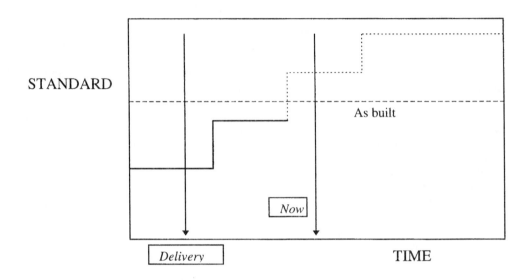

Fig. 1 The staged improvement in standards

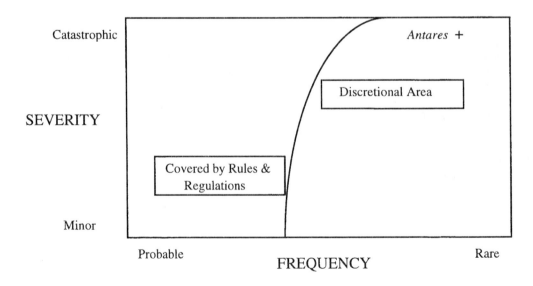

Fig. 2 The Safety Case Approach

8

PAPER NO.2.

RAPID FAILURE, RAPID SINKING

by D Brown
Independent Consultant Naval Architect, Gourock, UK

Paper presented at the

International Conference

**DESIGN AND OPERATION FOR
ABNORMAL CONDITIONS**

21 22 OCTOBER 1997 GLASGOW

RAPID FAILURE, RAPID SINKING

Douglas Brown
Independent Consultant Naval Architect, Gourock, UK

SUMMARY

The aim of this paper is principally to focus on the many instances of structural failure which have occurred on ships at sea in the latter years of this century. Analysis and comment on a number of these incidents is offered.

The procedures for loading and discharging in port are commented on, as these have been found to expose the ship's structure, both overall and locally, to stresses which are often at a level much above those envisaged by the ship's designers.

Among the conclusions reached is that further research is needed into the strength of hatches in bulk carriers and their protection from heavy seas, as well as the freeboard presently assigned to this type of ship. Comment is also made on the strength of ship structure at sea, including transverse bulkheads in bulk carriers and shell plating in large ships, particularly those with single side shells.

AUTHOR'S BIOGRAPHY

Douglas Brown is a qualified naval architect whose early experience was gained in shipbuilding. He has recently completed 20 years as lecturer in ship stability and construction within the Faculty of Maritime Studies at Glasgow College of Nautical Studies. During this time he has had wide experience of offering courses leading to a BSc and a Higher Diploma in Maritime Studies, as well as to Deck Officers taking courses at all levels up to Extra Master qualifications, including those for Masters, Chief Officers and Command Endorsements.

He is now an independent Consultant Naval Architect and has recently been involved in work on the loading, discharging and dry-docking of FPSO (Floating Production Storage and Offloading) vessels.

Additionally he has been appointed retained Consultant Naval Architect to a leading firm of UK ship managers. He has also been invited to take part as a visiting lecturer in the delivery of postgraduate courses in Ship Construction at the University of Strathclyde.

1. INTRODUCTION

The author intends to establish the two themes included in the title to this paper by looking, first, at the theme "rapid failure" illustrated by two examples in which a ship's hull has failed rapidly, followed by a further two cases to illustrate the second theme of "rapid sinking".

The author takes the view that a ship's hull is exposed to abnormal conditions both when at sea (e.g., episodic waves leading to higher than normal values of stress) and in harbour (e.g., extremes of bending stresses and shearing stresses, due to unanticipated sequences of loading or discharging cargo).

1.1 RAPID FAILURE

1.1.1   In May 1981, off South East Africa, while on passage from the Arabian Gulf, the large loaded oil tanker M.V. ENERGY ENDURANCE, 205,807t dwt, lost her forward ballast tank, just aft of the collision bulkhead. The complete bottom and side shell plating port and starboard, together with internal stiffening and securing brackets, simply dropped out of the ship. (Presumably those on board, some 220m further aft, learned of the event when attempting to take a tank sounding - with a record breaking result - many tens of fathoms because the tank simply was not there!)

Fig. 1   M.V. ENERGY ENDURANCE

The damage suggests that there was insufficient strength aft of the collision bulkhead, although there may well have been great strength <u>forward</u> of the collision bulkhead

It is a long established fact that the well subdivided hull of a tanker, even when loaded, is able to survive the loss of a single tank, in this case a ballast tank, and remain afloat.

The ship reached port for repairs in Cape Town, where the 110,000t cargo of crude oil was discharged. As South Africa was experiencing an oil embargo at that time it is likely that it came in very useful.

1.1.2   In November 1994, M.V. TRADE DARING, a 134,999t dwt bulk carrier, was loading ore at Ponta da Madeira, Brazil.   Suddenly, and without warning of previous deformation, the ship cracked right across in way of No.2 hold and settled on the bottom at the loading berth.

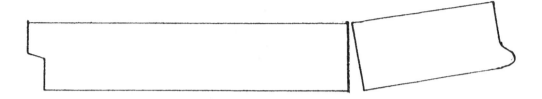

Fig.2 M.V. TRADE DARING

It is understood that the consequent effects caused by the seriously damaged ship occupying the loading berth for some months caused a major economic effect on Brazil's ore industry. The ship was eventually raised and towed clear of the berth to allow other vessels to load.

It should be specially noted that each of the above ships was in isolation, and that no other ship was involved in the incident.

1.2   RAPID SINKING

1.2.1   In September 1990, shortly after she had departed from loading a cargo of ore at Tubarao in South America, it was discovered that the bulk carrier M.V. GALLANT DRAGON 123,126t dwt, was suffering ingress of water.

The vessel returned immediately to a sheltered anchorage where pumps were maintained at full capacity and just managed to keep up with the inflow of water. The ship was kept afloat for some time in this way but eventually a decision was taken not to attempt a repair but to tow the ship to sea and allow her to sink.

When the pumps were stopped, the ship, loaded with ore, disappeared below the surface of the sea in seconds. Observers at the scene were astonished at the short space of time it took to sink.

1.2.2   On 22nd June 1995 a collision occurred in thick fog in the East China Sea between Korea and Japan in which the bow of a 151,023t dry cargo vessel impacted on the side of the loaded bulk carrier M.V. MINERAL DAMPIER, 170,698t dwt.

The Belgian owned MINERAL DAMPIER (built 1985) sank so rapidly that none of the crew, neither those who were asleep at the time or those who were awake and on duty, were rescued. All 27 men on board lost their lives, as the ship sank rapidly. There was no time for a distress message to be sent.

It is very sad to record that incidents similar to the above are all too common in the 1990's, and have occurred with a frequency in the latter years of this century which is, in the opinion of this author, quite unacceptable in terms of the losses of men's and women's lives.

It is hoped, in the discussion which follows, to contribute to the analysis of why these failures happen, and to comment on possible remedies.

2.   DISCUSSION

The discussion which follows has six headings:

2.1   Are we designing correctly at the initial design stage for all that may happen to the structure of a ship during her life? [1]

2.2   Are the reviewing arrangements for structural deterioration during a ship's life adequate?

By reviewing arrangements is meant annual and periodic surveys, both those concerned with load line and with classification.

2.3   Are the requirements for freeboard and protection of water ingress appropriate in the light of the industry's experience in the last 30 years of large ships, both dry cargo and oil carrying vessels.

2.4   Are the personnel who are currently involved in decision making being given adequate training?

2.5   Can a ship which experiences temporary machinery failure be given an immediate auxiliary source of power and/or steering?

2.6   Can the Safety Case Concept be of assistance in ship operation where these operations might otherwise lead to rapid failure and sinking?

The comments which now follow are ordered in the following way: Heading 2.1 is discussed in paragraph 3.1, etc.

3. RELEVANT COMMENT AND FURTHER INCIDENTS

3.10   In most of the ships built during, say, the 1970's and now featuring in the title to this paper, the longitudinal strength at sea was investigated <u>only in a vertical plane</u>, with the ship being supported on an assumed 'worst' wave, of length equal to the ship's length. It is suggested that this scenario was (and is) far too simplistic and that the stresses to which the hull is subjected are much more complex and require far more thorough investigation. Recent advances should, it is hoped, go some way to remedying this severe lack of knowledge [2].   The use of stress monitoring equipment, fitted as a standard, specified item of ship's equipment and regularly monitored, is to be welcomed.

3.11   It is questionable whether loading and discharging practices are adequately taken into account when a ship is designed.

One occasion on which a ship's girder was subjected to abnormal loading in port (due, in this incident, to human decisions and error) was when the tanker M.V. ENERGY CONCENTRATION (215,675 dwt) was discharging at Europoort in July 1980 and a sharp report was heard. The ship had cracked due to the end tanks being kept full while tanks near to midships were emptied. The ship settled on the bottom of the berth with her stern on the bottom, the midship part rose up while the forefoot also sank to the bottom.

Fig.3 M.V. ENERGY CONCENTRATION

Fortunately there was, almost miraculously considering the hazards present, no explosion and the 43 crew were able to leave the ship safely. The loading manual carried on board had not been adequately consulted by the officers responsible.

The captain and chief officer subsequently faced charges in court. The ship herself had the remainder of her cargo carefully and safely discharged. Each end of the ship was subsequently towed away for scrapping, the forepart in Yugoslavia, the afterpart later in Spain.

The similarity to the Trade Daring incident (a dry bulk carrier) in 1.11 above is obvious.

Many ships require most careful attention to longitudinal bending and shearing stresses while loading and discharging. Safe values can easily be exceeded by lack of attention to the guidance given in the loading manual [3].

3.12   It is common practice at the end of bulk carrier discharge to lower a small bulldozer into the hold to assist in the final stages of discharge. One task that the bulldozer is often given is to use a metal prong to clear accumulated cargo debris from the side frames and connecting brackets. This repeated impact stress on internal steelwork is clearly very damaging yet is not taken into account at the design stage [4].

A further example of internal damage occurs when the discharge grab itself is swung against the inside of the hold frames and inner surface of the shell plating to release, often successfully, the last remnants of cargo.

As this grab often weighs many tonnes, the subsequent damage can be imagined.

The ship is simply not designed to take this type of abnormal local loading. The strength of the steelwork in subsequent voyages must be weakened by this practice.

3.20   A question which must be raised is that of the time devoted to annual inspections for the renewal of load line and classification. The historical background is that the surveyor is present annually to check if there have been any changes which would affect the conditions of assignment of freeboard, or of structural strength. In many cases this, in the small ships of 100 years ago (indeed, even of 50 years ago) was visualised as taking a day or less.

What has happened at the present time is that the surveyor is faced with the daunting task of surveying many square metres of steelwork, often at a considerable distance from the surveyor himself. While recent improvements (e.g. by using surveying technicians skilled in abseiling techniques) have taken place, this observer wonders whether a greater allocation of time might be considered.

3.21   As high tensile steel became readily available in the 1970's, designers found it appropriate to use it in certain parts of large ships. It offered, because of its reduced thickness for the same strength, a reduction in weight which could be applied to increase the deadweight able to be carried by a given design.

Thus it was attractive to a ship's first owners, i.e., those for whom she was designed and built.

It was used in many parts of a ship, including the sheer strake and side shell plating. It is here, of course, in a tanker or bulk carrier that the inner surface of the plating is exposed to contact with cargoes which may often have corrosive properties.

In older ships, corrosion margins were often adequate for many years of service (e.g., to second or third ownership). In the ships fitted with high tensile steel the corrosion margin has often been found to be inadequate. Current designers are looking much more closely before fitting high tensile steel to shell plating. There still exists, however, the problem that many existing members of the world's fleet suffer corrosion of those thinner plates.

3.22   The author has heard it said, during a friendly debate on what constituted an older bulk carrier (see 3.21 above), that an old ship was one which had completed her first loaded voyage. While this is clearly an exaggeration, a ship carrying highly corrosive cargoes, like coal, can age very quickly indeed.

3.23   When preparing this paper, it was found by the author that there were very many cases of both bulk carriers and tankers from which, in the last few years, a section of side shell plating has simply fallen off whilst the ship was at sea. This has occurred in way of No.1 hold, at or near to midships and also further aft. There are many examples to choose from; the one selected is M.V. PACIFICOS, an oil tanker of 268,000t dwt which was on passage off Durban in October 1989. The shell plating of this VLCC's port side midships ballast tank fell off, leaving a hole some 15m long by 8m high.

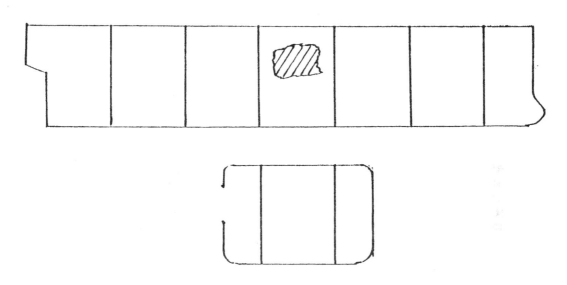

Fig. 4 VLCC PACIFICOS

Shell Plating Failure. The shell plating fell off at sea

The PACIFICOS was able to move under her own power into the Mozambique Channel where calmer seas allowed a ship-to-ship transfer of the full cargo of crude oil, which was bound for Brazil.

Men equipped with abseil-type ropes and harnesses were employed to drill holes at the ends of cracks to prevent propagation of the cracks upwards to the sheer strake and across the deck. The ship was able to reach Durban for temporary repairs, where, despite a safety and construction certificate having been issued only five months previously, it was found that the corresponding ballast tank on the opposite (starboard) side was also in poor condition and required immediate attention. Permanent repairs were undertaken later in Dubai.

3.24   The above is only one example of many such incidents in the author's records. A large proportion of those incidents have taken place in the last twenty years [5].

One other that comes to mind readily is from February 1990 when M.V. TRIBULUS, a bulk carrier loaded with ore, was bound for Rotterdam from Canada. The vessel had to divert because of heavy weather to the south of Ireland, where it was found that a 30 square metre section of shell plating had fallen off in way of No.8 hold.

3.25   One of the most striking examples of the shell plating falling off is M.V. San Marco which arrived in port (in this case Cape Town) with both port and starboard sections of shell plating having fallen off. It was possible for photographs to be taken, not merely showing Cape Town's seafront from within No.1 hold, but from a camera on the quayside looking right through No.1 hold and out the far side [3].

Clearly something is wrong with current design, survey and maintenance practices if this can happen, and not just in isolated instances.

3.26   It is worthwhile noting the frequency of occurrence of damage to shell plating which occurs whilst a loaded vessel is on passage southward off south east Africa. It has been regularly reported that large British - registered oil tankers on voyages in this

part of the world suffer damage to the port forward quarter of the shell, i.e., on the port side only, in way of No.1 tank. This damage, due to wave action on the shell plating occurs on the port side only. There is little or no damage to the starboard side (Fig. 5).

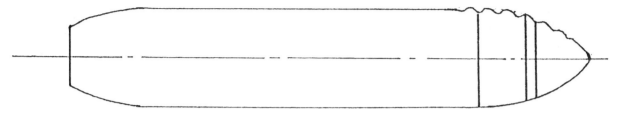

Fig. 5

3.27   One aspect of a loaded OBO's behaviour when pitching is worth recording. In the loaded condition, at the same total displacement and longitudinal radius of gyration, it is reported that the OBO will pitch 'softly' when loaded with an oil cargo, yet pitch in a 'hard' way when loaded with ore. The latter results in hazards such as burying of the bow, etc.

This result may be due to sloshing effects in the oil cargo, but may be worthy of further research.

3.28   One feature of bulk carriage by sea, whether liquid or dry cargo, is that the cargo (often by its nature corrosive) is in direct contact with the inner surface of the shell plating. Arguments have been made for and against double hulls for both types of cargo, and this debate is ongoing [6] [7].

A worthwhile analogy which the author would like to put forward is that of cargo-carrying aircraft where the shell plating forms an envelope which is part of the pressure hull. There is no intention in the aviation industry of placing cargo in direct contact with the inner surface of the pressure hull, yet it is commonly done at sea. This observation lends support to the proposed provision of double hulls in ships.

One further point to be made is that it is common practice in the aircraft industry to continuously monitor the condition of hull plating, and frequently to replace fatigued sections. The effect is considerable; an 'old' aircraft will have been replated, at critical areas, many times during its life. Technology is currently being developed for the intelligent aircraft wing which monitors itself [8].

3.29   Continuous and intelligent operator usage of stress monitoring equipment on board ships at sea is a matter of some concern.

Many ships have been fitted, and currently are being fitted, with sophisticated stress monitoring equipment which is designed to send appropriate information to the bridge from remote sensors positioned in the hull [2]. The efficiency of this equipment is only as good as the use made of the information received from it.

The author is aware that on many occasions the equipment is switched off "because it was giving maximum readings and audible warnings" both at sea and in port during loading and discharging operations.

One hopes and trusts that the aviation industry does not allow those in charge of an aircraft similarly to switch off vital stress monitoring equipment yet it happens, and regularly, in ships at sea.

3.30   Concern has been expressed in recent years about the size of the freeboards assigned to dry bulk carriers. While the modern tanker fleet consists of ships which are permitted to have small freeboards (known as Type A Freeboards), these are ships which are basically strong, are well sub-divided and have small hatch openings leading to cargo carrying spaces which have a low permeability.

A dry cargo ship is given a larger freeboard known as a Type B Freeboard.

The dry bulk carrier is often assigned a reduced freeboard, known as a Type B - 60 or a Type B - 100 Freeboard.

The 'B minus 60' freeboard gives a bulk carrier a reduced freeboard which can be up to 60% of the difference between a Type A and a Type B freeboard; it is usually associated with the ability to have sufficiently strong and closely enough spaced bulkheads (and adequate reserve buoyancy) to withstand the flooding of any one hold. Around 1600 of the world's 4000 bulk carriers have a B - 60 freeboard.

The 'B - 100' freeboard gives a bulk carrier a reduced freeboard which can be up to 100% of the difference between a Type A and a Type B Freeboard; it is usually associated with the ability to have sufficiently strong and closely enough spaced bulkheads (and adequate reserve buoyancy) to withstand the flooding of any two adjacent holds. This implies a suitably designed dry cargo ship having the same freeboard as a tanker.

3.31   In recent years the strength of transverse bulkheads in some bulk carriers has been called into question and the IACS has taken steps to review the requirements, particularly of the bulkhead between No.1 hold and No.2 hold [9].

3.32 The industry must be aware that a dry cargo ship's hold boundary bulkheads, unlike a tanker's, are not designed to take hydrostatic pressure. Only those specifically designed to do so, i.e., the fore peak bulkhead and any bounding bulkheads of holds which are designed to carry storm ballast (commonly No.5 hold in a nine hold ship) are able to withstand flooding.

3.33 To illustrate the above point, there comes to mind the report about the M.V. L......., a bulk carrier, which in the early 1980's arrived off a remote west coast South American ore loading port. The vessel was found to have too great an air draught forward to get under the loading gantries. The chief officer realised that his total forward ballast tanks when full, including the fore peak tank, would not bring the ship's bow down sufficiently. He was not well versed in ship construction but had read somewhere that other ships were able to have salt water loaded into their holds. He therefore decided to fill, with a hose, No.1 hold.

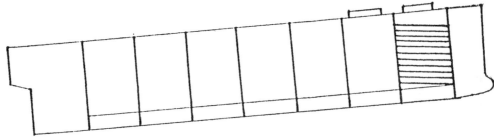

Fig.6 M.V. L.........

As the level in No.1 hold rose not very much happened to start with, but as the level increased to almost deck level the predictable happened. The fore peak bulkhead held, but the one between No.1 and No.2 split suddenly at a welded seam. Some thousands of tonnes of water rapidly transferred from No.1 hold to No.2 hold causing No.1 hatch lids to be sucked into the hold and the deck to be set down some 20 centimetres. The water, on suddenly entering No.2 hold, blew off the hatch lids and pushed the deck up some 10 centimetres. By this time the ship was considerably altered in strength and deck layout forward. (This may be hearsay, but one understands that what happened took place in the early afternoon and therefore disturbed, somewhat abruptly, the master's traditional after lunch snooze).

The ship was temporarily wired together for a voyage to a repair yard some 3000 miles away, another ship was chartered to take the awaiting cargo and the chief officer sought fresh employment elsewhere!

3.34 The author has recently become aware of a loading on a dry bulk carrier's bulkheads which is, he understands, a common occurrence on long ocean passages.

This appears, as illustrated in Fig.7, as an increase in depth of the ore against the forward bulkhead of each hold. It presumably takes place as a direct result of surge, i.e., the alternating forward movement of the deeply laden ship when heading into a heavy swell. It therefore, is a dynamic, rather than a static, load.

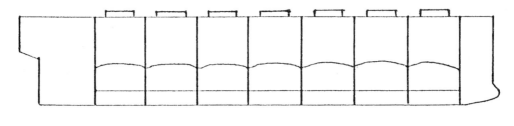

Departure Condition

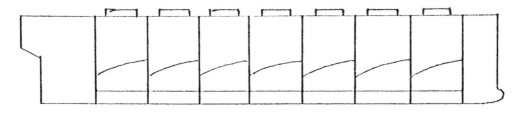

Arrival condition, with ore increased in depth against each forward bulkhead.

Fig. 7

It is reported as having regularly occurred during long voyages (say from the St. Lawrence River to Japan) rather than short ones (say from North Norway to Holland). Clearly it involves additional stresses, of the impact/fatigue type, on the bulkhead plating.

Additionally, the effect of the transfer of a considerable weight forward in the vessel, towards the end of a long ocean voyage, results in a trimming effect by the head, with consequent loss of bow height, which in turn can lead to an increased risk of the shipping of green water over the bow.

3.35   There exists considerable concern about whether the strength of hatch lids has been adequately calculated for abnormal conditions [10]. At least one classification society has recently increased scantlings for bulk carrier hatch covers, and this is to be welcomed.

3.36   There also exists considerable concern about the provision of adequate breakwater and/or forecastle arrangements in B - 60 and B - 100 ships. This is a topic which urgently requires further research.

The evidence given in this paper of rapid sinking and the apparent lack of reserve buoyancy of some bulk carriers leads to concern about the strength, watertight integrity and methods of protection from green seas of the hatch covers on these ships. This has been dealt with in many recent technical papers, e.g., [11], and this interest is to be welcomed.

3.40   This observer is greatly encouraged by the relatively recent moves by ship owners and ship managers to require ship's officers (and all those on board) to take an active part in decision making (and funding/financial decisions) regarding both minor and major repairs and renewals. He questions, however, the amount and quality of training in ship construction which is currently being offered to deck officers.

His recent experience in a nautical college suggests that deck officers trained in the 70's and 80's were well educated, but would welcome the opportunity, on a future occasion, to discuss the present, to his mind, less adequate training being offered in naval architecture and ship construction. More, rather than less, knowledge should be given to a ship's officer who is going to take part in decisions regarding repair and renewal of a ship's structure.

3.50   Whilst the principal aim of this paper is to draw attention to rapid structural failure, there is also concern where a ship suffers loss of her main machinery or her ability to steer (the AMOCO CADIZ and BRAER disasters require no repetition here).

3.51   This concern has, in part, been addressed by the recent requirement for emergency towing apparatus to be fitted to tankers over 20,000t dwt.

A basic disadvantage of this method is that, in order to make this system a success, another vessel with towing capability must be able to get close to the casualty.

3.52   The author strongly welcomes other recent moves towards a ship possessing her own method of independent emergency power and steering. This can take the form of independently powered azimuth thrusters (as in the case of some recent Swedish product tanker designs [12]) or independent systems of main machinery provision, such as are being currently developed by some of the world's largest shipowning companies.   This is to be generally welcomed. The system has been described by some of its proponents as a get - you - home system, but its benefits in keeping a ship clear of a hazardous coast until remedial work is completed and/or adequate towage assistance arrives, are obvious.   As naval architects, we are all aware that only a relatively small amount of power is required to move a ship at a slow speed, even in relatively severe storm conditions, to take the vessel clear of a hazard.

3.53   It is not just large heavily laden vessels which suffer in the event of main machinery failure. Light draught broad beam vessels, such as Ro-Ros, can experience severe damage both to cargo and structure, after having suffered machinery failure.

Their natural roll period is much more likely to be in phase with the period of a wave, resulting in synchronous rolling, which, associated with large values of GM, can, and often does, result in severe damage and in a number of cases, sinking [13].

3.60   SAFETY CASE CONCEPT

The argument here leads logically to a brief consideration of the recent trend to applying the safety case concept to ships.

This extremely worthwhile concept developed as a result of the Flixborough Chemical Works disaster in 1974, calls for quantified hazard identification, risk assessment and risk reduction to be applied to ship management and operation [14]. It has been applied, with considerable success and acceptance, in the nuclear industry and the offshore oil industry and has much to commend it.

One wonders, if that concept had been in place 30 years ago, just how differently the design of ships might have changed, for the better. The " what if " technique, when applied to rapid sinking would, it is suggested, lead to a much improved design of, for example, bulk carrier.

4.   BULK CARRIERS

There are many sources of data which give details of the severe losses of dry bulk carriers, and of lives, which have occurred in the last two decades of the 20th century. It is indeed a matter for great sadness to this author that phrases like "1100 men have been lost in these ships since 1988" have become commonplace. Even our own RINA Journal, "The Naval Architect", has carried reports like "bulk carriers continue to be lost at the rate of about two a month" [15].

While this paper was being prepared two loaded bulk carriers were lost, within weeks of each other, each with the loss of the entire crew. In one case, M.V. LEROS STRENGTH (21,673t dwt) while sailing southwards off the coast of Norway was able to send a brief distress message indicating that she was taking in water forward. 20 men were lost. In the other incident M.V. ALBION II (29,676t dwt, built 1976) was proceeding westwards in the English Channel - no distress signal was received, the ship being subsequently found on the sea-bed in 430ft of water, 65 miles west of Ushant, with its hull broken into several pieces. All 25 members of the crew lost their lives.

The media showed very little interest in each case, there being little evidence of sea-birds having been covered in oil, or of beaches being polluted; only men's lives were lost, with consequent shattering effects on the lives of those who would immediately become widows and orphans.

In the author's opinion, this should be an unacceptable level of loss in any industry in the late 20th century. It is hoped that perhaps the marine insurance industry may take note of some, at least, of the conclusions in this and similar papers in order to stem the flow of unnecessary sudden deaths. Over the 20 years there have been produced a huge number of reports and publications on the situation [16] [17]. Almost all have been ignored.

One of the most telling is reproduced as Table 1, and is taken from a Lloyd's document published in January 1996 [18]. The black dots denote total losses. The only comment that needs to be made is that the proportion of dots is devastatingly and totally unacceptably high for an industry that aspires to such hollow sounding aims as "Safer Ships, Cleaner Seas".

5.   CONCLUSIONS

5.1   It is the present writer's hope that many of the requirements which have been illustrated in the presentation of this paper will be addressed by ongoing discussions at such bodies as IMO, IACS, etc. With this in mind it does seem worthwhile to set down some of these, in summary form, as follows:

5.2   Should, perhaps, an investigation be carried out into reserve buoyancy for ships of the bulk carrier type? Is it possible that increase of freeboard is necessary?

5.3   Is it also possible that an investigation of additional requirements regarding protection of the forward hatches is necessary, possibly with statutory requirements for breakwaters, or, more obviously, a requirement for bulk carriers, even the very largest, to have forecastles?

5.4   Although some classification societies have recently increased requirements for the strengthening of hatch covers, that more quantified research needs to be undertaken into this important aspect of bulk carrier safety.

5.5   That corrosion allowances, particularly in ships fitted with high tensile steel, should be far more thoroughly investigated than hitherto.

5.6   That the whole question of the time allocated to annual condition surveys (for Load line and Classification renewal) be reviewed, with the intention of increasing the time greatly, in order that more than a superficial survey is possible in the time allocated.

5.7   That much greater attention be paid by those in design offices (and, indeed, in classification society plan approval departments) to what actually happens to the steelwork of a ship, particularly a bulk carrier, when loading and discharging. It appears, for instance, that many of the formulae for hull strength in longitudinal bending and shearing do not take into account the many violent practices to which a ship is exposed when loading or discharging ore.

5.8   That the rule bodies should look much more carefully further aft, in way of No.1 and No.2 holds, when requiring additional strengthening to be provided against panting.

5.9   That the knowledge imparted to a ship's officer during his training (even, and especially, under the recently introduced Standards for Training and Certification in Watchkeeping (STCW) Convention) should be closely investigated, with a view to increasing that knowledge. The author would welcome an opportunity to discuss this subject more fully, together with manning levels, on a future occasion [19].

5.10   That not merely the fitting of pressure sensors and stress monitoring strain gauges should be strongly recommended, but that their output should be used intelligently on board ship.

5.11   That much more attention should be paid by ship managers and operators to the procedures and stresses to which a ship's hull is subjected in port even before she proceeds to sea to meet, and this is likely during a modern ship's long life, abnormal conditions of wind and wave [20].

Fig. 8

Two examples of the many instances of bow plating failure, forward of the collision bulkhead, caused by the power of the sea.

1) M.V. TOCHAL, 300,000t dwt tanker, SE Africa, June 1994.

2) M.V. ATLAS PRIDE, 244,677t dwt ore/oil carrier, SE Africa, August 1991.

6.   ACKNOWLEDGEMENT

The author acknowledges with thanks the encouragement given by Professor Douglas Faulkner in the preparation of this paper.

7.   DISCLAIMER

All opinions expressed are those of the author.

8.   REFERENCES

[1]   BUCKLEY, W, 'A Study of Extreme Waves and their Effects on Ship Structures', SSC 320, US Coast Guard, 1984.

[2]   'Ship Hull Integrity Programme (SHIP) helps stress monitoring', BMT News, September 1995.

[3]   American Bureau of Shipping seminars on Bulk Carrier Safety, London, December 1994 and Hong Kong, October 1995.

[4]   FERGUSON, J.M., 'Bulk Carrier Safety - Today's Enigma', Lloyd's Register discussion paper, 1996,.

[5]   HOOKE, N, 'Maritime Casualties 1963 - 1996', Lloyd's of London Press 1997. This is a revised edition of 'Modern Shipping Disasters 1963 - 1987' by the same author, published in 1989.

[6]   COLL, G, 'Safety of Bulk Carriers - Are Two Skins better than One?', RINA Spring Meetings, 1996.

[7]   CORKHILL, M, 'Double Hull Tankers prove worth', Lloyd's List 14.03.97.

[8]   FRIEND, C, 'Even aircraft have feelings', New Scientist, 3.02.96.

[9]   GREY, M, 'Warning on bulk carrier sinking risk', Lloyd's List, 22.01.96.

[10] FAULKNER, D, 'Design for Abnormal Conditions', within Lord Donaldson's Assessment on M.V. Derbyshire, Cm 3128, presented to Parliament, December 1995.

[11] WILLIAMS, R.A. and FAULKNER, D, 'M.V. Derbyshire, The Search Assessment & Survey', RINA Colloquium Proceedings, London, March, 1996.

[12] 'Swedish chemical tanker Ek River', The Naval Architect, January 1994.

[13] ANDERSSON, P, et al, 'Cargo Shift and Cargo Securing on Passenger Ro-Ro Vessels', RINA international seminar on The Safety of Passenger Ro-Ro Vessels, IMO, London, June 1996.

[14] KUO, C, et al: 'A Safety Case for Stena Line's High Speed Ferry HSS 1500', RINA Spring Meetings, 1997.

[15] RAWSON, K, RINA Safety Committee, The Naval Architect, October 1996, page 34.

[16] Bulk Carrier Practice, Jack Isbester, ed., Nautical Institute, 1993.

[17] Steamship Mutual Underwriting Association (Bermuda) Ltd, 'Structural Damage to Bulk Carriers', August 1991.

[18] 'Bulk carriers - an update', Lloyd's Register, January 1996.

[19] 'People Matter', leading article in Lloyd's List, 19.12.96.

[20] HICKEY, J, ABS Underwriters' Special Committee, 'Bulk Concern', Fairplay 27.07.95.

SEE TABLE 1

A number of other significant examples of rapid failure and/or rapid sinkings, not referred to above, are listed below, for reference:

BETELGEUSE (Bantry Bay,1979)

EDMUND FITZGERALD (Lake Superior, November 1975)

KOWLOON BRIDGE (SE Ireland, November 1986)

MARINA DI EQUA (Bay of Biscay, December 1981)

MIMOSA (West of the Hebrides, Scotland, January 1995)

TOLEDO (English Channel, March 1990)

YARRAWONGA (North Atlantic, January 1989)

TABLE 1

Bulk, ore/oil, ore and OBO casualties - (deadweight >20000 tonnes)
Missing, lost or serious damage where structural failure may have been a factor,
January 1990 - December 1995

Name	Age	Type	Cargo	Case date	Casualty details
Ship 1	15	Bulk	Grain	Jan 90	•Missing
Ship 2	17	Bulk	Coal	Jan 90	Side shell lost No 1 Hold
Ship 3	19	OBO	Iron Pellets	Jan 90	Heavy weather damage
Ship 4	9	Bulk	Iron Ore	Feb 90	No 8 side shell lost
Ship 5	24	Bulk	Phosphate	Feb 90	•Damage in No 2 hold (flooded)
Ship 6	20	Bulk	Ballast	Feb 90	Fracture No 1 hold
Ship 7	23	Ore	Iron Ore	Mar 90	•Foundered
Ship 8	21	Ore	Iron Ore	Mar 90	•Ballast tank leak
Ship 9	22	Bulk	Barytes	Apr 90	2 m fracture in No 6 hold
Ship 10	19	Bulk	Iron Ore ?	May 90	•Hull damage. Holds flooded
Ship 11	13	Bulk	Iron Ore	May 90	•Hull damage. Flooded
Ship 12	12	Bulk	Iron Ore	May 90	•Fractures in holds 2 & 3
Ship 13	23	Bulk	Iron Ore	Jul 90	•No 3 hold flooded
Ship 14	18	Bulk	Cement	Jul 90	•Bow lost & keel fractured
Ship 15	9	Bulk	Coal	Aug 90	Side Shell damage
Ship 16	17	OO	Iron Ore	Sep 90	•Missing
Ship 17	24	Bulk	Iron Ore	Oct 90	Fractured side shell
Ship 18	19	OO	Iron Ore	Oct 90	•Presumed to have foundered
Ship 19	17	Bulk	Iron Ore	Oct 90	Wasted side shell framing in No. 3 hold
Ship 20	21	Bulk	Bauxite	Nov 90	Fractures in holds 2, 3 & 6
Ship 21	19	Bulk	Ballast	Nov 90	12 m fracture in No. 5 hold
Ship 22	18	Bulk	Iron Ore ?	Dec 90	Bulkhead frames loosened
Ship 23	17	Bulk	Potash	Dec 90	•Fractures in No. 2 hold
Ship 24	18	Bulk	Iron Ore	Jan 91	Damage to frames in No.1 hold
Ship 25	24	Bulk	Iron Ore	Jan 91	•Nos 2 & 4 holds flooded
Ship 26	19	Bulk	?	Jan 91	Fractures & detached frames in two holds
Ship 27	24	Bulk	Iron Ore	Jan 91	•Fracture in No. 5 hold. Flooded
Ship 28	21	OBO	Iron Ore	Feb 91	•Fracture in No. 1 hold
Ship 29	14	Bulk	Ballast	Feb 91	Fractures in No. 3 WB hold
Ship 30	24	Bulk	Pig Iron	Feb 91	•Took water after striking object
Ship 31	17	Bulk	?	Mar 91	Frames detached from No. 6 hold
Ship 32	24	Bulk	Iron Ore	Apr 91	•No. 1 hold flooded
Ship 33	21	Bulk	Iron Ore	Apr 91	•Fracture in No. 4 hold. Flooded
Ship 34	9	Bulk	Iron Ore	Apr 91	•Missing
Ship 35	16	Bulk	Iron Ore	May 91	Fracture in No. 1 hold
Ship 36	16	OO	Iron Ore	May 91	Fracture in hull below waterline
Ship 37	15	Bulk	Iron Ore	July 91	•No. 3 hold flooded
Ship 38	21	Bulk	Steel	Aug 91	•Grounded No. 1 hold
Ship 39	21	Bulk	Iron Ore	Aug 91	Severe crack No. 7 hold
Ship 40	16	Bulk	Iron Ore	Aug 91	•Ingress of water No. 1 or 2 hold
Ship 41	12	Bulk	?	Aug 91	Shell fracture frames detached No. 3 hold
Ship 42	14	Bulk	?	Aug 91	Heavy weather frames cracked
Ship 43	23	Bulk	?	Aug 91	Disabled towed to safety
Ship 44	24	Bulk	?	Aug 91	No. 5 hold frames fractured
Ship 45	18	OO	Oil	Aug 91	Hull fractures
Ship 46	18	OO	Oil	Sept 91	Shell fracture oil leakage
Ship 47	23	Bulk	Phosphate	Oct 91	•Sank in Mediterranean
Ship 48	18	Bulk	To load coal	Oct 91	Fractures in deck
Ship 49	14	Bulk	?	Nov 91	Extensive corrosion of shell plating
Ship 50	25	Ore	Iron Ore	Nov 91	•Leakage in heavy weather
Ship 51	18	Bulk	Steel Machinery	Nov 91	No. 2 hold flooded rip in side
Ship 52	18	Bulk	Iron Ore	Nov 91	•Cracks in side shell most holds
Ship 53	20	Bulk	Iron Ore	Dec 91	Side shell fracture

• = missing/sinking

TABLE 1 (continued)

Bulk, ore/oil, ore and OBO casualties - (deadweight >20000 tonnes)
Missing, lost or serious damage where structural failure may have been a factor,
January 1990 - December 1995

Name	Age	Type	Cargo	Case date	Casualty details
Ship 54	26	Bulk	?	Jan 92	Hull leaks when on voyage to breakers
Ship 55	25	Bulk	Calc Nitrate	Jan 92	Leakage into fore peak and double bottom
Ship 56	21	Bulk	Coal	Jan 92	Detained for extensive repairs
Ship 57	18	Bulk	?	Feb 92	Upper deck fracture heavy weather
Ship 58	23	OBO	Iron Ore	Mar 92	• Engine room flooded
Ship 59	24	Bulk	Iron Ore	May 92	• Side shell fracture and progressive flooding
Ship 60	20	Bulk	Iron Ore	Aug 92	Bulkhead between holds 8/9 collapsed
Ship 61	19	OO	Iron Ore	Sept 92	Damage to side shell P & S
Ship 62	22	Ore	Iron Ore	Oct 92	• Missing in typhoon
Ship 63	18	Bulk	?	Oct 92	No. 5 hold side frames adrift
Ship 64	19	Bulk	Coal	Nov 92	Severe structural wastage to topside tanks, fractures etc.
Ship 65	20	Bulk	Coal	Nov 92	Structural cracking
Ship 66	16	Bulk	Iron Ore	Dec 92	Taking water No.1 hold, hull fractures
Ship 67	19	Bulk	Gypsum	Mar 93	• Sank in heavy weather
Ship 68	24	Bulk	Coal	May 93	• Sank after loss of hatch
Ship 69	19	OBO	Iron Ore	June 93	Damage frames in No.3
Ship 70	19	Bulk	Steel	July 93	No. 4 hold internals adrift and buckled
Ship 71	19	Bulk	Iron Ore	July 93	No. 5 hold framing damaged
Ship 72	25	Bulk	Phosphate	Nov 93	Hole 12m x 6m in No 1 hold P & S
Ship 73	21	OBO	Iron Ore	Dec 93	No. 2 hold side shell leak
Ship 74	13	Bulk	Wheat	Dec 93	Took water in Nos. 1 and 7 holds
Ship 75	21	OO	Iron Ore	Jan 94	• Sank in North Atlantic
Ship 76	24	Bulk	Scrap	Feb 94	• Reported water in No.1 hold
Ship 77	21	Bulk	Manganese	Mar 94	• Cargo damage, sailed with incomplete repairs, class deleted, sank June.
Ship 78	18	Bulk	Ballast	Mar 94	No. 4 hold side shell and framing damage
Ship 79	20	Bulk	Iron Ore	Mar 94	Heavy weather damage to hull
Ship 80	13	Bulk	Iron Ore	June 94	47m crack in topside tank
Ship 81	13	Bulk	Iron Ore	June 94	No 1. side shell hold
Ship 82	21	Bulk	Iron Ore	June 94	• Disappeared
Ship 83	23	Bulk	Manganese Ore	Aug 94	Side shell fracture
Ship 84	26	Ore	Iron Ore	Sept 94	• Crack on starboard side and water ingress
Ship 85	22	OBO	Iron Ore	Nov 94	• Broke back while loading
Ship 86	22	Bulk	Grain	Nov 94	• Sank North of Guyana
Ship 87	20	Bulk	Cu Ore	Nov 94	No.3 hold crack, 2 holds flooded, heavy weather
Ship 88	12	Ore	Iron Ore	Dec 94	Buckling of cross deck strips, typhoon
Ship 89	20	Bulk	Iron Ore	Mar 95	Cracks in side shell/frames
Ship 90	22	Bulk	Potash	Apr 95	Shell fracture
Ship 91	22	OBO	Ballast	July 95	Cracks in bow section
Ship 92	21	Bulk	?	Nov 95	Deck fracture

• = missing/sinking

PAPER NO.3.

LONG TERM TRENDS IN ALTIMETER MEASURED SIGNIFICANT WAVE HEIGHT AND THE IMPLICATIONS FOR EXPECTED EXTREME VALUES

by P D Cotton and P G Challenor
Southampton Oceanography Centre - James Rennell Division, and
D J T Carter, Satellite Observing Systems, UK

Paper presented at the

International Conference

**DESIGN AND OPERATION FOR
ABNORMAL CONDITIONS**

21 22 OCTOBER 1997 GLASGOW

LONG TERM TRENDS IN ALTIMETER MEASURED SIGNIFICANT WAVE HEIGHT, AND THE IMPLICATIONS FOR EXPECTED EXTREME VALUES

P D Cotton and P G Challenor, Southampton Oceanography Centre - James Rennell Division, and
D J T Carter, Satellite Observing Systems

SUMMARY

There is now a considerable body of evidence, derived from in-situ (buoy and ship borne wave recorder), satellite, model, and observational data indicating that there has been a long term increasing trend in annual and winter mean significant wave heights in the North Atlantic. However, detailed analysis of this phenomena has been hamstrung by the inhomogeneity, irregular availability and spatial limitations of in-situ data. Satellite altimeter wave data, regularly available since the launch of Geosat in 1985, and providing consistent reliable global coverage, show no such limitations. They therefore provide a highly valuable tool for investigations into large scale wave climate change.

The authors employ altimeter wave data, covering the period 1985-96, to establish the spatial extent and temporal characteristics of large scale wave climate variability, in the North Atlantic and other ocean regions, and include an analysis of the latest data to assess the continuity or otherwise of established long term trends. They show that, over the last ten years, the increase in significant wave heights in the North Atlantic has been strongest in the North-Eastern Sector, and indeed that this region is the most strongly affected over the whole of the world's oceans during this period. For a number of specific locations they carry out further statistical analyses to investigate whether a change in mean wave climate is accompanied by a change in statistical extreme values.

AUTHORS' BIOGRAPHIES

Dr Cotton's early scientific career, when he gained his PhD, was in the field of upper atmospheric physics, and included a two year period working on a research base in the Antarctic (with the British Antarctic Survey) and a year spent at the University of Otago, New Zealand, funded by a Royal Society Fellowship. He moved fields in 1991, to remote sensing oceanography, when he joined the Institute of Oceanographic Sciences (now part of Southampton Oceanography Centre), originally as data manager/remote sensing scientist. Dr Cotton now leads the satellite waves research programme at SOC which is directed to understanding the nature and causes of large scale wave climate variability. He has also been a member of the ESA commissioning working groups for the ERS-1 and ERS-2 satellites, validating wind and wave measurements from the radar altimeter on these satellites.

Mr Peter Challenor gained an MSc in Biometry from the University of Reading and a BSc in Mathematics from the University of Exeter. After joining the Institute of Oceanographic Sciences in 1978, he initially worked on wave statistics, in particular the estimation of extremes and design heights. This led to an interest in the estimation of wave parameters from radar altimeter data and eventually to a general interest in satellite remote sensing of the ocean. He has been Head of Satellite Remote Sensing in the James Rennell Division of the Southampton Oceanography Centre since 1994.

Mr David Carter gained a BSc in mathematics from King's College London and is a qualified RN meteorologist having spent 15 years in the Royal Navy as a meteorologist and oceanographer. This was followed by 20 years at the Institute of Oceanographic Sciences, Wormley, UK, mostly studying ocean waves, especially the statistics of extremes and, since 1985, the analysis of wave climate from satellite altimeter measurements. He is responsible, with others, for the estimates of extreme wave heights around the UK in the 4th edition of the Department of Energy's "Offshore Installations: Guidance on Design, Construction and Certification", 1990.

1.   INTRODUCTION

A number of authors [Carter and Draper, 1988; Bacon and Carter, 1991] have analysed in-situ data to show that average wave conditions have been increasing, steadily but significantly, over the North Atlantic during the last 25 years, at a rate of 1% per year. These authors demonstrated [Bacon and Carter, 1993] that there was a connection to anomalies in the sea level pressure difference between the Azores and Iceland (a measurement equivalent to the North Atlantic Oscillation Index), but were not able to demonstrate a causal link. Van Hoof [1994] provides a discussion of these early studies and their implications. In more recent years, large scale wave models have been driven by hindcast wind fields in a attempt to recreate this observed increase, and to develop an understanding of its causes [e.g. Sterl et al, 1997; and others]. These efforts have met with mixed success, evidence of long term trends often being masked by higher frequency variability. The realism of wave fields from these models is also uncertain, being dependant upon the accuracy of the wind forcing fields input to the model and the algorithms used within the model to represent the complex non-linear physics of wind/wave and wave/wave interactions.

The authors of this paper have generated a global wave climate data base from satellite radar altimeter measurements of significant wave height, covering the period 1985 to the present day. Satellite data provide a direct and accurate measurement of significant wave height, and provide genuine global coverage. They therefore form an ideal tool for investigating large scale spatial patterns of variability in wave climate. They can help to place local in-situ measurements of variability into a global context and establish whether such measurements are representative of a larger area. It has also been demonstrated that statistical techniques can be successfully applied to satellite wave data in order to derive statistically important wave parameters such as exceedance values [Carter et al., 1995].

In this paper satellite altimeter wave data are used to establish the characteristics of variability in larger scale wave climate, and to investigate the presence or otherwise of long term trends in climate. These data are then applied to the problem of 'abnormal' conditions. The paper concludes with a discussion of whether altimeter data can be used to determine whether expected extreme conditions have changed in the NE Atlantic as a result of an increase mean wave climate.

2. WAVE HEIGHT MEASUREMENTS FROM SATELLITE ALTIMETERS

Two forms of altimeter wave data, covering the period 1985-97, are analysed in this paper: 1Hz data records, which are used to compile the statistical data base for calculation of extremes; and a gridded wave climate data base, used to assess the large scale characteristics of climate change. The data set analysed in this paper was generated from a combination of measurements from altimeters on three satellites: Geosat (1985-89), ERS-1 (1991-95), and Topex (1992-97).

Satellite radar altimeters provide an estimate of significant wave height (H_s) from the slope of the leading edge of the pulse reflected from the ocean surface [Brown, 1977]. Extensive comparisons with co-located in-situ data have shown that this altimeter measurement of H_s is remarkably accurate, these comparisons giving r.m.s. values as low as 0.3m [Cotton et al, 1997, Gower, 1996]. However, in order to generate a long term data set it has been necessary to combine measurements made from different satellites, and because of the different characteristics of each altimeter, both in the engineering and data processing, wave measurements from different altimeters are not necessarily consistent. Comparisons with wave buoy data has confirmed that in order to generate a single consistent data set, each altimeter wave data set requires the application of individual calibration corrections. The corrections applied to altimeter data in this paper were derived by Cotton and Carter [1996], and bring all altimeter data into agreement with data from 24 open ocean data buoys operated by the NOAA Data Buoy Center (selected because of their reliable records and their open ocean locations), equations 1-3.

$$H_{s(buoy)} = 0.089 + 1.069\ H_{s\ (Geosat)} \quad (1)$$
$$N=706 \qquad rrms=0.42\ m$$

$$H_{s(buoy)} = 0.333 + 1.126\ H_{s\ (ERS-1)} \quad (2)$$
$$N=1277 \qquad rrms=0.26\ m$$

$$H_{s(buoy)} = -0.082 + 1.049\ H_{s\ (TOPEX)} \quad (3)$$
$$N=1189 \qquad rrms=0.28\ m$$

Satellites repeat their tracks at intervals of 10 - 35 days, so give measurements at one location at these widely spaced intervals. Figure 1 illustrates the ground tracks of the Geosat altimeter, on a 17-day repeat orbit, in an area to the West of Ireland. ERS in a 35-day orbit has tracks at half the spacing, TOPEX in a 10-day orbit at about twice this spacing. This gain in spatial resolution is obtained at the expense of a loss in temporal resolution. The outlined area delineates a region which is considered in more detail later (inspection of the data indicated no significant differences in wave climate throughout this region). To get sufficient data for analysis it is necessary to combine data from an area of ocean; often data from all transects of an area of $2°$ latitude by $2°$ longitude are combined (see dotted outlines in figure 1).

However, whilst there are several days between successive transects, the measurements are obtained every second along a transect, i.e. every 6 - 7 km, and H_s values along such a transect are highly correlated. So it is generally preferable to use the mean or median value from each transect rather than the 1 Hz data. From one altimeter, this results in 5 - 10 values each month in a $2°$ bin. These 5 - 10 median values are then combined to form our climatological data set, monthly mean files on a $2°$ latitude by $2°$ longitude grid, determined as the best resolution possible after taking into account the sampling characteristics of the altimeters, and the variability of oceanic wave fields.

Where data from more than one satellite were available, separate gridded files were generated, and these files merged, with appropriate weighting. Cotton and Carter [1994] demonstrated, by comparisons with buoy data, that monthly means generated in this way were indeed representative of the mean wave climate in a grid square for that period. Figure 2 provides an example of altimeter derived wave climatology, for the first three months of 1996. The expected characteristics of a Northern Hemisphere winter are seen. Highest waves are found in the mid-latitudes in the central North Atlantic and North Pacific oceans, a lower wave climate predominates in the tropics, and then a broad band of high waves (which remains throughout the Austral summer) has a peak centred on $50°$ S, circling all longitudes.

3. CHARACTERISTICS OF VARIABILITY

3.1 THE ANNUAL CYCLE

The biggest signal of variability in wave climate is the annual cycle. To parameterise this seasonal cycle, and properly assess its significance, a simple sine/cosine model has been fitted to each grid square in the climatological data set, equation 4.

$$A(m) = B0 + B1\ \sin(2\pi m/12) + B2\ \cos(2\pi m/12) + \varepsilon_m \quad (4)$$

where $A(m)$ = Significant wave height in month m.

Figure 3 presents the annual cycle fitted to the 12 monthly means for two regions, the area to the West of Ireland indicated in Figure 1 (top panel), and from an area south of Australia (44°-46°S, 120°-130°E). The curve representing the annual cycle fitted in the top panel (W. of Ireland) accounts for 98.9% of the variance in the twelve values. The total range in monthly means (from 1.9m to 5.0m) is almost as large as the average value throughout the year (3.5m). In the southern ocean the annual cycle is not such a good fit to the within-year means, the annual cycle fitted in the bottom panel of figure 3 (S. of Australia) explains 77.4% of the variance (cf. 98.9% above). Note also the annual range, 1.47m, is about half of that in the region off Ireland (3.1m).

Looking now on the global scale, figure 4 shows parameters for the mean annual cycle fitted to all monthly mean data between 1985 and 1996. We can see from panel (a) that the annual mean wave height peaks in mid-ocean at mid-latitudes, and is a minimum in the tropics and in coastal regions sheltered from swell. The mean wave height is greatest in the Southern Oceans, being higher than 4m across most longitudes at approximately 50° S, whilst it is between 3m and 4m in the central North Atlantic and the North Pacific Oceans.

The biggest range in the annual cycle (calculated as the difference between the maximum and minimum monthly mean significant wave heights in the fitted cycle) occurs in the Northern Hemisphere, middle panel (b). The annual range in the central North Atlantic and North Pacific reaches 3m, illustrating the great difference between the winter and summer months in these regions. In contrast, across most of the Southern ocean the annual range is 1m or less, indicating that higher waves (and winds) remain throughout the year due to the lack of large continental land masses.

The phase of the annual cycle is illustrated by the month of the maximum wave height in panel (c). As would be expected, the maximum wave height consistently occurs in January/February throughout the Northern Hemisphere, apart from localised regions on the eastern boundaries of the Pacific and Atlantic, and in the Arabian Sea. The Southern hemisphere oceans show more variability, with the maximum wave height occurring between June and August. In areas where the annual cycle is not well defined the month of maximum wave height is not particularly meaningful (primarily in the tropics, but also some regions in the southern oceans e.g. to the east of Australia).

The ability of the simple model to account for the variability in the monthly mean data is illustrated in the figure 5, where the percentage reduction in variance is illustrated. It can be seen that the model explains much more of the variability in the data in the Northern Hemisphere than it does in the South. For instance, for much of the Northern Hemisphere between 80-90% of the variance in the data is explained by the model, whereas in the tropics, less than 10% reduction in variance is obtained and even across mid and high latitude regions in the Southern Oceans only 40-50% reduction invariance is achieved. Taken as an average over the whole global

ocean, the simple model for the annual cycle characterised by equation 4 explains 64% of the total variance.

Having established that a simple annual cycle can be used describe a significant proportion of the observed variability of wave climate, the remaining or residual variability can be characterised on two time scales, long term climate trends (5-10 years) , and short term inter-annual, and intra-annual variability (year to year, and month to month).

3.2   SHORT TERM VARIABILITY

Although long term change in the wave climate has generated the most interest both in the scientific community and more widely, the interannual variations are also of great scientific and practical interest. Variability on this time scale has the most significant short term impact on ocean users and an accurate characterisation of this variability would be of immense practical value.

Figure 6 presents time series of monthly means for four regions in the North Atlantic with the mean annual cycle removed. There is evidence of much high frequency variability in these means, (ranging up to ± 1m, standard deviations about the long term average of 0.3m - 0.56m). Appreciable increasing linear trends (up to 0.05m per year, fitted to the period 1985-94) can be seen for the regions of OWS Lima (Fig. 6a) and Mike (Fig. 6c) - see next sub-section.

Although the magnitude of this short term variability is appreciable, at first sight there appears to be little evidence of any predictable form (e.g cyclical behaviour) to this variability. It is apparent that much of the observed short term variability in wave fields is high frequency (intra-annual) and hence a consequence of immediate reaction to changes in wind field patterns, so the problem here is connected to that of short to medium term weather prediction. Evidence of this short term connection between variability in wave climate and atmospheric features can be seen in figure 7, whereby there is seen to be good agreement between the high frequency variability in the NAO and monthly mean wave height residuals at OWS Lima (these two time series of data show a correlation of 0.56).

Further analyses (not presented here) have demonstrated that there are connected patterns of variability in different ocean regions. For instance the North East Pacific and North East Atlantic have been found to exhibit an anti-phase correlation whereby when one of these regions is rougher than the long term average the other is calmer. This correlation is clearly evident and occurs on an inter-annual time scale. There is some further evidence, though as yet less convincing, that this correlation is in turn connected to variability in the Southern Oscillation Index and hence the El Niño cycle.

The relative scales of the short term variability and the annual cycle can be demonstrated by focusing on the area to the west of Ireland identified in Figure 1. The means calculated for the 88 individual months from

November 1986 to April 1997 for which we have transects, (excluding six with fewer than 15 transects) were analysed and the spread of values about the mean (figure 8a) is seen to be very large. For instance, August 1992 had a monthly mean of 3.21 m, almost equal to that of 3.24m for January 1987. (The number of transect values averaged to obtain these means and the s.e. of the means, calculated assuming the transect values are independent, were: Aug.92: 31, 0.21m; Jan.87: 41, 0.13 m.) Note also that the highest monthly mean was 7.79m from 17 values (s.e. 0.40m) in February 1997.

The sine curve fitted through these 88 monthly means now only accounts for 66.4% of the variance. Thus the between-year variability on monthly mean wave height is only about 30% of the within-year variability, but clearly cannot be ignored.

3.3   LONG TERM CLIMATE TRENDS

When discussing abnormal conditions, of particular concern is the possibility of long-term trends, over decades. Such changes in the climate might result in what could be regarded today as very abnormal conditions becoming common place within the lifetime of an offshore structure or of coastal defences. However, the very large short term variation in wave height, at least in mid-latitudes, can make it very difficult to detect any trend. This suggests that any structure designed to withstand the worst expected today should not be upset by any barely discernible trend, at least for a few years. Nevertheless, such a trend could have a significant effect on marine operations and on fatigue damage (Haver, 1995).

There has been considerable discussion as to whether the North East Atlantic has become rougher in recent years [Bacon & Carter, 1991]; and buoys in the North West Atlantic have measured a number of severe storms in the past ten years - with wave heights exceeding the previously estimated 100-year return level [Cardone & Swail, 1995] (but these observations are perhaps due in part to the increase in the number of buoys deployed).

In demonstrating that there had been an increase in average wave height in the North East Atlantic between the mid 1960's and late 1980's, Bacon and Carter [1991] used data from the shipborne wave recorder on OWS Lima (stationed at 57°N, 20°W). The +'s in Figure 9 show the values from Lima used in their paper, the increase is clearly seen despite a large degree of interannual variability. The o's show equivalent altimeter data from the 2° square which contains the nominal Lima position.

Considering the difference between a spatial average represented by the altimeter and a temporal average from the ship the comparison in the overlap is very good. The altimeter data clearly shows that the increase in wave height has continued through the early 1990's. However, Bacon and Carter were unable to address the question of how widespread this increase was. The altimeter climatological wave data base can be used to investigate this problem, and to see whether other oceanic regions have shown equally significant trends.

To achieve this end, mean annual cycles have been fitted to the two periods 1985-89 (Geosat) and 1991-95 (ERS and Topex) for each grid square of the entire global data set. The difference between the two periods were then calculated. Figure 10 illustrates the differences between the mean and the maximum of the annual cycles fitted to the two periods.

The rise in wave height in the North East Atlantic is clear in Figure 10. The situation in the rest of the globe is more confused and there is little evidence for similar trends over any other large regions. In some areas, for example the Western Mediterranean, significant wave height seems to have actually gone down over the period. Thus it would appear that the North East Atlantic is unusual, in that it has been seen to exhibit a significant long term trend in wave climate. The only other region that show a trend of a comparable magnitude is a region immediately to the South of Australia.

One should maintain some caution however, given the still relatively short time scale of the altimeter data set. One or two abnormally stormy or calm years could easily bias the observations (the previous subsection has demonstrated the significant variability on short time scales, with standard deviations about the mean of 0.3 to 0.56m, larger than the trend in the annual means over this period), producing results similar to those illustrated in Figure 10. It is only because longer term in-situ data are available for the North Atlantic that it is possible to be confident of the existence of a long term trend in this region.

The question of the cause of this long term increasing trend in the North Atlantic remains open. It is a question that has occupied the minds of many researchers in recent years, and although the increase has been linked to a similar trend in the North Atlantic Oscillation Index, the full physical sequence of atmospheric and wind/wave interactions has not yet been satisfactorily established. Some researchers [Munnich et al., 1997] have postulated that the coupled North Atlantic Ocean Atmosphere system has a natural feedback process generated through deep convection and advection within the sub-polar gyre circulation, which has a periodic, cyclical, time scale of close to 30 years. The North Atlantic Oscillation also exhibits some low frequency periodicity on the decadal scale. However, it remains difficult, if not impossible, to predict the future behaviour of the current increasing trend in the North Atlantic wave climate.

4.   ABNORMAL CONDITIONS

4.1

To allow for abnormal conditions when designing structures or planning operations requires:

a)   an understanding of what is meant by abnormal conditions;

b)   an ability to predict such conditions.

For wave height, 'abnormal conditions' is usually taken to mean conditions when wave heights are unusually high - although for some operations the possibility of unusually low waves can be important. For design purposes, the 100-year return value of individual wave height is often a useful measure, but for operational planning and some other design needs, such as fatigue calculations, a more general knowledge of the distribution of wave height is needed.

Altimeter data can be used to address both requirements, a and b. The use of both monthly mean and individual altimeter wave heights are considered in this application.

4.2 ABNORMAL CONDITIONS FROM MONTHLY MEAN DATA

For the purposes of this discussion, attention is again focused on the region to the west of Ireland indicated in Figure 1.

Table 1 gives the averages and the standard deviations of the individual monthly means for each calendar month, together with the monthly means from the fitted annual cycle.

TABLE 1 Monthly means shown in Figure 9

Month	Nb	mean (m)	s.d (m)	sd/mean	fitted mean (m)
1	8	4.91967	1.11859	0.2274	5.04264
2	8	5.11426	1.48984	0.2913	4.79502
3	8	4.44184	0.86482	0.1947	4.19908
4	9	3.17289	0.64342	0.2028	3.41450
5	8	2.50304	0.31972	0.1277	2.65150
6	8	2.07728	0.43673	0.2102	2.11455
7	7	2.17344	0.39647	0.1824	1.94750
8	6	2.18449	0.51906	0.2376	2.19512
9	5	2.75082	0.39526	0.1437	2.79107
10	6	3.67411	0.52702	0.1434	3.57565
11	7	4.37837	0.95180	0.2174	4.33864
12	8	4.62092	0.79431	0.1719	4.87560

We could fit the individual monthly mean residuals about the sine curve to some distribution, but the variation in standard deviations between months indicates that these residuals are not identically distributed. The standard deviations have an annual cycle with maximum in the winter months, so a more homogeneous data set can be obtained by normalising the residuals by dividing them by the monthly means - see Table 1. Figure 11a shows the cumulative probability distribution of the 88 normalised residuals plotted on Fisher-Tippett Type 1 (Gumbel) scales. (We have normalised using the fitted means, not the calculated values.) The FT-1 distribution fitted by maximum likelihood is also shown, it has location and scale parameters (α and β) of -0.0907 and 0.161 respectively.

The FT-1 distribution is given by

$$\text{Prob}(X < x) = e^{-e^{-\frac{x-\alpha}{\beta}}} \quad (5)$$

where in this case X is the normalised residual given by

$$X = \frac{y_{(m)} - y_{fm}}{y_{fm}}$$

where $y_{(m)}$ is the individual monthly means (with m denoting the calendar month, m=1,12) and y_{fm} is the fitted

value for month m,.

So the probability distribution for mean in month m is given by

$$P = \text{Prob}(Y_{(m)} < y) = e^{-e^{-(y - y_{fm}(1+\alpha))/y_{fm}\beta}} \quad (6)$$

or

$$Y_{(m)} = y_{fm}\left\{(1 + \alpha) + \left[-1n\,(-1nP)\right]\beta\right\} \quad (7)$$

So for example, there is a 10% probability that the monthly mean in any one month would be exceeded by the value of $Y_{(m)}$ given by P=0.9. Using the derived values for α and β:

$$Y_{(m)} = 1.27 y_{fm}$$

Extrapolating further, the 100-year return value is given by P = 0.99,. i.e.

$$Y_{(m)} = 1.65 y_{fm}$$

So, for example the monthly mean H_s in February exceeded on average once in a hundred February's is 7.9m. The value in February 1997 appears (from only 17 observations) to have been very close to this.

4.3 ABNORMAL CONDITIONS FROM INDIVIDUAL WAVE HEIGHT DATA RECORDS

So far we have only analysed monthly means, comparing the within- and between-year variability, but of course there is further variability in individual wave heights within a month. Figure 8b shows calendar monthly means as in Figure 3 this time with +/- the standard deviations of the individual H_s values within each month.

The annual cycle can be fitted to the individual observations (allowing for the time of the observation within the month). This gives, for the 3863 transect values from the area outlined in Figure 1, a highly significant annual cycle with mean of 3.46 m, amplitude of 1.57 m, and maximum on 14 January; the reduction in variance is 35.5%.

This fit and the individual observations are shown in Figure 12. (The semi-annual cycle was also highly significant, but its amplitude was only 0.1m so has been neglected.)

One way to estimate return values of individual values of H_s is to follow that often employed with a few years of buoy data: to fit all the data to a distribution and extrapolate to a probability corresponding to the required return value. This probability value is by no means obvious! With buoy data, that corresponding to the number of 3 hours in the return period is widely used, and Carter [1993] found that this, when applied to Geosat data from around the UK gave very similar 50-year return values to those in the Department of Energy's "Guidance Notes".

A more acceptable approach, statistically, would be to analyse residuals, similar to the method used above for monthly means. The skewness in the residuals, clearly seen in Figure 12 (the range of points above the fitted curve is much larger than that below), suggests that analysing log(H_s) might be advisable.

The problem with these methods is that the probability distributions of the data or the residuals are not known. We fitted the normalised monthly mean residuals to a Fisher-Tippett Type 1 (FT-1) distribution. This distribution was also employed by Carter [1993] to fit individual H_s values. Often 2 or 3 parameter Weibull distributions are used. But there is no theoretical or physical justification for any distribution. This is a particular problem when, as here, extrapolation is required to get estimates of abnormal conditions such as the 100-year wave height. Methods based on extreme value analysis or peaks-over-threshold do have a sound theoretical basis, but techniques to apply these to satellite altimeter data, with their widely intermittent data sampling, have yet to be developed.

4.4 THE EFFECT OF LONG TERM TRENDS ON EXTREMES

The detection of long term climate change is usually treated as a problem of estimating differences in mean conditions - or some other location parameter such as the mode or median. This is clearly a useful first step; and, moreover, has the advantage that there exist robust tests for checking the statistical significance of differences in the mean.

However there is no reason to assume that changes in a climate parameter are limited to changes in the location parameter of the distribution and that the scale parameter will remain constant; and changes in the scale parameter, or in the variance of the distribution, could have a much greater effect upon variation in the extreme values than indicated by a change of location.

To test for such changes in the distributions, and hence in predicted extremes, altimeter data from the study region to the West of Ireland have been extracted for the two continuous periods of altimeter data available: 1985-89 (from Geosat) and 1991-97 (from ERS-1 and Topex). Distribution functions for each period are plotted in Figure 13. It can be seen that the distribution function of the later data has a higher mode, and is slightly broader. These data were then fitted, using maximum likelihood estimation (MLE), to an FT-1 distribution. Results are given in Table 2.

TABLE 2 FT-1 Parameters fitted by MLE to Altimeter H_s transect medians in selected region West of Ireland (N.B. calibrations have been updated since the paper)

EFFECT OF LONG TERM TRENDS ON PREDICTED EXTREMES

Data Set	Alpha (Location)	α std. err.	Beta (scale)	β std. err.	100 yr rtn H_s	std. err.
Geosat (1985-89)	2.51	0.05	1.29	0.03	18.70	0.42
ERS-1/Topex (1991-97)	2.60	0.03	1.33	0.02	19.34	0.25
All Data (1989-97)	2.58	0.02	1.32	0.02	19.19	0.22

The first two rows in Table 2 confirm the visual impressions from Figure 13, and shows that there are differences between the location and scale parameters of the FT-1 distributions fitted to the two series of altimeter data, and that both have increased with time. The predicted 100 yr return value of H_s can similarly be seen to have increased (from 19.15m to 19.90m). 1.96 multiplied by the standard error is often taken as a measure of (95%) significance, and for the above results this measure would seem to indicate that there is a significant difference between the parameters of the distributions and the predicted extremes of the two series of data, 1985-89 and 1991-97 (using the standard errors from the second series of data). However, in the case of analysis of statistical distributions, defining the true test for significance is not a trivial exercise, and more work needs to be done in this area.

For comparison with the distribution fitted to the monthly mean data, the fit to the FT-1 distribution of the entire data set (final row in Table 2), is illustrated in Figure 11b.

5. CONCLUSIONS

The most striking feature of the wave height climate over much of the globe, including the North Atlantic, is the large variability. Besides the annual cycle (within-year variability) there are also considerable variability between-year and within-month. Since 1986, satellite altimeters have provided us with routine global, open-ocean measurements of significant wave height which are enabling us to estimate the variability on these time scales, and hence begin both to quantify 'abnormal conditions' and to give probabilities of occurrence.

The satellite database, now extending over 12 years, is just sufficient for us to start looking for variability over decades but can only be used to investigate trends in mean conditions and the spatial scales of such trends. Significant changes in extreme conditions are much harder to detect. Nevertheless the database is an invaluable start and, assuming the routine monitoring of the waves by altimeters continues, it will become a useful source of measurements to determine decadal trends and hopefully to indicate the physical forcing responsible for the variations.

6. REFERENCES

1. BACON, S & CARTER, D J T: 'Wave climate changes in the north Atlantic and North Sea', Int. J. Climat., 11, 545-558, 1991.

2. BACON, S & CARTER, D J T: 'A connection between mean wave height and atmospheric pressure gradient in the North Atlantic', Int. J. Climat., 13, 423-436, 1993.

3. BROWN, G S: 'The average impulse response of a rough surface and its applications', IEEE Trans. Antennas Propag., AP-25, 67-74, 1977.

4. CARDONE, V J, and SWAIL, V R: 'Uncertainty in prediction of extreme storm seas (ESS)', pp.1-20 in, Preprints 4th International workshop on wave hindcasting and forecasting, Banff, Alberta, October 16-20, 1995, (ed.V.R.Swail). Downsview, Ontario: Environment Canada, 358pp, 1995.

5. CARTER, D J T: 'Estimating extreme wave heights in the NE Atlantic from Geosat data', Health and Safety Executive Offshore Technology Report No. OTH 93 396. HMSO, London, 24pp, 1993.

6. CARTER, D J T and DRAPER, L: 'Has the North East Atlantic become rougher?', Nature, 332, p494, 1988.

7. CARTER, D J T, CHALLENOR, P G & COTTON, P D: 'Surface wave statistics from satellite altimeters, in "Seakeeping and Weather" ', RINA International Conference, Royal Institution of Naval Architects, London, March 1995.

8. COTTON, P D, CHALLENOR, P G & CARTER, D J T: 'An assessment of the accuracy and reliability of Geosat, ERS-1, ERS-2 and Topex altimeter measurements of significant wave height and wind speed'. Proceedings CEOS Wind and wave validation workshop, 3-5 June, 1997, ESTEC, Noordwijk, The Netherlands.

9. GOWER, J F R: 'Intercalibration of wave and wind data from TOPEX/POSEIDON and moored buoys off the west coast of Canada', J. Geophys. Res., 101(C2), 3817-3829, 1996.

10. HAVER S: 'Possible impacts of climate changes regarding safety and operations of existing offshore structures', pp.21-30 in Preprints, 4th Intern. Workshop on Wave Hindcasting & Forecasting, Banff, Alberta, 16-20 Oct. 1995.

11. MEARNS L O, KATZ R W & Schneider S H: 'Extreme high temperature events: Changes in their probabilities with changes in mean temperature', J. Climate Appl. Meteor., 23, 1601-1613, 1984.

12. MUNNICH, M, LATIF, M VENZKE, S, MAIER-REIMER, E: 'Decadal oscillations in a simple coupled model', Max-Planck-Institut fur Meteorologie, Hamburg, Report No. 225, 25pp, 1997.

13. STERL, A, KOMEN, G J & COTTON, P D: '15 years of global wave hindcasts using ERA winds-Validating the reanalysed winds and assessing the wave climate', accepted, J. Geophys. Res., 1997

14. VAN HOOFF, R W: 'Trends in the wave climate of the Atlantic and the North Sea: Evidence and Implications', Underwater Technology, Vol 19, no. 4, pp20-23, 1994.

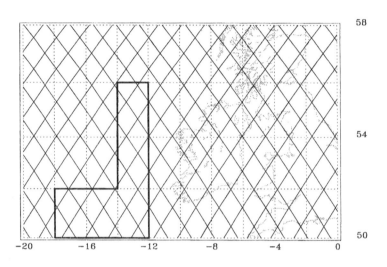

Fig. 1 Ground tracks, to the west of the British Isles, of the altimeter of Geosat in a 17 day repeat orbit. Area of data subsequently analysed is outlined.

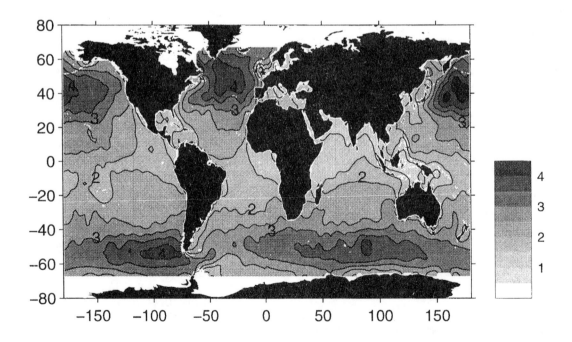

Fig. 2 Mean significant wave heights (m) from the (2° x 2°) gridded altimeter wave climatology, for January-March 1996. Contours at 0.5m intervals, the graded grey scale, is given in the key.

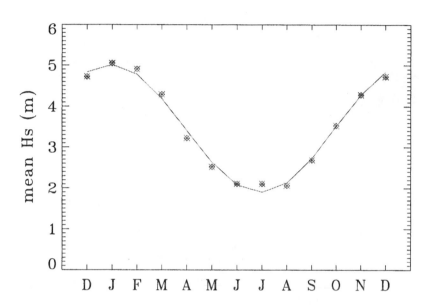

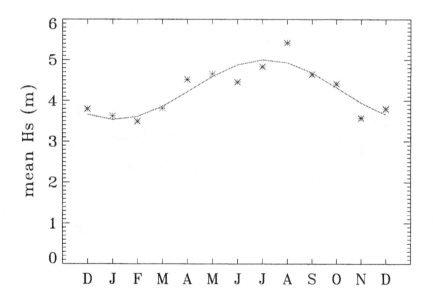

Fig. 3 Monthly mean significant wave height, and the annual cycle sine curve fitted to these twelve values, for all transects by Geosat, ERS-1 and TOPEX (1986-1997) of the 2° bins (top) outlined in Figure, and (bottom) from 44° -46°S. 120°-130°E

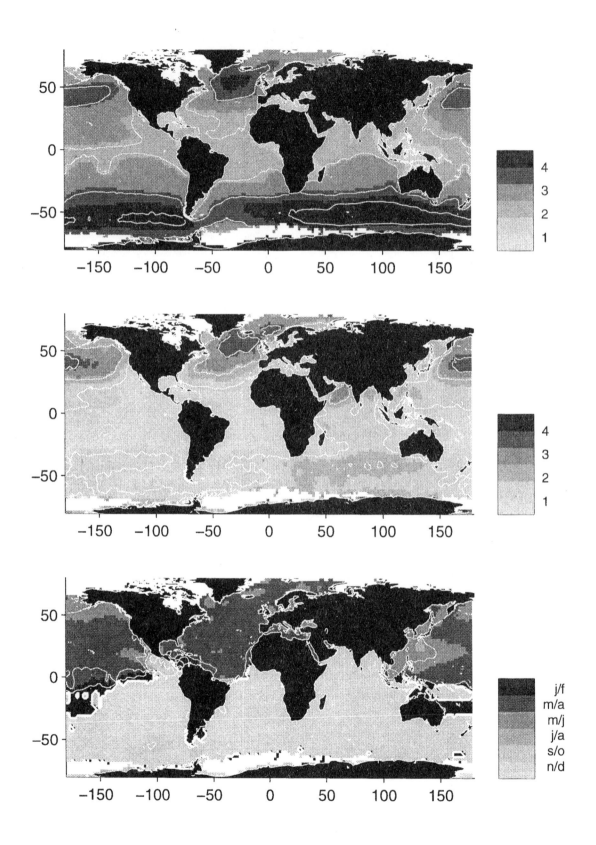

Fig. 4 Parameters calculated from the annual cycle fitted to monthly mean altimeter data from 1985-96. (a) Top panel, annual mean significant wave height. (b) Middle panel, range of annual cycle, (c) Bottom panel, month of maximum wave height

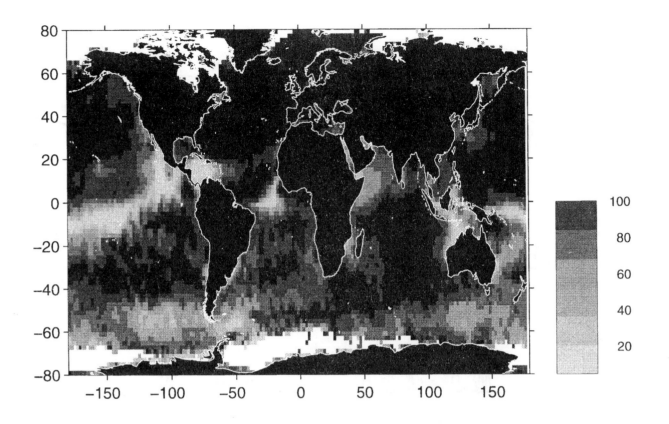

Fig. 5 Percentage reduction in variance obtained after fitting and removing annual cycle to monthly mean data 1985-96

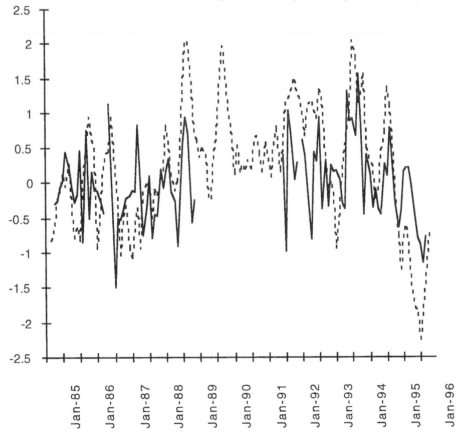

Fig. 7 The monthly North Atlantic Oscillation Index (5 month moving average - bold dotted line) and significant wave height residual at OWS Lima (thinner solid line)

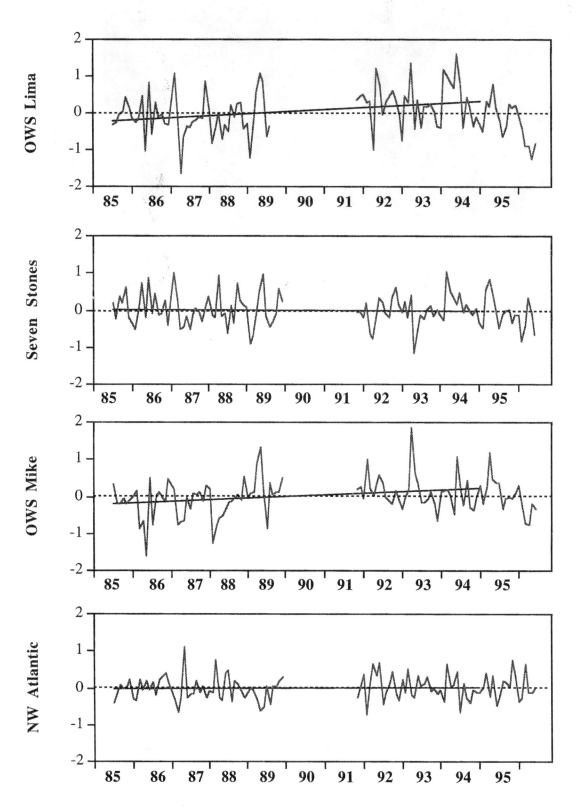

Fig. 6 Residual Monthly Mean Significant Wave Heights (1985-96) for Four North Atlantic Regions: (a) OWS Lima, (b) Seven Stones, (c) OWS Mike, (d) NW Atlantic. Linear trends have been fitted for 1985-94

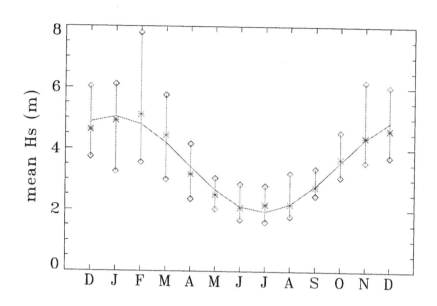

Fig. 8a Mean and range of individual monthly mean H_s values from the area outlined in Figure 1, with the annual cycle fitted to all 88 monthly means

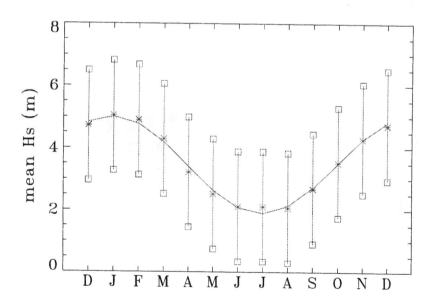

Fig. 8b Monthly mean H_s with +/- standard deviations of the measurements (about 300 in each month)

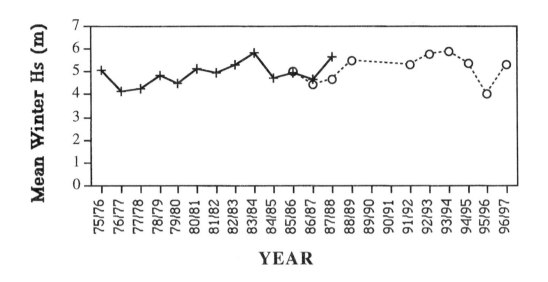

Fig. 9 Winter Mean SWH from OWS Lima (+), and altimeter data (o)

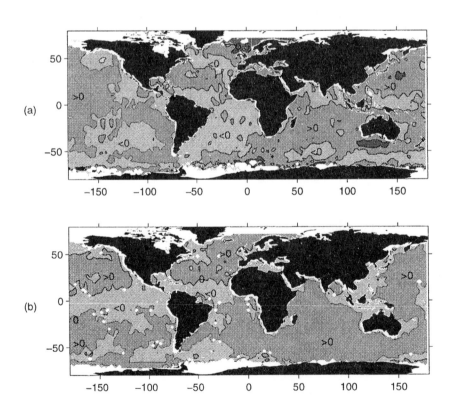

Fig. 10 Difference in SWH Annual Cycle Maximum (top) and Mean (bottom) between the periods 1985-89 and 1991-95. Contours are at 0.5m intervals, with the lightest grey areas showing a *decrease* (from 1985-89 to 1991-95) of between -0.5 to 0m, the next lightest an *increase* of 0.0 to 0.5m, and the darkest grey an *increase* of *more* than 0.5m

14

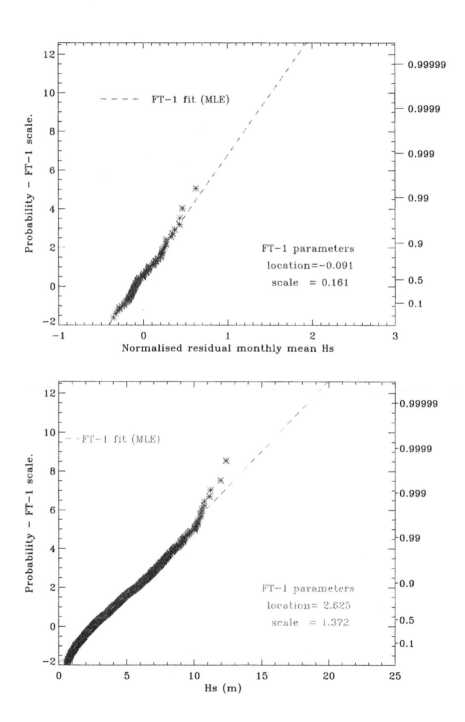

Fig. 11 Probability distribution and Fisher-Tippett Type 1 distribution fitted by maximum likelihood to (a) upper panel, of the 88 individual normalised monthly mean wave heights 1985-97, and (b) lower panel, of all H_s transect medians, 1991-97

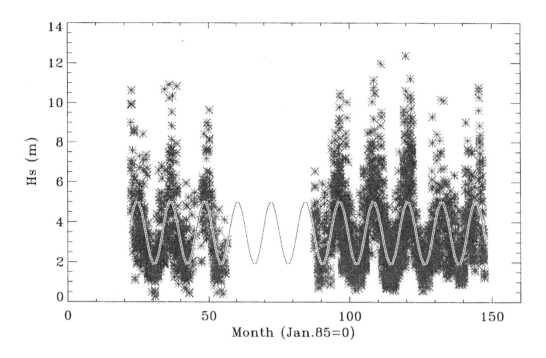

Fig. 12 H_s values from all transects by Geosat, ERS-1 and TOPEX, 1986-1997, across the 2° bins outlined in **Figure 1**, with the fitted annual cycle

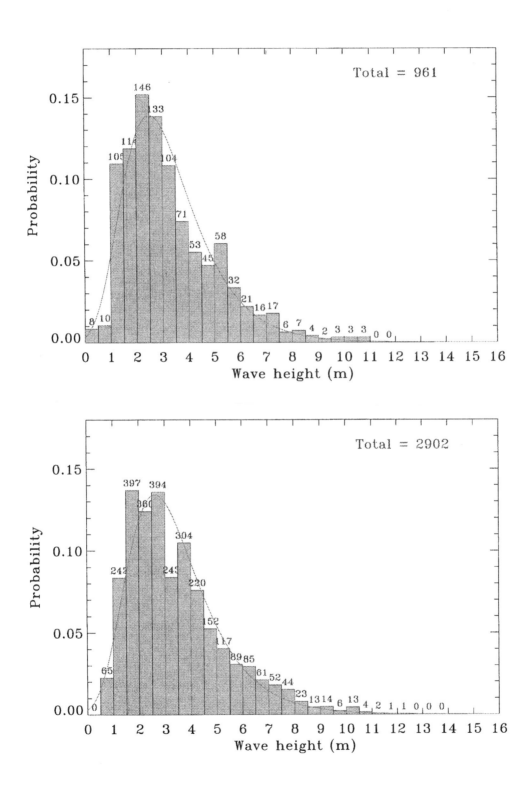

Fig. 13 Distribution functions for all H_s transect median values within study region (Figure 1). For (a) upper panel, 1985-89, and (b) lower panel 1991-97

PAPER NO.4.

WAVE PROFILES ASSOCIATED WITH EXTREME LOADING IN RANDOM WAVES

by K R Drake
Department of Mechanical Engineering, University College London, UK

Paper presented at the

International Conference

DESIGN AND OPERATION FOR ABNORMAL CONDITIONS

21 22 OCTOBER 1997 GLASGOW

WAVE PROFILES ASSOCIATED WITH EXTREME LOADING IN RANDOM WAVES

K R Drake

Department of Mechanical Engineering, University College London

SUMMARY

This paper investigates the wave surface profiles associated with specific types of extreme loading for ship structures in gaussian random waves. The methodology is based upon an established statistical relationship for a gaussian random process, which indicates that in the vicinity of an extreme event the most probable shape of the time history approaches that of the autocorrelation function.

For illustration purposes, the methodology is applied to the quasi-static response of a constant beam vessel in head seas. The wave surface profiles associated with extreme relative motion at the bow and extreme bending moment at midship are investigated for both Pierson-Moskowitz and JONSWAP wave spectra. Second order corrections to the wave surface profiles are also considered. It is shown that the case of extreme relative motion at the bow is associated with a wave surface profile which is steep-fronted and has significant asymmetry in the horizontal direction. This result is particularly significant because it closely resembles the scenario considered by Faulkner and Williams [1] for green water loading on the fore deck and hatch covers of a bulk carrier.

NOMENCLATURE

g	gravitational acceleration;
i	$\sqrt{-1}$
k	wave number ($= 2\pi/\lambda$)
l	vessel length;
m	wavelet counter;
n	wavelet counter;
t	time;
x	horizontal coordinate;
A	complex amplitude of wave surface elevation;
B	vessel beam;
H_{ζ_b}	linear transfer function of relative motion at the bow;
H_2	quadratic transfer function;
M_m	complex amplitude of bending moment at midship;
N	total number of wavelets;
S_{ζ_b}	spectrum of relative motion at the bow;
α	magnitude of extreme response;
λ	wavelength;
η	first order wave surface elevation;
$\eta^*_{\zeta_b}$	most probable wave elevation associated with extreme relative motion at the bow;
$\eta^*_{M_m}$	most probable wave elevation associated with extreme midship bending moment;
$\eta^{(2)}$	second order wave elevation;
ρ	density of seawater;
σ	standard deviation of response;
τ	time relative to occurrence of extreme event
ω	wave frequency
ξ_2	complex amplitude of heave response
ξ_6	complex amplitude of pitch response

ζ_b	complex amplitude of relative motion at the bow
ζ_b^*	most probable value of relative motion at the bow

AUTHOR'S BIOGRAPHY

Dr Kevin Drake, CEng, MICE, studied civil engineering at Leeds University and ocean engineering at University College London (UCL). After obtaining a PhD in 1984 he worked for Shell UK Exploration and Production for five years before joining Kvaerner Earl and Wright. His industrial experience has included the design, fabrication and installation of various offshore structures for the oil and gas industry. He returned to UCL in October 1995.

1. INTRODUCTION

Offshore measurements in extreme storm conditions have recorded individual waves with steep symmetric elevated crests[2] and also steep-fronted waves with pronounced asymmetry in the horizontal direction[3]. Similar wave profiles have been recorded during model tests in random waves[4]. The largest waves are formed by the superposition and interaction of various wave components which combine at a particular location and time before dispersing. Because of the temporary nature of these waves, they are sometimes referred to as transient waves.

A gaussian random wave model is unable to fully represent the time histories of wave surface elevation in extreme storms because nonlinear effects tend to sharpen the crests and flatten the troughs. However, an improved representation is obtained when second order corrections are applied to the underlying gaussian random process [2,3,4].

The significance of wave shape will depend on the characteristics of the structure being loaded. The work that is described in this paper is aimed at developing *design waves* for specific types of loading on ship structures. The paper has been written in response to a recommendation made by Faulkner and Williams [1] concerning the need for improved design methods when determining the profiles of extreme waves.

Although nonlinear loading mechanisms and nongaussian waves will have a significant influence on extreme loading, it is hypothesised that there may be important design cases where the occurrence of extreme nonlinear response is closely correlated with the wave surface profile which maximises the linear response. For example, it is considered that extreme green water loading on the foredeck of a ship will be generated by wave profiles that maximise the first order relative motion between the wave surface and the bow of the vessel.

When the underlying wave shape has been defined, it is straightforward to compute the corresponding second order corrections which sharpen the crests and flatten the troughs. The overall methodology results in short duration wave sequences being used to characterise extreme design events; this has potential benefits for wave tank testing, computational modelling and design.

2.   ANALYSIS METHOD

2.1   STATISTICAL BASIS

Tromans et al.[5] investigated the shape of the water surface for the region around a wave crest in a random sea. The main purpose was to produce a more realistic formulation for design waves, compared to deterministic methods, when computing the extreme wave loads on fixed offshore platforms. The analysis was based upon gaussian random waves and considered the following random variables: wave elevation and slope at time t_1 and wave elevation at time t. By defining a crest at time t_1, and using standard relationships for the joint and conditional probability distributions, it was shown that in the vicinity of the wave crest the expected and most probable shape of the time history is described by the autocorrelation function. This result is only exact for a narrow band process due to the omission of curvature when defining the wave crest. However, for the general case the shape of the autocorrelation function is approached when the excursion is large[6]. Tromans et al.[5] advocated using the autocorrelation function as a model for a design wave and referred to the concept as New Wave.

Jonathon et al.[6] analysed the measurements recorded at the Tern platform in the northern North Sea during three severe winter storms. It was found that the autocorrelation function provided a good model for the underlying shape of a large wave after second order effects had been taken into account.

The spectral density of a random process is defined by the Fourier transform of its autocorrelation function. In design, it is common practice to evaluate response spectra using linear transfer functions and input wave spectra. It is relatively unusual to compute the autocorrelation function of a random process, however, this can be readily obtained from the inverse Fourier transform of the appropriate spectrum.

Extreme global wave loads for fixed steel jacket structures are generally dominated by drag forces associated with extreme horizontal fluid velocities. For a particular seastate, it is expected that the extreme global loading will be closely correlated with the occurrence of the largest wave crests. The New Wave formulation is based upon the wave profile in the vicinity of a crest and is specifically directed towards predicting the extreme nonlinear loads for jacket structures. For ship structures, however, the correlation between specific types of extreme loading and wave shape may be rather different. For example, wave steepness may be more important than crest elevation, and the ratio of the length between successive crests (or troughs) and the length of the vessel may also be significant.

In the following sections, autocorrelation functions are used to approximate the shape of the extreme response time histories of a linear system responding to gaussian random waves. When the time histories of extreme response have been defined, it is then possible to compute the associated wave profiles.

2.2   LINEAR TRANSFER FUNCTIONS

For illustrative purposes, it is useful to consider a slender stationary vessel, of constant beam, responding in a quasi-static manner to head seas. Response parameters of interest are the relative vertical motion at the bow and the longitudinal bending moment at midship. The reasons for selecting these cases are, firstly, to investigate the wave profiles that are likely to generate green water loading on the fore deck, and secondly, to provide a basis for comparison with the deterministic design methods used for longitudinal strength checks. The formulation of the linear transfer functions is given below.

For a regular wave, propagating in the negative *x* direction, the first order wave surface elevation is defined by

$$\eta(t,x) = \mathrm{Re}\big[A\exp\big(i(\omega t + kx)\big)\big] \qquad (1)$$

For a slender vessel responding quasi-statically to waves, the vertical force is dominated by the hydrostatic restoring force and the Froude-Krylov exciting force[7]. The heave and pitch responses are found by integrating the forces and moments along the vessel and solving for equilibrium. For a vessel of length l in head seas, with the location of midship at $x = 0$, the complex heave and pitch responses may be estimated from the following equations

$$\frac{\xi_2}{A} = \frac{2}{kl}\sin\frac{kl}{2} \qquad (2)$$

$$\frac{\xi_6 l}{2A} = \frac{12i}{(kl)^2}\left(\sin\frac{kl}{2} - \frac{kl}{2}\cos\frac{kl}{2}\right) \qquad (3)$$

where the heave response is positive in the upward direction and the pitch reponse is positive when pitching causes upward motion at the bow. The complex relative vertical motion at the bow is obtained by combining the above equations, thus

$$\frac{\zeta_b}{A} = \cos\frac{kl}{2} + i\sin\frac{kl}{2} - \frac{\xi_2}{A} - \frac{\xi_6 l}{2A} \qquad (4)$$

The midship bending moment is found by integrating the moments due to hydrostatic and Froude-Krylov forces along half of the vessel to obtain

$$\frac{M_m}{\rho g A B l^2} = \frac{1}{(kl)^2}\left(1 - \cos\frac{kl}{2} - \frac{kl}{4}\sin\frac{kl}{2}\right) \qquad (5)$$

The midship moment M_m is positive when the ship is hogging.

2.3   WAVE PROFILES

For the case of extreme relative motion at the bow, the most probable shape of the time history of relative motion can be approximated by the corresponding autocorrelation function. The latter may be obtained from the inverse Fourier transform of the spectrum of relative motion. Thus, the most probable time history of relative motion at the bow may be computed from the following expression

$$\zeta_b^*(\tau) = \frac{\alpha}{\sigma^2}\int_0^\infty S_{\zeta_b}(\omega)\cos(\omega\tau)\,d\omega$$

$$\approx \frac{\alpha}{\sigma^2}\sum_{n=1}^N S_{\zeta_b}(\omega_n)\cos(\omega_n\tau)\Delta\omega_n \qquad (6)$$

where α is the extreme relative motion, σ is the standard deviation of relative motion and S_{ζ_b} is the spectrum of relative motion.

The amplitudes of the various wavelets for the associated wave profile are obtained by dividing the frequency components of the relative motion time history by the appropriate values of the linear transfer function. The profile of each wavelet is then determined using Equation (1). Thus, the most probable wave elevation associated with extreme relative motion at the bow is obtained from the following summation

$$\eta_{\zeta_b}^*(\tau, x) = \frac{\alpha}{\sigma^2}\text{Re}\left[\sum_{n=1}^N \frac{S_{\zeta_b}(\omega_n)}{H_{\zeta_b}(\omega_n)}\exp(i(\omega_n\tau + k_n x))\Delta\omega_n\right] \qquad (7)$$

where H_{ζ_b} is the linear transfer function obtained from equation (4).

The above methodology can also be applied to the midship bending moment and various other design parameters.

3.   RESULTS AND DISCUSSION

The linear transfer functions for bow relative motion and midship bending moment in head seas are shown in Figures 1 and 2. The results are presented in non-dimensional form, as a function of the ratio of vessel length to wavelength, and are computed from Equations (4) and (5). In both cases, it can be seen that the maximum responses arise when the wavelength is approximately equal to the vessel length.

The remaining figures are based upon the results obtained for a vessel of length 300 metres, subjected to stationary seas with a peak period of 13.5 seconds. Results are presented for both Pierson-Moskowitz and JONSWAP wave spectra [8]. The parameters have been selected in order to provide a basis for comparison with the scenario investigated by Faulkner and Williams [1] for green sea loading on the fore deck and hatch covers of a bulk carrier.

Figures 3 to 8 are based upon the use of linear transfer functions and deep water gaussian random waves. Figure 3 shows the response spectrum of relative motion at the bow for a Pierson-Moskowitz wave spectrum. The peak value of the reponse spectrum occurs at a frequency which corresponds very closely to the peaks of the transfer function and the wave elevation spectrum. Figure 4 shows the most probable time history associated with extreme relative motion at the bow. The results have been computed using Equation (6) and normalised by setting the extreme relative motion at the bow to unity. With the time history presented in normalised form, the values correspond directly with the autocorrelation coefficient for the response spectrum shown in Figure 3.

Figures 5 and 6 show the most probable wave profiles associated with the instant of extreme relative motion at the bow for Pierson-Moskowitz and JONSWAP wave spectra. The wave profiles have been computed from Equation (7) with time $\tau = 0$. It is noted that the direction of wave propagation is from right to left (ie. in the negative x direction). The JONSWAP wave profile is, as expected, more narrow-banded in appearance. Also shown in the figures are the corresponding orientations of the still waterline (SWL) of the vessel. At the bow of the vessel, which is located at the 150 metres position, it can be seen that the relative elevation between the wave and vessel SWL is unity , and therefore consistent with Figure 4. For the selected parameters, it is evident that the occurrence of extreme relative motion at the bow - and hence, green water loading on the fore deck - is associated with the vessel bow pitching downward into a steep-fronted wave which has significant asymmetry in the horizontal direction. It must be emphasised that this observation is pertinent only to the instant of extreme relative motion, because the wave profile will vary continually with time, due to dispersion effects in the random wave model.

Also presented in Figures 5 and 6 are the expected wave profiles obtained from numerical simulations. In each case the profiles have been computed by averaging the normalised profiles obtained from 100 separate simulations of the selected seastate. Time histories of bow relative motion were produced using inverse fast Fourier transform techiques to compute 8192 (i.e. 2^{13}) data points at 0.25 second intervals, thus representing a duration of approximately 34 minutes per simulation. The general numerical procedure was based on the approach recommended by Tucker et al[9]. For each simulation, the time corresponding to maximum relative motion was identified and the corresponding normalised wave profile (ie. wave profile associated with unit relative motion) then computed. It is noted, from Troman's derivation[5], that the most probable values of surface elevation around a crest are equal to the expected values. In both figures, the wave profiles predicted using Equation (7) are found to be in close agreement with values obtained from numerical simulations.

In Figures 7 and 8, results are presented for the case of extreme midship bending moment. The results have been obtained using the linear transfer function given in Equation (5) and the same procedure as for relative motion. From both figures, it can be seen that the case of extreme midship bending moment is associated with a symmetric wave profile with the crest (or trough) located at midship. Due to symmetry, the pitch of the vessel is zero. It is observed that the profiles are very similar in appearance to the shape of the profiles used in deterministic design methods for checking longitudinal strength. For the latter, it is common practice to consider a regular wave with a wavelength approximately equal to the length of the ship.

For Figures 9 to 12, second order corrections have been applied to the wave profiles using the procedure described in the Appendix. The key parameters which determine the wave profiles have been defined in accordance with the scenario considered by Faulkner and Williams[1] namely, a seastate of 36 hours duration with a significant waveheight of 14 metres and a peak period of 13.5 seconds, in conjunction with a 5 % probability of exceedance for extreme values. The scenario corresponds to a seastate of limiting steepness with extreme linear responses which are approximately five times the standard deviation. Values obtained for the extreme relative motion of the bow are 19.5 and 20.8 metres respectively for the Pierson-Moskowitz and JONSWAP wave spectra.

Figures 9 and 10 show the first and second order wave profiles associated with extreme first order relative motion at the bow for Pierson-Moskowitz and JONSWAP wave spectra. It can be seen that the principal effect of the second order correction is to significantly sharpen the largest crests and flatten the adjacent troughs. No attempt has been made to assess the influence of the second order wave elevation on the response of the vessel. The main purpose of computing the second order profile has been to give an indication of the degree of wave surface nonlinearity that is to be expected, and also to provide a methodology for computing realistic profiles for design waves.

Figures 11 and 12 show the second order wave profiles described above, but re-plotted over the horizontal distance -50 to 250 metres using equal length scales for the horizontal and vertical axes. The main features are annotated and the related wave profile parameters are compared in Table 1. Values obtained for the instantaneous mean wave front steepness and vertical asymmetry are very similar to the values used by Faulkner and Williams[1], whilst the horizontal asymmetry is more severe. When comparing the values, it should be noted that the results presented in this paper represent the shape of the water surface at the time of extreme response. As the individual wavelets disperse, the shape of the wave profile will change with time.

Although second order corrections will provide an improved representation of the wave surface, it is noted that Baldock et al.[10] have demonstrated that nonlinear effects beyond second order can become significant for very large waves. The results presented in Table 1 and Figures 9 to 12 should therefore be treated with an appropriate degree of caution.

4.   CONCLUSIONS AND RECOMMENDATIONS

An outline methodology has been presented for predicting the most probable wave profiles associated with specific types of extreme loading on ship structures in stationary random seas. The theory is based upon an underlying gaussian random wave model and uses

4

autocorrelation functions to approximate the response time histories for extreme events. The validity of the theoretical approach has been confirmed by the results of numerical simulations.

For the illustrative case considered in this paper, the principal conclusions are as follows :

- extreme relative motion at the bow - and hence, green water loading on the fore deck - is associated with the vessel bow pitching downward into a steep-fronted wave which has significant asymmetry in the horizontal direction;

- extreme midship bending moment is associated with a symmetric wave profile that closely resembles the wave shapes used in deterministic design methods with the crest (or trough) located at midship;

- for the largest waves, in seastates of limiting steepness, nonlinear effects will contribute significantly to sharpening the crests and flattening the troughs.

The following recommendations are made for future work :

- Numerical simulations and physical model tests to investigate the correlation between wave profiles which generate extreme nonlinear responses in extreme seas and profiles which maximise linear response in moderate seas of the same peak period.

- A design study to estimate green sea loadings, using the proposed methodology in conjunction with an analysis of nonlinear vessel response and latest guidance on fluid loading aspects (e.g. Buchner[11, 12]).

- Although there has been considerable research on the generation of extreme transient waves for model testing purposes (e.g. Clauss and Kuehnlein[13]), the potential for structure and loading specific wave profiles should be investigated.

ACKNOWLEDGEMENTS

The author would like to thank Rod Rainey of W S Atkins Consulting Limited for helpful discussions, and Professor David Andrews of University College London for reviewing the manuscript.

REFERENCES

1. FAULKNER, D. and WILLIAMS, R.A., 'Design for abnormal ocean waves', RINA Spring Meetings, Paper No. 1, 1996.

2. ROZARIO, J.B., TROMANS, P.S., TAYLOR, P.H. and EFTHYMIOU, M., 'Comparisons of loads predicted using New Wave and other wave models with measurements on the Tern structure'. In *Wave Kinematics and Environmental Forces* , 29, SUT, Kluwer, 1993, pp. 143-58.

3. BUCKLEY, W.H., 'Analysis of wave characteristics in extreme seas', Ship Structure Committee Report, SSC-353, 1991.

4. DUNCAN, P.E. and DRAKE K.R., 'A note on the simulation and analysis of irregular nonlinear waves', Applied Ocean Research, 1995, Vol. 17, No. 1, pp. 1-8.

5. TROMANS, P.S., ANATURK, A.R. and HAGEMEIJER, P: 'A new model for the kinematics of large ocean waves - application as a design wave', Proc. 1st Int. Offshore and Polar Engineering Conference, Edinburgh, 1991, Vol. 3, pp.64-71.

6. JONATHON, P., TAYLOR, P.H. and TROMANS, P.S., 'Storm waves in the northern North Sea', Proc. 7th Int. Conf. on Behaviour of Offshore Structures (BOSS), 1994, Vol. 2, pp. 481-494, MIT.

7. NEWMAN, J.N., 'Marine Hydrodynamics', MIT Press, 1977, ISBN 0-262-14026-8.

8. FALTINSEN, O.M., 'Sea loads on ships and offshore structures', Cambridge University Press, 1990, ISBN 0-521-45870-6.

9. TUCKER, M.J., CHALLENOR, P.G. and CARTER, D.J.T., 'Numerical simulation of a random sea: a common error and its effect upon wave group statistics', Applied Ocean Research, 1984, Vol. 6, No. 2, pp. 118-122.

10. BALDOCK, T.E., SWAN, C. and TAYLOR, P.H., 'A laboratory study of nonlinear surface waves on water', Phil. Trans. Roy. Soc. London, 1996, Series A, Vol. 354, pp. 649-676.

11. BUCHNER, B., 'The Impact of Green Water on FPSO Design', 27th Annual Offshore Technology Conference, Houston, 1995, OTC 7698, pp. 45-57.

12. BUCHNER, B., 'An Investigation into the Numerical Simulation of Green Water', Proc. 8th Int. Conf. Behaviour of Offshore Structures (BOSS), 1997, Vol. 2, pp. 113-125.

13. CLAUSS, G.F. and KUEHNLEIN, 'A New tool for Seakeeping Tests - Nonlinear Transient Wave Packets', Proc. 8th Int. Conf. Behaviour of Offshore Structures (BOSS), 1997, Vol. 2, pp. 269-285.

APPENDIX - SECOND ORDER WAVE PROFILES

Second order contributions to the wave surface elevation in random seas are associated with the sum and difference frequencies of first order wave components. The sum frequency components are of particular interest for the extreme loading on a freely floating vessel.

For deep water waves these components may be calculated from the simple quadratic transfer function

which defines the amplitude of the second order interaction of two first order regular waves [4]

$$H_2(\omega_m, \omega_n) = \frac{(\omega_m^2 + \omega_n^2)}{2g} \quad \text{(A1)}$$

For irregular waves the sum frequency components of the second order wave elevation are obtained from

$$\eta^{(2)}(t, x) = \text{Re}\left[\sum_{n=1}^{N} \sum_{m=1}^{N} \frac{A_m A_n}{2} H_2(\omega_m, \omega_n) \exp\left(i(\omega_m + \omega_n)t + i(k_m + k_n)x\right)\right] \quad \text{(A2)}$$

where A_m and A_n are the complex amplitudes of the first order wave components.

TABLE 1 Comparison of wave profile parameters

Wave Profile Parameters	Faulkner and Williams[1]	Pierson-Moskowitz Spectrum (Figure 11)	JONSWAP Spectrum (Figure 12)
mean wave front steepness $m = A_c/OF$	0.5	0.50	0.43
vertical asymmetry $a_v = A_c/H$	0.65	0.66	0.62
horizontal asymmetry $a_h = OF/OR$	0.7	0.38	0.46

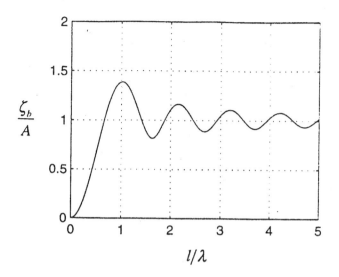

Figure 1   Linear transfer function of relative vertical motion at the bow

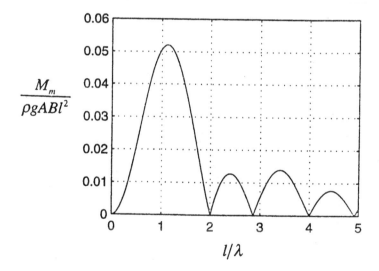

Figure 2   Linear transfer function of bending moment at midship

7

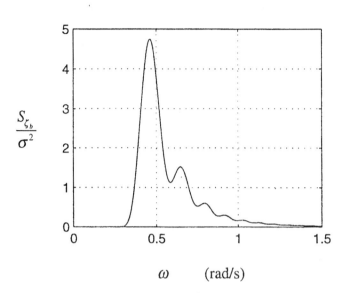

Figure 3   Spectrum of relative motion at the bow for
             a Pierson-Moskowitz spectrum

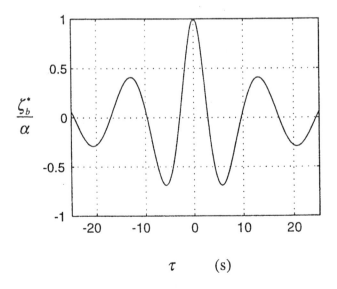

Figure 4   Time history of most probable relative motion
             in the vicinity of an extreme event for a
             Pierson-Moskowitz spectrum

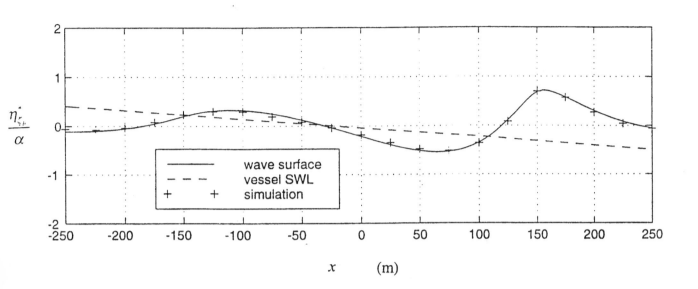

Figure 5   **Wave profile associated with extreme relative motion at the bow for a Pierson-Moskowitz spectrum**

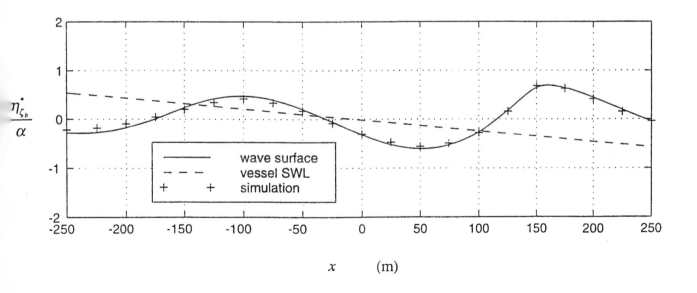

Figure 6   **Wave profile associated with extreme relative motion at the bow for a JONSWAP spectrum**

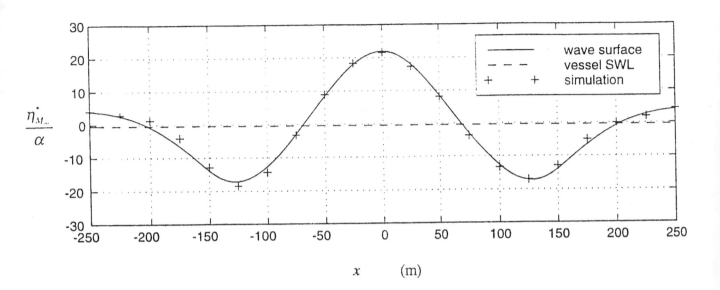

Figure 7   Wave profile associated with extreme midship bending moment for a Pierson-Moskowitz spectrum

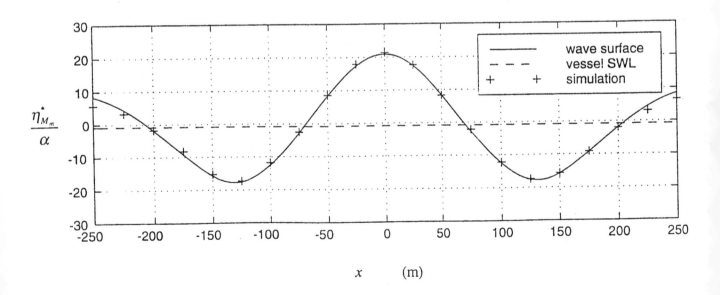

Figure 8   Wave profile associated with extreme midship bending moment for a JONSWAP spectrum

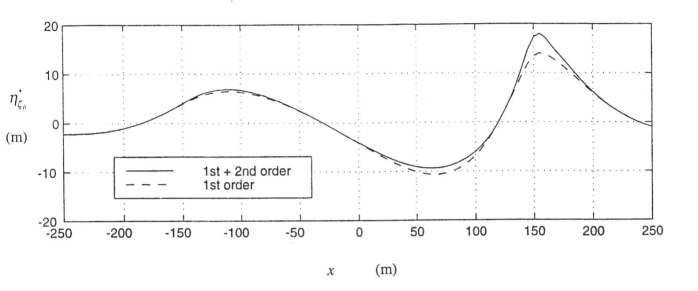

Figure 9 First and second order wave profiles associated with extreme first order relative motion at the bow for a Pierson-Moskowitz spectrum

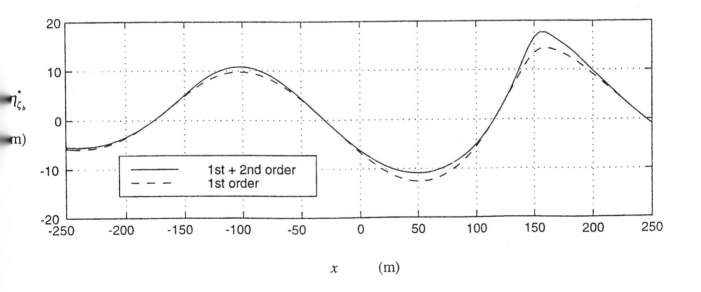

Figure 10 First and second order wave profiles associated with extreme first order relative motion at the bow for a JONSWAP spectrum

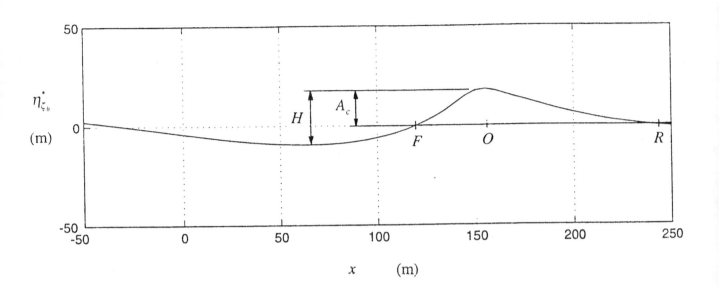

Figure 11   Combined first and second order wave profile associated with extreme first order relative motion at the bow for a Pierson-Moskowitz spectrum

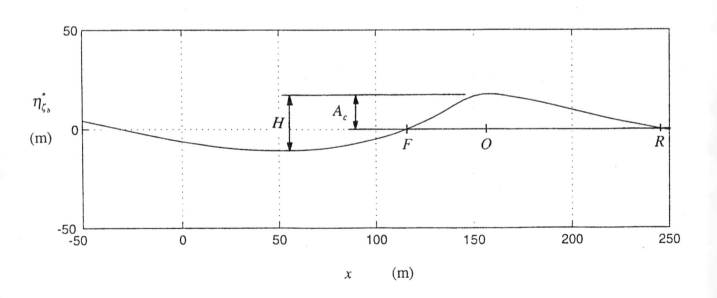

Figure 12   Combined first and second order wave profile associated with extreme first order relative motion at the bow for a JONSWAP spectrum

PAPER NO.5.

DEMAND AGAINST CAPABILITY - BREAKING WAVES AGAINST SHIP DESIGN AND OPERATION

by E A Dahle
Governmental Fishing Vessel Accident Commission,
Norwegian Ministry of Justice, Oslo, and
D Myrhaug
Department of Marine Hydrodynamics
Norwegian University of Science and Technology,
Trondheim, Norway

Paper presented at the

International Conference

**DESIGN AND OPERATION FOR
ABNORMAL CONDITIONS**

21 22 OCTOBER 1997 GLASGOW

DEMAND AGAINST CAPABILITY - BREAKING WAVES AGAINST SHIP DESIGN AND OPERATION

Emil Aall Dahle
Governmental Fishing Vessel Accident Commission
Norwegian Ministry of Justice, Oslo, Norway, and

Dag Myrhaug
Department of Marine Hydrodynamics,
Norwegian University of Science and Technology, Trondheim, Norway

SUMMARY

Adjusting capability to demand has always been a central task in engineering design for fixed structures. Calculation methods have taken over from trial and error. When age is taking its toll, the capability may deteriorate below the required minimum if compensation is not fully provided for by maintenance, or by over-design.

Realising that demand as well as capability may be associated with uncertainty, methods have been developed to express the safety of a design in statistical terms. The most relevant way of expressing safety is considered to be the expected probability of collapse of the design within a specified time span, preferably by presenting the marginal distribution of the probability.

For a moveable structure such as a ship, as opposed to a fixed structure, demand can be strongly influenced upon by the operator.

In the paper, risk management of a ship in terms of design and operation is discussed, concluding that safety can be obtained by adjusting operation to the design. However, the operative restrictions that have to be imposed must be expressed in a clear and explicit manner. Preferably, instrumentation should be provided to aid the operator by giving tactical warnings when action is needed to reduce the risk level.

AUTHORS' BIOGRAPHIES

Dr Emil Aall Dahle has been a member of the Governmental Fishing Vessel Accident Commission since 1980. He is Senior Principal Engineer in Det Norske Veritas, Høvik, Norway.

Dr Dag Myrhaug is Professor of Marine Hydrodynamics at the Faculty of Marine Technology, Norwegian University of Science and Technology.

1. INTRODUCTION

For fixed structures, risk management is restricted to over-design to avoid extensive maintenance, and to maintenance in various forms. These measures are related to the capability of the structure to withstand the demand from the environment in the form of wind, waves and sea currents exposure.

On some fixed structures at sea, critical operations are also undertaken. On oil installations, simultaneous drilling, oil well maintenance and oil production may take place. For such installations, the demand in terms of explosion and fire loads must be met by capability so that a specified safety level is obtained. For such accidents, the safety may be investigated by risk analysis, and design as well as operational measures may be employed to adjust the capability to a specified safety level.

For ships, the flexibility is wide because operations can have a very strong bearing on the safety level, by adjusting the demand as well as the capability. Typically, the speed or heading in heavy seas can be changed to reduce the demand, and the probability of structural damage. Alternatively, more capability can be added in the design stage to improve the capability.

2. DESIGN AND OPERATION TO OBTAIN A SPECIFIED SAFETY LEVEL

For capsize of ships to occur, the demand in terms of steep and high waves must exceed the capability in terms of stability. For this accident type, the capability is decided by:

- design features that influence upon the stability;

- operational measures that improve or damage the stability, including loading.

The demand is decided by:

- wave characteristics;

- operational handling of the vessel.

The factors can be considered as means for risk management. Bad design can be compensated for by good operation. More commonly, bad design in combination with bad operation is what causes accidents. On the other hand, good design and good operation is commonplace, resulting in a capsize risk that is not necessarily alarming.

In the following, a simple method is suggested for moderately safe ship design, for which good operation is needed to obtain an acceptable safety level. The method uses the principles applied in structural design on the basis of reliability analysis. To use the method, the marginal statistical distribution of capability (stability parameters) as well as demand (wave occurrence over time, and corresponding ship response) must be known. The influence that the operations have on capability and demand must also be known.

To numerically practice risk management for ships with regard to capsize, a level of acceptance must be formulated. If the present level is considered satisfactory, this level can serve the purpose.

2.1   DEMAND

Consider a ship lying beam to the sea, with waves breaking onto the ship from within a sector of 90°. This constitutes demand. Breaking waves are relatively high and short. The probability of encountering such waves at a random location at sea has been studied, see Ref. (1). For seastates defined by T_z and H_s, the probability of occurrence of dangerous waves, i.e., waves above specified threshold values for steepness and wave heights, has been calculated, and is given by

$$P = \text{Prob}[(\varepsilon > \varepsilon_c) \cap (H \geq H_c)|H_s, T_z] = \int_{\hat{\varepsilon}_c}^{\infty} \int_{\hat{h}_c}^{\infty} p(\hat{\varepsilon}, \hat{h}) d\hat{h} d\hat{\varepsilon}$$

(1)

H is the zero-downcross wave height, and ε is the crest front steepness defined by

$$\varepsilon = \frac{\eta'}{\frac{g}{2\pi} T^2 \cdot \frac{T'}{T}} = \frac{\eta'}{\frac{g}{2\pi} TT'} \qquad g = 9.81 \ m/s^2$$

The symbols are defined in Fig. 1. ε represents the mean crest front inclination of a zero-downcross wave in the time domain, and the definition is obtained by transforming the length scale to a time scale using the dispersion relationship $L = gT^2 / 2\pi$ for linear deep water waves. This is an approximation for the nonlinear wave form given in Fig. 1 and may therefore distort the results. The subscript c denotes the threshold value of the parameter. p is the joint probability density function of $\hat{\varepsilon} = \varepsilon/\varepsilon_{rms}$ and $\hat{h} = H/H_{rms}$, where the rms (root-mean square) values ε_{rms} and H_{rms} are related to the seastate

parameters H_s and T_z (see Ref. (1) and Ref. (2) for more details). The probability in Eq. (1) is illustrated by the shaded area in Fig. 2a.

This means that to express the demand, the seaway must be measured, and T_z and H_s must be made available for users. This is the case in many locations, and Iceland can be put forward as a good example. Already, 7 weather stations are in operation, and T_z H_s and wave direction are made available for users within minutes after the sampling has been made.

2.2   CAPABILITY

The ability of the ship to withstand breaking waves depends upon the intact stability. When being slowly forced to heel over by an external moment, the ship opposes the heeling until the intact stability becomes zero. When being exposed to a dynamic moment, energy from the breaking wave is transferred to the ship. The ship stores the energy by heeling over, until the static stability becomes zero. If the ship is able to store the transferred energy, capsize will not occur, otherwise it will.

Some of the energy transferred from the wave is also consumed by hydrodynamic damping, and some energy is consumed by transverse motion, which also is imposed by the wave, but the major part is stored by the heeling itself. Thus, the capability to withstand breaking waves from the side is expressed mainly by the area under the intact GZ-curve of the ship, multiplied by the displacement.

What remains is to ascertain the relation between this capability with demand. Some theoretical considerations were presented in Ref. (2), concluding that the problem was complex, and that model experiments could be used to establish an approximate relationship.

Also, in Ref. (2), it was argued that ship design was the most effective way to ensure capability against capsize in breaking waves, providing strong, watertight super-structures that could be effectively closed. In this way, the intact stability would effectively prevent capsize, if not large angles of heel.

2.3   DEMAND AGAINST CAPABILITY

Because a ship is free to move, and because its stability can be subject to changes by operational measures, demand and capability can be considered in conjunction, and risk management can be exercised. Obviously, such an approach will contain several uncertainty factors, basically:

Capability:

· uncertainty in GZ- and displacement calculations, mostly in weight and centre of gravity calculations with changing amount of cargo and fuel (a roll period instrument can be of great assistance to assess the GM);

2

- uncertainty in model experiments to ascertain the capsize limits;

- uncertainty in the operational handling of the ship, in particular if openings are closed or not.

Demand:

- uncertainty inherent in wave measurements;

- uncertainty in fitting of parametric models to wave data.

The combined uncertainties of these two effects are given by the standard deviations $\sigma_{\dot{\epsilon}_c}$ and $\sigma_{\hat{h}_c}$ of critical crest front steepness and wave height, respectively. This gives an uncertainty in the probability of occurrence of dangerous waves as illustrated by the shaded area in Fig. 2b.

Having realized these uncertainties, there remains the crucial task of assessing an acceptance criterion for capsize. It might be argued that such a criterion is not necessary, but as long as it seems to be accepted that ships can be designed with the ability to capsize, also administrators should have the courage to set an acceptance criterion for capsize.

Choosing a generic level of capsize risk of frequency per year, that has prevailed for some years and not considered to be unacceptable, can be considered as a means to avoid future deterioration of the situation.

3.   RISK MANAGEMENT

With the approach outlined above, a risk management procedure for capsize in breaking waves from the side can be outlined as follows:

1. Establish the capability of the ship in terms of internal energy expressed by area under GZ-curve, multiplied by displacement.

2. Relate this energy, for several relevant combinations, with steep breaking waves of varying height by model experiments, thereby establishing the relation between capability and demand (a quite sharp cut-off between safe and unsafe can be expected).

3. Divide the chosen acceptance criterion of frequency of capsize per year by number of expected days of operation per year, thus establishing an acceptance criterion per hour of operation.

4. Use the data (T_z, H_s) from the weather station nearby to find the probability of capsize in beam seas, based upon the immediate capability of the ship (GZ, displacement).

5. If the probability is above what is acceptable, hove to or go to port.

More details are given in Ref. (3).

4.   CONCLUSIONS

By applying risk management, the skipper can use his ship in a safe way. More important, the stability will be related to relevant wave parameters in severe weather, and operational measures can be made in time, such as closing of openings, securing cargo or taking it from the deck and into the hold.

In fair weather, the stability can be less than in bad weather, and this will be fully acceptable, in contrast to what is the case today.

The principles for risk management outlined above will not provide a uniform, day to day risk, but will yield a conservative risk figure because administrations will normally be unwilling to accept stability below IMO guidelines.

5.   REFERENCES

1. MYRHAUG, D and KJELDSEN, S P: 'Prediction of Occurrences of Steep and High Waves in Deep Water'. Journal of Waterway, Port, Coastal and Ocean Engineering, ASCE, Vol. 113, 1987, 122-138.

2. DAHLE, E Aa and MYRHAUG, D: 'Capsize Risk of Fishing Vessels'. Ship Technology Research (Shiffstechnik), Vol. 43, No. 4, 1996, 164-171.

3. DAHLE, E Aa, MYRHAUG, D and VIGGOSSON, G: 'Information System on Waves and Stability of Small Fishing Vessels'. Report No. 2, July 1997, Icelandic Maritime Administration, Kopavogur, Iceland.

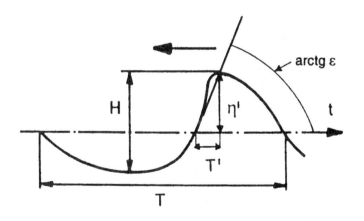

Fig. 1   Definition of zero-downcross waves

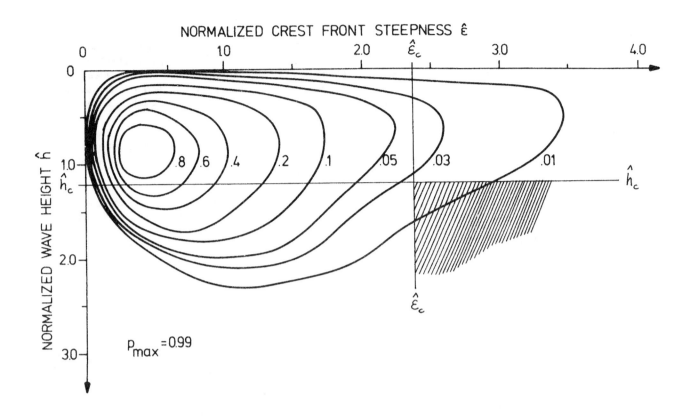

Fig. 2(a) probability of occurrence of dangerous waves according to Eq. (1)

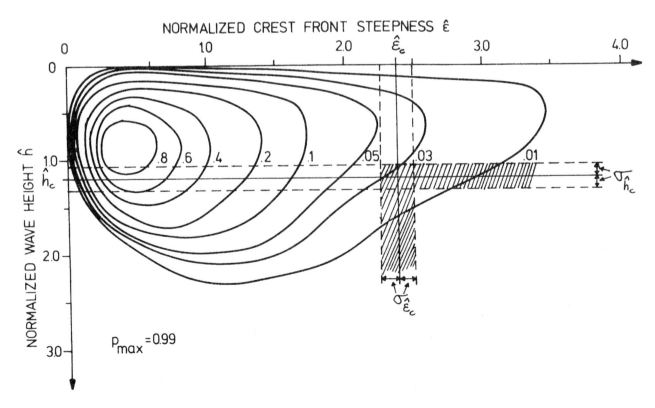

Fig. 2(b) associated uncertainties originating from $\hat{\varepsilon}_c$ and $\hat{h}_c$

PAPER NO.6.

CRITICAL SURVIVAL CONDITIONS FOR SHIP DESIGN

by D Faulkner, Emeritus Professor and Consultant, Glasgow, UK
and
W H Buckley, Consultant, USA

Paper presented at the

International Conference

**DESIGN AND OPERATION FOR
ABNORMAL CONDITIONS**

21 22 OCTOBER 1997 GLASGOW

CRITICAL SURVIVAL CONDITIONS FOR SHIP DESIGN

D Faulkner, Emeritus Professor and Consultant, Glasgow, UK
W H Buckley, Consultant, USA

SUMMARY

A central argument in this paper is that ships are not at present designed explicitly for anything like the worst sea conditions they might experience in their lifetimes. Nor does experience suggest that weather routeing provides a sufficient safeguard against encountering such conditions. Based on casualty experience, reason, and in some cases experiment, present methods are felt to be inadequate for certain aspects of design and operation.

It is suggested that present design methods should in essence remain, but in certain cases which need to be examined further they need to be supplemented by Survival Design procedures. These aim to ensure that all ships have at least some low safety capability to survive critical operational conditions under abnormal sea waves even though most ships are unlikely to meet them. Based on previous work of both authors, a First Principles Methodology (FPM) is advocated in which the essential elements are outlined. Three of these are to establish:

- critical design conditions;
- appropriate seaway criteria, and
- appropriate analytical methods and criteria.

The paper discusses the first two and illustrates the third by offering some possible methods for dealing with water impact design. Theoretical methods will in general need to be non-linear and need to be developed and in general supported by experimental work in qualified wave tanks, etc.

The paper ends with specific conclusions and recommendations for further R&D and for more relevant and effective feedback from service experience.

AUTHORS' BIOGRAPHIES

Professor Douglas Faulkner, PhD DSc FEng, is an Emeritus Professor of the University of Glasgow, and a Consultant, heavily involved at present with the final survey of the m.v. DERBYSHIRE. His prior experience follows: 1954-73 Royal Corps of Naval Constructors engaged in Surface Ship and Submarine Design and Construction; Research at NCRE; Teaching at RNC, Greenwich; Staff Constructor on the British Navy Staff, Washington Embassy; Defence Fellow at MIT. From 1973-95 he was Head of Department of Naval Architecture and Ocean Engineering at the University of Glasgow. He has held many other associated positions and was the UK Standing Committee Member of the ISSC for 12 years.

Mr William H Buckley graduated in 1948 from MIT with a BS in Aeronautical Engineering and an SB in Business Administration. For 20 years Bell Aerospace Co. employed him as a structural engineer where he was responsible for the design loads for the VTOL research airplane and for the Navy's first large air cushion and surface effect ships. In 1971 he joined the David Taylor Research Center where he held positions related to various advanced marine vehicles and loading research for displacement ships incorporating analyses of casualties, statistics of non-linear waves, extreme waves and spectra for long-term design loading. In 1982 he received a Masters degree in Ocean and Marine Engineering from The George Washington University. He is a member of ASNE, SNAME and

SIGMA Xi. He is currently an active member of SNAME's Ad hoc Load Lines Panel with responsibilities for ship safety and new methodologies.

1. INTRODUCTION

1.1 BACKGROUND TO FIRST PRINCIPLES DESIGN

Seeds of Unrest

"Freak" and "Rogue" waves or troughs have been discussed for centuries by mariners who see them as coming from nowhere and violating normal behaviour. The 1960s and 70s saw an increasing interest by oceanographers. Draper[1] suggested that "exceptionally high waves are not curious and unexplained quirks of nature" and that "their occurence can be calculated with an acceptable degree of precision". The implications for ship design were clear, but Oceanus is not widely read by naval architects. The dangers of the Agulhas current-wave interactions are however well known[2] and disasters still occur.

SNAME's Hydrodynamics Committee surveyed actual data for high steep waves which was summarised by Sellars in 1978[3]. Buckley and Stavovy showed real time wave profiles in 1981[4] measured during hurricane CAMILLE (1969). From these one finds wave crest heights are frequently 0.6H to 0.7H where H is the total crest to trough height and mean front face wave crest slopes can be as steep as 0.4 to 0.6. Faulkner used such data when modelling typhoon ORCHID (1980) for the Annex to Ref. 5 in which his derived most probable wave height was 30m. He also provided a definition and classification of abnormal waves[6] and casualty evidence of their damaging effects on large and small ships. Earlier, for the US Ship Structure Committee, Buckley studied extreme waves and their damaging effects on U.S. ships[7] and he defined wave characteristics[8].

The underlying message throughout is that the real sea which causes damage and ship loss is far more severe than the idealised low amplitude linear waves presently used in design. To their credit, SNAME in October 1995 established an Ad Hoc Panel on Load Lines, one of whose goals is to provide a means to deal with "novel vessels" and new design features. This is with a view to contributing to a new load line convention and to bring the everyday experiences of industry (and operators) into the debate.

Meanwhile, as this paper reports, offshore operators have during the 1980s continually increased their 100-year design waves in the North Sea from 20 metres or so to 30m, and now for West of Shetland waters to 35-40m. They also acknowledge the existence of freak waves and are considering their design implications. Hopefully, this RINA conference will provide a similar groundswell of action among ship designers, classification societies and the IMO to consider survival wave actions with a view to initiating required R&D and implementing any necessary design and operational changes.

Ship Safety and Design

Broadly, there are three main attributes for which naval architects attempt to provide adequate models and safety margins:

- *primary strength* of the hull girder
- *stability* to resist cargo shift and capsize
- *watertight integrity* to resist water ingress

In terms of experience from casualty data which relate to inadequate design and/or construction, the above list is in inverse order of experience for ships over 20,000 tonnes displacement say, and for smaller ships stability is usually of greatest importance[9].

Ship Safety and Operation

It is an unfortunate fact that over the last 160 years the "cause of shipwrecks"[10] have essentially remained unchanged[9]. Moreover ships are no exception to the fact observed in land based structures that the majority of disasters and losses are due to human errors and incompetence. In ships these include navigational errors, poor seamanship and/or crew negligence such as inadequate preparation for rough weather,

inadequate maintenance, inappropriate loading, and even drunkenness.

The reasons for this regrettable state of affairs are well known but perhaps the three main factors are the priority of economy over safety, overregulation and inadequate standards and training. Offshore marine activities are better served.

Emerging Trends

The current trends which affect structural design principles and criteria have been noted from Ref. 11 as moves toward:

1. more explicit consideration of safety of life, property and the environment ("safer ships and cleaner seas");

2. first principles based structural design with explicit consideration of performance objectves and failure modes and non-prescriptive goal oriented design standards;

3. inclusion of maintenance, repair and survey considerations as part of an integrated life cycle approach;

4. use of probabilistic (reliability) technologies as part of design and maintenance, and code development and validation;

5. integration of statutory and classification aspects of structural design into the total structural safety concept;

6. addressing the human element as part of overall safety;

7. use of advanced information technologies to integrate design and operation.

It will be recognised that many of these trends reflect what is or has happened in the generally more enlightened offshore industries.

The only addition suggested is the adoption of Formal Safety Assessment as illustrated in Fig. 1 from Discussion of Ref. 12. The risk matrix illustrates the value of combining judged risk and consequence when decisions are required regarding the ranking, for example, of loss scenarios. This discipline may be useful when ranking the importance of critical conditions in section 1.4 or the recommendations in 4 for future action.

1.2   OBSERVED SEAS AND DISTRESS

Abnormal Seas and Their Effects

Reference 6 provides a fuller description and classification of unusual extreme seas which are not

2

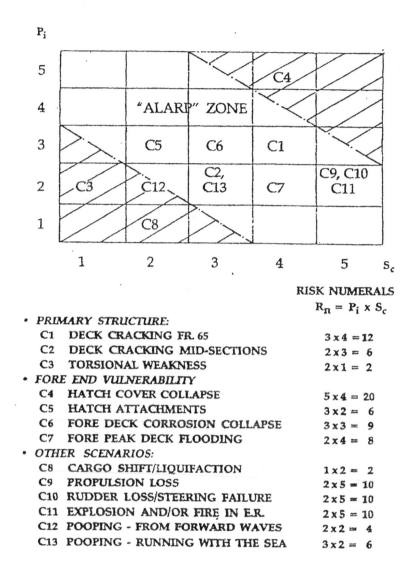

RISK NUMERALS

$$R_n = P_i \times S_c$$

- *PRIMARY STRUCTURE:*

  C1   DECK CRACKING FR. 65 $3 \times 4 = 12$

  C2   DECK CRACKING MID-SECTIONS $2 \times 3 = 6$

  C3   TORSIONAL WEAKNESS $2 \times 1 = 2$

- *FORE END VULNERABILITY*

  C4   HATCH COVER COLLAPSE $5 \times 4 = 20$

  C5   HATCH ATTACHMENTS $3 \times 2 = 6$

  C6   FORE DECK CORROSION COLLAPSE $3 \times 3 = 9$

  C7   FORE PEAK DECK FLOODING $2 \times 4 = 8$

- *OTHER SCENARIOS:*

  C8   CARGO SHIFT/LIQUIFACTION $1 \times 2 = 2$

  C9   PROPULSION LOSS $2 \times 5 = 10$

  C10 RUDDER LOSS/STEERING FAILURE $2 \times 5 = 10$

  C11 EXPLOSION AND/OR FIRE IN E.R. $2 \times 5 = 10$

  C12 POOPING - FROM FORWARD WAVES $2 \times 2 = 4$

  C13 POOPING - RUNNING WITH THE SEA $3 \times 2 = 6$

Fig. 1   Risk Matrix for Loss Scenarios for the m.v. DERBYSHIRE (Ref. 12)

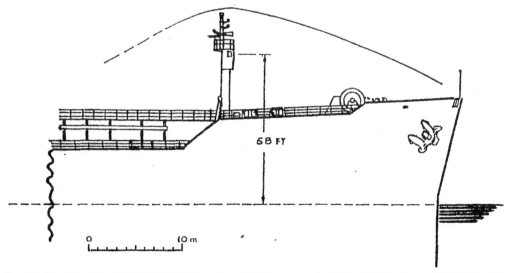

Fig. 2   Sketch of the VLCC ATHENE and a 100 ft wave met off Port Elizabeth in 1977 (Ref. 12)

covered by the conventional design wave concept. Section 2.2 of this paper suggests criteria for abnormal waves which apply to all ship sizes. It is inevitable that unusual sea conditions which might distress small vessels will occur more frequently than the higher sea states which damage larger ships. Short steep and crossing seas are common in coastal waters, and can be very dangerous, for example, causing fishing vessels to capsize.

In contrast, the lower freeboard and greater length and mass of larger ships suggest that they are likely to be more vulnerable to steep elevated plunging waves because they will tend to burrow into oncoming wave fronts Although the predictability of abnormal conditions is less well understood than for normal linear sea waves, section 2.2 does provide some guidance on this.

Section 2.1 provides some data on observed and maximum design waves. Not mentioned is the 112ft (34.1m) wave encountered by the American Tanker USS RAMAPO in the North Pacific in 1933. It is often quoted because the report is regarded as being reasonably reliable. Also well known are the unusual long troughs and steep, elevated wave fronts encountered off South Africa's SE coast which arises from the interaction of normal storm waves and the strong opposing Agulhas current. Such interactions also occur off Peru, Greenland and Japan.

The QUEEN ELIZABETH slid into a trough of a huge wave off the coast of Greenland in world war II. The wave which followed shattered the bridge windows more than 90 feet (27.4m) above the waterline and the foredeck was smashed 6 inches (152mm) below its normal level. Since then, similar wave-current inter-actions off SE Africa have claimed at least 12 ships and damaged many more, including the oft quoted BEN CRUACHAN which in 1973 had her fore body set down 7° from a 15m wave impact. In 1977 the 256,000 dwt VLCC ATHENE met a much higher 30m wave off Port Elizabeth, as depicted in Fig. 2. It submerged all the fore mast knocking out all the windows of the crows nest 58 feet (17.7m) above the laden sea level. Had the vessel been a B minus 60 bulk carrier, with no forecastle, her forward hatch covers would have burst.

Damage to breakwaters, sea walls and lighthouses can be quoted. But enough has been said to indicate the nature of the cruel sea and the forces which can arise on decks and higher structures. Section 3.1 quotes a graphic example of bridge front damage and shattered reinforced windows.

Feedback of Service Experience

Classification Societies pride themselves on their extensive records of casualties and damage. The incidence statistics alone are certainly valuable and are often quoted. But they usually lack detail of the failure and seldom state the sea conditions and other relevant actions which caused the damage or failure. Another shortcoming noted in the discussion of Ref. 12 is that naval architects seldom talked sufficiently to operators and owners and vice versa.

One Master Mariner wrote in with his experiences at sea as regards inadequacies he noted in construction, ship control and stability, systems and safety. This was invaluable, and strong pleas were made by many delegates to improve a range of service feedbacks with well thought through forms, to improve communications, and to enable more naval architects to gain seagoing experience.

There are moves afoot through the IMO to fit shipborne voyage data recorders. These would maintain a store of information concerning the position, speed, heading, physical status (including hull openings, watertight and fire door status), command and control status of a ship over the period leading up to and following an important incident. This information should be made available to the administrative authorities and the ship owner, and is for use during any subsequent investigation into the cause(s) of the incident. It is to be hoped these moves are approved and implemented.

Weather Routeing

Many Master Mariners have voiced unhappiness that weather routeing today pays too much attention to meeting tight charter arrangements rather than to storm avoidance. Some owners it seems are not happy to leave their Captains free to follow their judgement even in extreme storm conditions. Others prefer playing safe than being sorry.

Certainly, instances are known of errors in weather routeing plots, of Captains assuming they can pass ahead of a storm only to find the storm had accelerated, or an unknown tropical disturbance had confused the picture. Some quoted cases of ships caught in rotating tropical storms where had the ship taken early appropriate avoidance actions, as given in The Mariners' Handbook, their loss could in all probability have been averted.

Since Weather Routers bend over backwards to ensure car carriers avoid rough weather, it would seem that they may implicitly assume all other unrestricted service ships can survive the weather. This is demonstrably untrue.

It does seem that the economic emphases on meeting charter dates and minimising fuel used is not acting in the best interests of ship safety. This unfortunate trend is well known in design, construction and maintenance, but the real danger is at sea where safety considerations should be uppermost. Weather routeing would seem to be a topic in need of a wider debate.

1.3   ELEMENTS OF FIRST PRINCIPLE DESIGN

Designing vessels from first principles has in principle been available through "direct design" for more than 30 years, but seldom practised. It is desirable, if not essential, for novel hull forms, new materials or novel roles not covered by conventional classification society rules. In practice this was seldom completely followed because of the very high design cost, lack of uniformity in applying and interpreting the first principles and the difficulty of including service experience.

However, once the operational conditions become unusual, as it does when designing to survive abnormal seas and loadings, then a first principles approach becomes essential, even for conventional mono-hull ships.

Buckley first introduced his First Principles Methodology (FPM) for design in 1988[13] and at the STAB'94 conference and now at this conference[14]. The method aims to provide more realistic cause-effects relationships involving basic design variables. The necessary five elements are outlined here:

- **Operational Requirements:** which identify the roles and payloads of the ship, ocean areas and routes, speeds in calm and rough seas, operational life, etc.

- **Seaway Criteria:** which define both worldwide climatic (long-term average) and extreme wave conditions.

- **Critical Design Conditions:** which identify those particular operating and sea conditions which the designer should consider in satisfying survival response criteria. When identifying critical wave conditions the entire range of seaway criteria must be considered.

- **Analytical Methods:** which are suitable to establish ship design characteristics which satisfy the critical design conditions and response criteria. These methods must be capable of leading to deterministic results for preliminary and final design, and able to analyse linear and non-linear excitations and responses.

- **Response Criteria:** which define acceptable or unacceptable behaviour under critical design conditions for seakeeping and structural design.

With respect to vessel behaviour, two levels of design wave climates are defined:

- **The Operability Envelope:** an assembly of wave climates in which the vessel is required to operate without experiencing seakeeping distress or structural damage requiring repair or replacement. This would correspond to best present normal design practice.

- **The Survivability Envelope:** an envelope of extreme wave spectra parameters in which the vessel is required to operate without experiencing loss of watertight integrity, hull girder fracture or

collapse, capsize or loss of communications or survivability equipment.

The baseline envelopes will be described. They have been established using NOAA significant wave height (H_s) versus modal period (T_p) trend line data extrapolated to cover northern and southern hemisphere extremes. The survivability envelope has been checked and augmented by Hogben's Global Wave data and consists of two connected segments corresponding to seaways of limiting steepness and to seaways of extreme H_s.

1.4 CRITICAL DESIGN AND OPERATION CONDITIONS

Not surprisingly, Ref. [12] showed that for all the 13 loss scenarios the risk numerals (refer to Fig. 1) increased beyond normal design levels to varying degrees under abnormal sea conditions. On average, they more than doubled, but for the "other" machinery breakdown scenarios they more than trebled - mainly due to the increased risks of sinking arising from the bulk carrier becoming beam-on to the sea.

From this and other experience the following conditions may lead to loss or severe damage. They are listed (and in some cases discussed) for further possible study in the light of survival storm conditions defined later. The list is suggestive and clearly requires to be reviewed and put in priority. The two sub-headings used in some cases overlap.

1.4.1 Critical Ship Design Conditions

The following are offered for discussion and development as felt necessary.

Structure and Construction

- Hull strength - Buckley[15] was the first to suggest present standards may be inadequate; preliminary calculations[5,6] suggest that for large bulk carriers wave bending moments from survival waves may exceed the IACS standard [16] by more than 2 to 1.

- Fore end and aft end discontinuities - the transition from large open cargo holds to more cellular structure is an unavoidable global discontinuity, which is likely to be more important with higher stresses arising from bow and stern emergence and/or high slamming forces.

- Hatch covers and coamings - hatches form about 30% of the watertight integrity of the deck in many cargo ships and bulk carriers, and yet they are far weaker than the deck and very vulnerable to steep, elevated and plunging waves[17,18] all along the ship - especially for the B minus 60 bulk carriers; the evidence for action is compelling.

- Side shell fractures and cross-deck buckling become more likely.

- Need for fore end protection - raised forecastles, higher bulwarks and breakwaters offer substantial protection to vulnerable fore end hatches, vents and deck fittings and reduce water on deck.

- Hatch and ventilator securing cleats should be substantial and non ferrous, and weld connections to the deck must withstand extreme sweeping green seas.

- Bridge fronts and windows - see 3.1 below and elsewhere.

- Water impact - a major area to investigate as discussed for wave impact in section 3.1, and for slamming and sloshing.

- Corrosion - clearly excess corrosion does occur and can seriously reduce hull strength and will be more damaging for exposed hull structure.

- Collisions and groundings - need for adequate residual strength and stability with realistic accident scenarios as the basis for design as suggested by the ISSC[11] and offered by three classification societies at present.

- Accidental flooding - more likely, and water sloshing effects will need greater attention, including cargo liquifaction effects.

Seakeeping

- Capsize - see Ref. 14 at this conference; risks from beam-on scenarios, for example, arising from temporary loss of propulsion or steering are very much increased in steep elevated seas as they also are if ships attempt to run with stormy seas.

- Cargo shift - leading to list and greater risk of collapse of boundary side shell and bulkheads.

- Excessive water ingress with hatchless container ships.

- Severe motion induced damage to machinery, equipment, etc.

- Larger rudders and or transverse thrusters may be needed to maintain hove-to and for slow speed manoeuvring.

1.4.2 Critical Machinery, Equipment and Operational Conditions

Again, the following are for discussion; several are based on Capt. Richardson's written contribution to Ref. 12.

Machinery Breakdown.

- Engine shut down when propeller emerges.

- Lubricating oil system - excessive pitching can cause loss of oil pressure and engine shut down.

- Steering gear failure.

- Main propulsion failure.

- Loss of rudder.

- Loss of propeller or fractured shafting.

- Pooping damage - leading to possible fuel contamination and engine shut down.

- Engine room fire and explosion risks to be re-assessed.

Control and Other Systems

- Forepeak spaces require improved sounding arrangements and should be capable of being pumped out from the Engine Room/Pump Room.

- Steering gear motors switched on from the wheelhouse.

- All forward floodlights should be controlled from the Bridge.

- Lubricating oil cooling systems require inlet and outlet valves which are either both open or shut, to avoid main engine shut down.

- Preparing ship for rough weather - all hatches, doors and other openings fully secure and reported to the bridge; secure loose equipment.

- Loss of communications - examine scope for improvement.

- Loss of survival equipment - greater security and more protected positioning may be necessary.

- Weather routeing - to be reviewed.

1.4.3 The Human Element

It is commonly stated that in excess of 80% of high-consequence marine accidents are the result of compounded human and organisational errors. These occur in all stages of design, construction and operations. Moore and Bea[19] note that operations account for 80% of all marine accidents, that is, a total of 64% of all disasters. Making things "sailor proof" is not easy. But there are undoubtedly influences and interactions between human errors, in various stages of design, operations, procedures and management. Everyone needs to be involved.

In the wake of serious tanker accidents since 1989, IMO initiatives have led to two major products:

- the International Safety Management (ISM) Code, implemented from July 1998;

– the 1995 amendments to the Standards of Training, Certification and Watchkeeping (STCW) Convention, implemented 1 February 1997.

Given the changing roles of Classification Societies, several are now embracing these vital non-technical aspects of ship safety as part of their "Total Classification" concept.

There is now a detectable groundswell of activity to generate a "safety culture" throughout the marine industries. Even the ISSC '97[20] is advancing a four step strategy to address the human element problem in marine safety.

2.   SEAWAY CRITERIA DEVELOPMENTS

Only recently have survivability seaway conditions been suggested because:

- sufficient measured wave characteristics and spectra have only become available in the last decade or so;

- there has been no immediate demand for such criteria because existing empirical design methods were felt to be adequate.

2.1   WAVE CLIMATE

The word "climate" strictly applies to the average weather in a region. Nevertheless, phrases like "wave climate" and "climatic wave spectra" are frequently used as here to describe average weather induced waves Buckley[13]. Averaging implies over sufficient time to reduce irregularity (uncertainty).

However, it is well established that substantial global climatic variations have occurred throughout history. This has inevitably led to significant changes in wave climate, as several researchers have recently shown[21,22]. This presents a problem as human experience of these variations spans only a very short period. And yet, meteorologists and oceanographers today are frequently presented with relatively short sets of measured data from which to establish design criteria. Lynaugh[23] therefore concludes that the usefulness of these short-term data sets would be considerably enhanced if they could be placed in the longer term climatic cycle.

The authors are less sure that there is a "cycle" as such and suggest the words like longterm "trend" or "changes" might be more appropriate, especially as these are observed phenomena with as yet no satisfactory explanation. A recent international study of the dynamics of world climate and ocean actions provides conclusive evidence that wave climate changes are occurring on a global scale. Bacon, Carter, Hogben and Challenor have all reported recent satellite readings which show that in the western Mediterranean and the central South Atlantic average wave heights are

0.5m smaller than in the mid-1980s. But, for the North Atlantic from the Iberian peninsula to Greenland, waves are almost twice their size of 40 years ago. Challenor wonders if these global changes are indicators of global warming due to ozone depletion in the upper atmosphere.

It follows that significant shifts in long term climate continuously occur which brings additional uncertainty when attempts are made (as here) to establish climatic design wave criteria for critical operational scenarios. For similar reasons, offshore operators in the North Sea have needed to adjust their 100-year design wave heights - usually upward, as discussed earlier.

Design Wave Heights

Many naval architects only accept the need for specifying maximum wave heights when considering ship safety to withstand primary bending actions. In this they assume that waves of similar length to the ship are the most stressful and that these are unlikely ever to exceed about 10 to 11m height[16]. However, this historical perspective has recently been challenged[6] even for primary ship strength. But for inadequate watertight integrity, which accounts for the majority of design related ship losses[6,9], wave heights far in excess of 10m are the most likely initiating cause, especially for larger ships. Even ship stability can be severely compromised by unusually steep elevated waves[6,14]. The choice of period may be critical. Reference 24 suggests investigating a range in metric units:

$$13\,H_s < T_p^2 < 30\,H_s \qquad (1)$$

There have been many reports of bigger waves causing distress and damage to ships, including the BRITANNIA and the QUEEN ELIZABETH 2, and to oil and gas rigs. And yet, most naval architects continue to explicitly ignore the actions of waves more than about 10 m, or 15m at most, unless they are employed by the more enlightened offshore industries. This, like the weather, must change!

Sellars is more enlightened, and based on many years of operations from weather stations from most world oceans he provided extreme wave heights and steepness for design. Only that for the North Sea is summarised in Table 1, together with more recent data from Rainey:

Whilst the wave Rainey quoted for the TERN platform is the steepest, it is not actually the highest measured in the North Sea. A 28.3m wave was recorded about 1979 and during a storm 11-13 December 1991 a significant wave height of H_s = 16.6m was estimated from multiple measurements at the HUTTON tension leg platform. This would imply a most probable extreme height exceeding the 1980 100-year design wave of 30.3m height and 16.6 s period. This wave was also elevated, steep and compatible with extensive damages

TABLE 1

Wave Data Source	Height (m)	Period (s)	Steepness (H/λ)	Date
Sellars (Ref. 3)	18.6	13.3(T_p?)	0.067	11/69
Rainey (Ref. 6 Discussion)	26.9	12.5 (T_z)	0.110	01/92

to the topsides and cellar decks more than 20m above LAT of nearby platforms and an observed wave breaking over the heli-deck of the HUTTON platform.

From this we see that even Rainey's North Sea wave of 1992 is 45% higher than the 1969 value, and those of 30m or more are more than 60% higher. Now, offshore installations west of Shetland are being designed with significant wave heights of 18m, which implies 100-year design waves of about 40m. This is more than twice Sellars' North Sea maximum design wave and nearly twice Sellars' North Atlantic wave of 20.4m recorded in 1961. The wave which struck the QE2 off Newfoundland's Grand Banks in September 1995 has been estimated at about 29.3m which is 43% higher.

Even these isolated examples indicate the problems of climate shift, mentioned earlier, and perhaps also the effect of more extensive data gathering.

Actual extreme wave data from storms are quite sparse, but some good references and discussion are provided by Gaythwaite[25]. Yamanouchi and Ogawa's data for the N. Pacific[26] is of particular interest since between 20% to 30% of all ship losses occur in a 1000 nautical miles width of ocean between Japan and Papua New Guinea.

The maximum possible waves that could occur in the ocean have not yet been recorded but, based on Goldman's work, Ref. 27, suggests that the meteorological conditions required to produce long period waves of up to 219 feet (67m) in height have been investigated and are possible, for example, in the Gulf of Alaska and in the N. Atlantic near Iceland.

2.2 ORIGINS OF COMPREHENSIVE SEA-WAY CRITERIA

The National Oceanographic and Atmospheric Administration (NOAA) has an extensive database of hourly wave buoy measurements from a wide range of wave climates. Reference [13] has used this to define operability and extreme survivability envelopes from climatic wave spectra (long term averages) in terms of a range of significant wave heights H_s (H_{mo} in the US references) and peak or most probable wave periods T_p.

For design, three operability wave climates have been established, as shown in Fig. 3 [28]. The upper bounds O_1, O_2 and O_3 of these envelopes correspond to

occurrence levels at H_s of about once per year, just a little more severe than present design waves. The large survivability envelope encompasses the most extreme combined values of H_{mo} and T_p found in the NOAA data over an effective measurement period of about 10 years. It corresponds to a dominant wave steepnesses Hλ of about 1/20, or most probable extreme wave steepness of about 1/10.

Among several atlases of long term ocean area waves, Ref. 29 was found to agree best with NOAA data over a wide range on a probability of occurrence basis (see Refs. 28 and 30) and in terms of relative wave steepness. This is illustrated below. Hence, those northern and southern ocean areas of Ref. 29 which could be classified as climatically steep or climatically long period were identified and compared.

Operability Envelopes

Considering all the climatically steep ocean areas in Ref. 29, the one experiencing the highest H_s was found to be Area 11 (North Sea). At one event per year occurrence level this was about 1 metre higher than for Area 23 (US East Coast) which was used in Ref. 28 to define the *climatic steep waves* boundary. This increment was therefore added to establish the worldwide extremes for the design Operability envelope shown in Fig. 3. (The southern hemisphere provided a smaller increment in this case). In extending the *climatic long period seas* boundary a similar procedure showed that the Southern hemisphere provided a more extreme value.

Buckley[28] derived empirically a parametric equation which defines the left hand climatic boundary of Fig. 3. This can be shown to be of the form:

$$a \; H_{mo} = T_p^{\;b} \qquad (2)$$

where, using metric units:

a = 182 , b = 3.0 for Climatic Steep Seas

a = 1168 , b = 3.3 for Climatic Long Period

Recently, Hogben has provided additional information from section 8, volume 9, Part A of Ref. [31] which relate to Buckley's two climatic boundaries. Based on the mean values of the natural logs of the long term

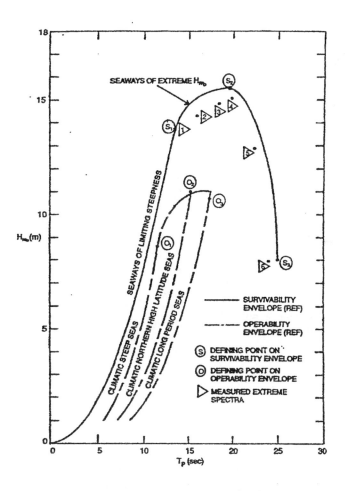

Fig. 3 NOAA Baseline Operability and Survivability Envelopes (Ref. 28)

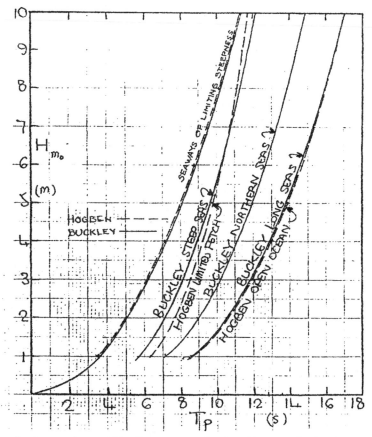

Fig. 4 Comparison of Significant wave Height and Modal Period Boundaries

zero wave crossing period T_z and the associated H_s (note again $H_s = H_{mo}$), Hogben's general wave climate relationship can be shown to be:

$$T_z = e^A H_s{}^B \qquad (3)$$

where

A = 1.818   B = 0.297 for Open Ocean areas

A = 1.515   B = 0.266 for Limited Fetch areas

Using the relationship $T_p \cong 1.4 T_z$ eq (3) can be written in the form of eq (2) where:

$$a = (1.4\, e^A)^{1/B} \text{ and } b = 1/B \qquad (4)$$

The equivalent Buckley constants a and b are then compared in the following Table 2 and in Fig. 4:

TABLE 2

Source - Sea type	a	b
Buckley - Long Period Hogben - Open Ocean	1168 1414	3.3 3.37
Buckley - Steep Seas Hogben - Limited Fetch	182 1054	3.0 3.76

The Hogben Open Ocean and Buckley Long Period seas formulations can be seen to be remarkably close considering that they were derived from different ocean areas, namely, Northwest European vs US East Coast offshore waters. The Hogben Limited Fetch and Buckley Steep Seas agree closely in the range 5m < H_{mo} < 8m, and differences outside of this range can be accounted for. At low H_{mo} values Buckley's curve is based on Gulf of Mexico data where swell is limited and wind driven seas tend to predominate. At high values of H_{mo}, Buckley's climatic steep seas boundary is constrained to avoid crossing the seaways of limiting steepness boundary.

Survivability Envelopes

In Fig. 3 no extension of the seaways of Limiting Steepness boundary was made to provide for hemispheric extremes because of the unusual severity of hurricane CAMILLE in 1969 which defined its upper end. The scarcity of other data precluded any further statistical extrapolation. As a result, the 1m increment used to extend the operability envelope was adopted even though a greater increment might have been expected; this would have been less "defensible". The resulting northern and southern hemisphere survivability envelopes derived from an analysis of Ref. 29 are shown in Fig. 5. More extensive discussions are provided in Ref. 28 and, to a limited extent, in Ref. 30.

With respect to the Seaways of Limiting Steepness boundary, Hogben recommends[31] using the relationship $H_s = 0.00797g\, T_p{}^2$ which in metric units is identical to the lower inequality of eq(1):

$$T_p{}^2 = 13 H_s \qquad (5)$$

and only 3% more than the $H_{mo} = 0.00776g\, T_p{}^2$ of Buckley[13].

During a severe winter storm in the North Sea at the Cormorant platform in December 1991[32] Hogben and Tucker quote a value of $H_s = 13.6$m with $T_z = 10.6$ secs. For a JONSWAP spectrum approximation this gives $T_p = 13.6$ secs. The H_s, T_p combination closely matches the 13.7 m, 13.5 sec. used to define the upper end of the Seaways of Limiting Steepness boundary of Fig. 3. Moreover, its steepness parameter is very close to Buckley's, while the JONSWAP shape parameter of $\gamma = 3.3$ is only 10% higher the upper end of the 1 < γ < 3 range recommended by Buckley.

Survival Design Storms

The above storm findings suggest that it is not unreasonable to move forward with a first principles methodology using the seaway criteria of Ref. 28. It is suggested that the extreme wave height H_e during the chosen survival design storm can then be estimated assuming individual wave heights H in each sea state follow a Rayleigh distribution. This leads to the Longuet-Higgins equation[33]:

$$H_e = H_s \left[0.5(\ln N - \ln(-\ln(1 - p_e))) \right]^{0.5} \qquad (6)$$

where p_e is a small but acceptable probability of H_e being exceeded (say 1% to 5%) during $N = D/T_p$ wave encounters in a chosen period D (12 to 24 hours say) during the storm. The procedure has been illustrated in Ref. 6 for hatch cover loading.

It is there noted that wave crest elevation and mean crest slope can be important parameters to incorporate in the analyses; advice is given based on hurricane CAMILLE measured wave profiles. Figure 6 from US Naval Oceanographic Office Data (reference 25) shows wave steepness vs wave age (celerity/wind speed). At C/V about 1.4 a fully developed sea is attained. Cyclones at Sea generate younger steeper waves, especially during tropical storms.

Revolving Tropical Storms

The data derived above includes the effects of hurricanes, typhoons and other revolving tropical storms (RTS). However, this additional note is added to emphasise:

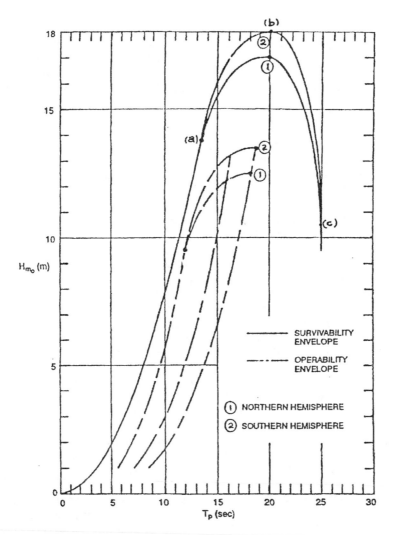

Fig. 5 Survivability and Operability Envelopes for Northern and Southern Hemispheres

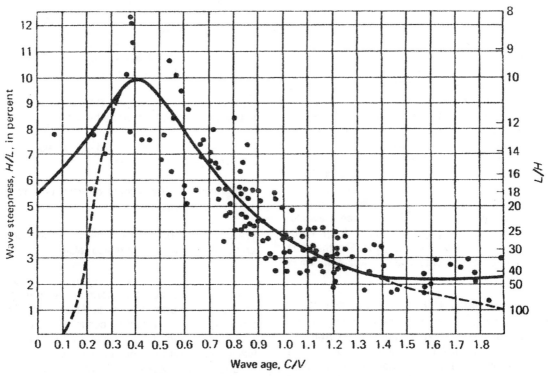

Fig. 6 Relation Between Wave Steepness and Wave Age (Ref. 25)

- the unusual nature of waves generated by these revolving storms;

- that they are not limited to tropical waters.

Wind-generated seas during RTSs are significantly different from those observed in ordinary storms because the input source of energy generating the waves is advancing at a speed of 5 to 12 knots. The rate of change of wind speed changes much faster than for ordinary storms. Moreover, the circulatory motion of the storm restricts the fetch. The time duration, therefore, of a given wind speed is short in contrast to seas generated by ordinary winds blowing continuously for several hours with constant speed.

For such reasons, even super-typhoons are unlikely to generate waves more than about 30m high. However, they are often highly non-linear with steep, elevated crests. When added to any existing ordinary swell and wind, waves generated over longer fetches they may well exceed 30m in height[5,6] with crests 20m or more above the MWL.

RTSs migrate away from the topics, and their depressions can increase and draw energy in from other nearby storms. In September 1995 hurricane LUIS generated far more severe sea conditions off Newfoundland's Grand Banks than it did earlier in the Gulf of Mexico. In April 1847 a hurricane of freak proportions unleashed its fury down the entire west coast of Scotland, sinking five emigrant ships. A similar, but more sustained period of hurricane generated storms in December 1883, sank 56 ships in one week. Most of these ships were carrying about 250 emigrants on average to the USA and Canada, and none survived[34].

Analysis of Wave Non-Linearities and their Simulations

Buckley's half-cycle matrix (HACYM) method[8] was used to analyse non-linear characteristics of the CAMILLE wave height data. Successive trough-to-peak and peak-to-trough time series events are entered in a square data matrix from which a statistic is determined, referred to as the Mean Value Distribution of Amplitude Events (MVDAE). For present purposes it is sufficient to note that if the MVDAE curve is non-linear, the random process is non-linear. Dashed lines to a point indicates that it has been defined by less than 5 events. Figure 7 shows the essentially linear plot from 1100-1130 hours for 17 August 1969 disturbed in the next half hour by a large, potentially dangerous wave appearing suddenly.

The upper time-series plot of Fig. 8 shows this 22.9m high wave which is 2.4 times greater than the significant wave height for that period of hurricane CAMILLE, where a typical value might be about 1.7 to 1. One could therefore regard this as a "freak wave", but note that similar characteristics are found in the lower plot which is for much smaller waves measured off the Irish

coast [35] where it will be noted the maximum H/H_s is 2.5. Both of these maximum waves support Faulkner's provisional definition of freak or abnormal wave heights suggested for survival design of large ships [5,6]:

$$H_d \geq 2.5H_s \quad \text{or} \quad \geq 25m \qquad (7)$$

and the $2.5\ H_s$ proposed was supported in the discussion of Ref. 6. These findings suggest that wave recording should be continuous to pick up such unusual waves because statistical sampling can fail to detect them.

At the height of the hurricane, when the MVDAE plot showed the seaway was clearly non-linear, time series wave records showed three of the highest waves during the interval 1500 to 1530 hours were steep and elevated. One 19.8m wave attained a crest height above mean water level of 14.6m (0.74 H), which would correspond to a linear wave 29.2m high. This would normally be regarded as relatively rare from a statistical point of view, which is not the case here. Such conditions could well be critical for hatch cover loadings or for water ingress in hatch-less container ships when pitching severely.

Buckley *et al* [36] showed from the CAMILLE HACYM analysis that large, steep, elevated waves are found near the height of the storm. A later Norwegian study[37] also concluded from analysing steep asymmetric waves that the wave spectrum alone is not sufficient to categorise the roughness of an irregular sea. The best way ahead is seen to be the collection of time series wave data during severe storms, for example, from offshore platforms in the North Sea, off E. Australia and off E. Brazil. In selected cases where HACYM analysis showed high non-linearities, these wave data should then be generated in quality wave tanks or basins, to examine critical seaway conditions for ship models. Suitable, time-domain studies, once validated, can supplement the experiments.

Some conclusions from the CAMILLE HACYM analysis are that non-linearity of wave height:

- correlates well with rapid increases in 30 minute average wind velocities

- is related to the amount of wave energy present in the higher frequencies.

Wave basin experiments show that short crestedness and wave non-linearity are also related.

Eilersen *et al* [38] have studied freak waves and their effect on steel jacket platforms. Assuming that the height of extreme waves is limited by the spilling breaking limit and that they occur in strongly directional seas, the authors demonstrate that the highest possible wave height will then be around $2.9\ H_s$. However, its probability of occurrence is conservatively estimated from limited data to be 2.5 times less than the most likely highest wave predicted using, for example, the

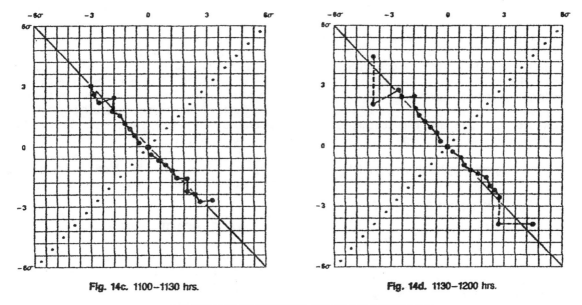

Fig. 14c. 1100–1130 hrs.   Fig. 14d. 1130–1200 hrs.

[---DENOTES LESS THAN 5 EVENTS AVAILABLE TO DEFINE MEAN.]

Fig. 7 Linearity of Hurricane CAMILLE Waves (Ref. 8)

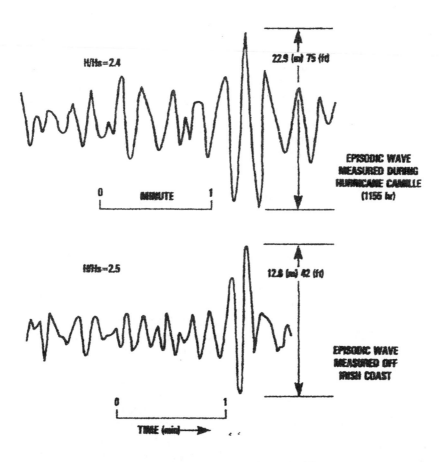

H/Hs=2.4

22.9 (m) 75 (ft)

0   MINUTE   1

EPISODIC WAVE
MEASURED DURING
HURRICANE CAMILLE
(1155 hr)

H/Hs=2.5

12.8 (m) 42 (ft)

0   1

TIME (min) ➝

EPISODIC WAVE
MEASURED OFF
IRISH COAST

Fig. 8 Similarity of Episodic Waves From Different Storms (Ref. 7)

Rayleigh distribution or eq. (6) above. They also provides some time series data of wave elevations which includes a crest elevation of 17.0m which is 0.72 times the wave height of 23.7 m. Measured maxima normal forces near the water surface on the bracings of steel jacket platforms were 3.6 times those calculated using relevant design methods. The authors conclusions relating to these freak waves are:

- freak waves do occur, usually in directional (3-D) seas in combination with wave groups;

- an absolute spilling breaking height limit is 2.9 H_s;

- crest elevation is at most 1.8 H_s (0.72 H_d from eq(7));

- steepest slope is tan 30° (0.577).

They also provide a limited amount of wave kinematics data which is compared with Stokes' fifth order wave model. Further work is recommended.

Wave steepness is usually measured by H/λ, but the crest elevation and mean steepness is considered to be more significant from a flooding and damaging viewpoint. Bitner-Gregersen et al[39] have examined these through numerical models and laboratory tests. Extreme wave steepness simulations of linear, 2nd and 3rd order wave model records compared well with laboratory models.

The 13th ISSC[40] discusses experimental modelling of irregular waves, and the 1994 international symposium "Waves - Physical and Numerical Modelling" provides a good source of papers on the topic. In this Gallez[41] describes a new device which generates short-crested waves in flumes with or without carrier current. Mathematical expressions which describe the wave field and related generator operation are summarised. Noting that an oblique cylindrical wave can be extracted from a short-crested wave field, Gallez suggests that proper combinations of generators in parallel flumes with various widths can produce predictable multi-directional seas in a wave basin.

From all this it follows that the phrases "extreme waves" or "extreme seas" take on meanings which are more complex than is often considered. Present wave-wave interaction theories have important limitations as applied, for example, to seaways driven by hurricanes and other rotating tropical storms, and to other equally non-linear extreme seas, including areas of strong current-wave interactions.

Survey of Mariners

A survey of 78 US masters and mates attending instructional classes over a year and a half was aimed at gathering information on ship handling in heavy seas. 36 of the 78 (i.e. 45%) responded that they had encountered seaway conditions severe enough to cause concern for crew and/or ship safety. Of these 36, 40%

had encountered long crested waves similar to those in Figs 9 and 10, and 22% had encountered rogue waves like that in Fig. 11 - all from winter storms.

Whilst acknowledging the subjectivity of the survey and the small sample size, it is believed fair to conclude that severe storm driven waves, such as those shown, are by no means rare. This was confirmed by the discussion in Refs. 12 and 14 and by the many outstanding photographs and storm data in Refs 35 and 42. It follows that explicit consideration of the actions of these types of waves is required in survival wave design. A strong recommendation is that more formal surveys of mariners be conducted, as recommended in Ref. 12.

3. WAVE IMPACT DESIGN

Several possible critical design conditions were introduced in section 1. However, this section will focus only on critical conditions for wave impact design to illustrate the first principles approach. Slamming loads on the hull are probably adequately treated in most monohull ship designs, but this does not appear to be the case for fast multi-hull vessels[43].

To establish rational loading and design criteria for unrestricted service, it is stipulated that such an approach requires the following developments:

- establish seaway parameters which reflect the range of conditions a ship may encounter;

- identify vulnerable structural components and their failure criteria which could compromise watertight integrity of the hull or deckhouse(s);

- characterise wave impact loads so they can be quantified for potentially critical seaway and operating conditions.

- an experimental approach is needed.

This last stipulation is important because of the highly non-linear character of wave impact. Model experiments in qualified seakeeping tanks are regarded as the most realistic means of identifying critical design conditions associated with these spatial and time-varying loadings. "Qualified" here means those facilities capable of recreating points (a), (b) and (c) on the survivability envelope of Fig. 4 of ref. 4 to generate wave-time profiles similar to those from storm wave records. Refer also to subsection 5.4 of Ref. 14 for a more complete discussion and to the non-linearities section of 2.2 above.

3.1 WAVE IMPACT LOADINGS

First a brief review of current design practice is given. The general time domain and other characteristics of water impact loads are outlined from which analytical and physical experiments and instrumentation may be considered. From this basic general understanding the

Fig. 9 Steep Long Crested Wave (Ref. 7)

Fig. 10 Long Crested Breaking Wave (from USS INDEPENDENCE) (Ref. 7)

Fig. 11 Rogue Wave (from m.v. SELKIRK SETTLER, G. Ianiev c. 1987)

Fig. 12 Bridge Damage Following Wave Impact (Ref. 4)

behaviour in particular cases may also then be better understood.

Current Design Practice and Real Sea Experience

Structural design to withstand wave impacts is typically based on static uniform pressure or head of water. This may be justified by general service experience, but it is unreal in storm driven seas because:

- it is not related to the physical characteristics of the wave impacts;

- rarely occurring extreme seas in which structural failures can lead to fatal flooding, has little or no relation to general service experience.

Experience with US commercial and Navy ships reveals that wave impact has been the most common cause of heavy weather damages[4,7].

Figure 12[4] illustrates these shortcomings. The front of the deck house of the naval vessel had been designed to withstand a single uniform static loading. The steel plating was dished and the frames between the canted windows were bowed and broken at their welded joints. The weld metal was clearly less able to withstand the overloading than the more ductile base metal. The laminated and tempered bridge windows were destroyed at five locations, and adjoining ones were crazed and nearly destroyed. The extent of failure of the window in front of the Commodore's chair can be appreciated by the damage done to the chair. The dynamic nature of the load is evident in the testimony of an officer "I turned my head toward Lt. .... to inform him of the high wave. As I turned my head, the window I was standing by exploded, as did several others".

Clearly, static load design is inappropriate. For this and other wave impact loads, criteria and methods need to be developed using the elements of FPM.

Impact Characteristics

In mechanics the word impact is usually reserved for collisions between essentially rigid bodies where the duration Δt of contact is very small or "sudden". Then the magnitude of the contact force is estimated from a vector quantity called the impulse I which is the integration over time Δt and is equal to the change in momentum $m\Delta v$ of each of the two bodies. The average force is then:

$$F = m(\Delta v)/\Delta t \qquad (8)$$

and is usually much greater than the weight of the colliding body.

For wave impacts the pressure induced force analysis is much more complex, but the concepts of suddenness and impulse are still relevant. Experimental data shows considerable scatter of local pressure coefficients with coefficients of variation of 0.2 to 0.7 or more. However, the total impulse imparted to the struck body shows much less variability. Typical characteristics of water impacts on flat surfaces as observed from drop tests, breaking wave and green sea actions can be summarised:

- an initial pressure spike, sometimes referred to as the gifle part or "hammer shock", which is of short duration - typically 2 to 5 milliseconds and is approximately proportional to Y^2; gifle[46]

- this is followed by a more nearly constant loading, sometimes referred to as the bourrage[46] part, which is between 0.1 to 0.5 of the peak pressure and decays to zero generally in less than a second; this is sometimes referred to as the momentum phase of the impact arising from the change in direction of the water flow and is approximately proportional to V;

- however, these pressure signatures vary in both space and time depending on the extent of the impact area and its inclination;

- the area over which hammer shock acts from breaking waves is generally very limited compared with the area acted on by the bulk of the wave;

- hammer shock pressures during flat bottom drop tests have been recorded which were several hundred times higher than the Bernoulli uniform flow pressure $0.5\rho v^2$, and even time and space averaged pressures can substantially exceed this, for example, in most cases of severe ship slamming - this is analogous to solid collision forces far exceeding the weight of the bodies involved;

- impulse loads usually cause dynamic amplification in elastic structures, and this is generally very sensitive to the shape and duration of the hammer shock and subsequent loading;

- entrapped air, or air entrained in the seawater, usually softens the impact but it can worsen the dynamic response of an elastic structure.

The first three characteristics are illustrated in Fig. 13(c). It follows that local pressure is a very uncertain measure of the effective time varying loading on any particular component which the designer needs to consider. He is interested in the area of impact, from which some effective area of assumed uniform pressure may be derived.

Experienced and Experimental Data

Reference 44 provides measured data on pressures arising from breaking waves, and Ref. 45 discusses wave impact pressures on composite breakwaters. The forces which pushed back a re-designed breakwater into Wick harbour were estimated as being equivalent to a sideways uniform static pressure over the entire structure of 6340 lbf/ft^2 or 30.2m of seawater head.

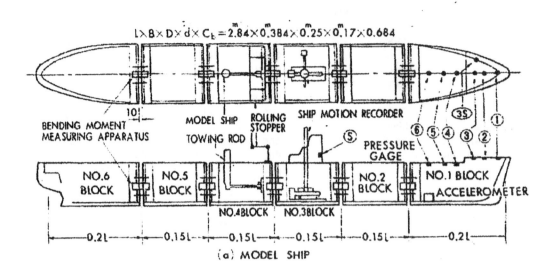

$$l \times B \times D \times d \times C_b = 2.84^m \times 0.384^m \times 0.25^m \times 0.17^m \times 0.684$$

(a) MODEL SHIP

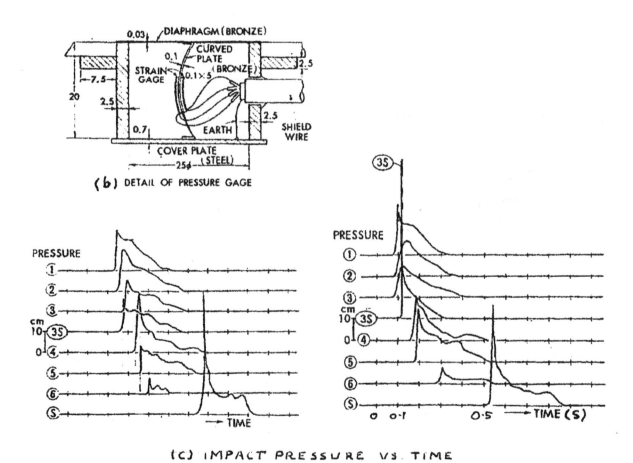

(b) DETAIL OF PRESSURE GAGE

(C) IMPACT PRESSURE VS. TIME

Fig. 13 Local Impact Pressures Due to Shipping Green Water (Ref. 4)

18

However, the magnitude and spatial distribution of wave impact forces on ship structural components will be quite different. This is because of the wide variation in local ship geometry and because the relative profile and speed of the oncoming wave is influenced by position and by the ship speed and motions. It follows from above that, for measuring component load effects, sensibly positioned strain gauges are far more satisfactory than pressure gauges.

The wave impact loadings arising from shipping green seas have been studied with tank experiments on a 1/50 scale model of a medium size cargo liner towed in regular waves at two speeds and free to move in heave and pitch[46]. Details of the model and strain gauged pressure sensors are seen in Figs. 13(a) and (b). At full scale the pressure gauges would each have an area of 1.23 m^2, which would represent average pressures over a typical area for plating design.

Large wave encounters were of two distinctive types: one where the bow threw water into the air which then fell and impacted on the deck resulting in a sharp but rapidly decaying load; in the second type the water surged over the deck as the forecastle penetrated into the wave and it showed a lower level impact followed by a more nearly constant loading of similar duration. The pressure-time traces of Fig. 13 suggest a mixture of both types. The pressure gauge on the bridge front showed a high but brief initial impact followed by a relatively constant loading, probably arising from the subsequent water flow.

Analytical and Experimental Models

A generalised time domain impulse expression which recognises the foregoing is:

$$P(t) = P_i \, e^{-kt} + C \,,\, 0 < t < t_m \tag{9}$$

where P_i is the initial impact loading excluding hammer shock, k and P_i are the pressure decay constant and effective duration of the impact, and C is a steady loading attained shortly after initial impact. It is suggested that these characteristics be selected from impulse experiments on models of specific ship components and with an appropriate range of realistic wave profiles and relative velocities between the wave and ship. Because of the various distortional modes which are possible in most structures, and their known sensitivity to different impulse characteristics, a modal analyses of the responses is recommended.

An alternative, more direct design related approach to consider for dealing with essentially normal impacts on flat surfaces is to make use of reputable drop test data. For example, from a worldwide sample of about 40 data points examined recently[47] it can be shown that for impact angles of 3 nd less the pressure coefficient:

$$C_p = \text{pressure}/0.5 \, \rho v^2 \tag{10}$$

as deduced from Fig. 14 [Ref. 47] small pressure gauge results take the following C_p values:

- mean value of the gifle peaks   135
- upper 5% of the gifle peaks   300
- mean value of the burrage pressure   45

However, what is required is spatially averaged simultaneous pressures over areas significant for design. For global response of stiffened plate panels the averaged burrage or momentum phase pressures are most likely to be relevant, but for local plate element behaviour the gifle peaks may in some cases be damaging. In this respect a time and space averaged mean value of $\underline{C_p = 9.0}$ might be considered for plating design based on an analysis of Zhu's work[47] and assuming 1.0 m^2 area. An upper 5% value of $\underline{C_p = 15}$ might be used with a low safety factor.

Such values are compared with C_p values below derived from Kawakami's measured green sea deck gifle pressures on the forecastle deck of a 1/50 scale model of a 142m cargo ship, as depicted in Fig. 13(a) We should note, however, that the water entry characteristics of a ship model in motion are different from those in drop tests, which mostly have little or no follow through.

TABLE 3

Figure 13(a) position	p(ton/m^2)	C_p
6 - centreline maximum	14	8.5
3S - maximum close to bulwark	50	30.4
Average on centreline	11.5	7.0

The strain gauged pressure transducers have a full scale area of 1.23m^2, which is very reasonable. The high value close to the forecastle bulwark is attributed to the growth of piled up spray and waves. Pressures were also measured without the bulwark fitted and on average they were less than 40% of those measured with the bulwark in place, no doubt because water can escape over the sides of the deck.

The Japanese have always believed in physical testing and the value of large scale experiments. Two other valuable papers are Refs 49 and 50. Korobkin[52] admirably reviews the complex physics of the various impact actions and complications including air-cushion effects.

Kawakami also measured pressure at position S in Fig. 13 on the bridge front. The maximum gifle pressures were very high, about three times higher than those on the deck. Because the deck is reasonably unobstructed, water on it behaves like a shallow water wave (bore) under the action of ship motions and gravity - pitching in particular. Water motions are therefore complex and so no C_p values could be derived.

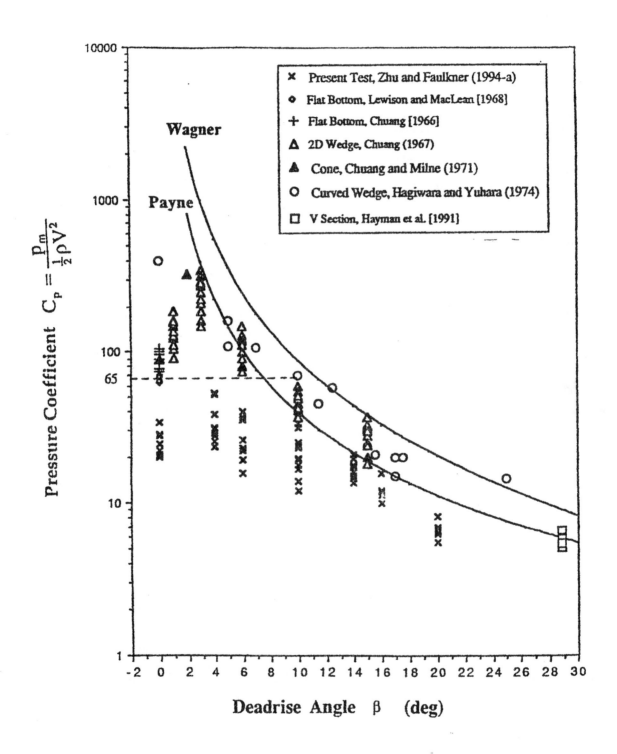

Fig. 14 Drop Test Pressure Coefficients Compared for Various Forms
and Design Proposals (Ref. 47)

Behaviour is likely to be different from plunging wave actions on the deck. Mizoguchi[48] presented some promising results for flow prediction on the deck using Glimm's method.

For a 1/50 scale model of the m.v. DERBYSHIRE pressures were measured at three positions on the forward coaming of no. 1 hatch[17]. These compared well with the Bernoulli term $0.5 \rho v^2$ in which the relative velocity v was assessed from[5]:

$$v = kc + v_s \qquad (11)$$

where wave celerity $c = \lambda/T = 0.4 \sqrt{g\lambda}$ v_s is the ship speed and k is a water flow augment constant arbitrarily set at 1.2. However, this method was very provisional to examine possible extreme sea loads on the coaming structure. These were equivalent to about 22.5m of uniform sea water pressure which suggests the coamings may be vulnerable to collapse.

Kvålsvold and Faltinsen have studied the hydroelastic effects during impact between a free water surface and an elastic wet deck of a multihull vessel. The hydrodynamic loads account for the vibrations of the structure based on an extension of Wagner's (1932) two-dimensional asymptotic theory. When the impact velocity is not too small (for an ultimate strength analaysis this requirement is easily achieved) the maximum stresses in the longitudinal beams between transverse frames are not sensitive to where the waves initially hit the deck or to the radius of curvature of the waves. Comparisons with the drop tests of Aarsnes (1994) indicate that under such conditions the maximum bending stress σ in the longitudinals at a fixed position can be written as [53]:

$$\sigma = K_\sigma z v \sqrt{\rho L_b E / I} \qquad (12)$$

where K_σ is a function of the longitudinal position between two transverse stiffeners and the beam end boundary conditions and ρ is the weight density of the water. For the beams z is the distance from the neutral axis, L_b is their length and I their second moment of area. In this equation, the only parameter that does not depend on the local geometry is v, the modulus of the relative impact speed, and the linear relation supports the importance of momentum effects. The equation has also shown some agreement for stresses in the plate elements between stiffeners.

The method shows promise of being easy to use directly in local design. However, there are effects that need to be studied further and more validation tests with models and full scale ships in realistic wave conditions are needed. Moreover, it should be noted that the theory should not be generalised to other slamming cases where the largest impact pressures are not highly concentrated in space and time.

To return to pressure on the deck and hatch covers, Buchner[51] shows that for green water the static head corrected for the verticle acceleration both play a role in the loading on the deck. But, for a falling breaking wave, as examined by Takezawa et al[49], Buchner shows that the impulsive loading is due to the rate of change of water height on deck. He therefore compared force measurements on the fore deck of models of a 122m frigate and a 260m floating production storage and offloading unit with those derived from the three components:

$$p = \rho w \left(\frac{\partial h}{\partial t} \right) + ph \left(g \cos \theta + \frac{\partial w}{\partial t} \right) \qquad (13)$$

where w is the vertical velocity of the ship and h is the water height on the deck. However, he concludes that the shipping of water and the green water loading are not linear phenomena. On a momentum basis an important component of peak force F per unit breadth of deck is:

$$F = \rho h U^2 \qquad (14)$$

where h is the maximum wave height above the deck and U is the incoming water flow, assumed constant. He also confirmed that for green water impacts the empirically based pressure coefficient approach of eq(10) was valid. These integrated pressure measurements supported the Suhara et al [50] value of $C_p = 2.8$ as a low probability peak but with a large scatter of lower values.

We conclude, as Buchner does, that the development or improvement of those types of prediction methods is indispensable for a better evaluation of the operability and safety of ships in rough seas. Meanwhile, designers have to design and the suggestions in this section may act as a guide in the absence of anything better to provide the bases for provisional design and assessment methods. Validation tests with models and full scale ships in realistic wave conditions are needed.

Structural Safety Criteria

At the same time that design loads are being advanced, acceptable structural performance criteria must also be considered. Since even moderately thick continuous plate elements have substantial reserves of membrane strength, it is suggested that the general long-plate membrane relation is used:

$$p_m = 8 \sigma_y \left(\frac{t}{b} \right) \frac{\Delta}{b} \qquad (15)$$

in which t and b are plate thickness and width and a plastic deformation of say $\Delta/b = 1/16$ would be acceptable since it implies a further load factor of about 2 before failure is likely to occur at the boundaries. However, before then the stiffeners are likely to fail as they are generally weaker and have little reserve strength beyond first yield. For these a load factor of say 1.25 on the formation of a collapse mechanism of plastic hinges would be quite adequate as the suggested loading is likely to be conservative.

With regard to watertight integrity for main hull or deckhouse structures, the usual criterion would be based on penetration of the hull or sides. This is usually induced by fatigue crack growth, and only very recently are such criteria being developed, for example, for the side shell of tankers and bulk carriers. Penetration can also be caused by breaking wave or other green sea actions, and this certainly has occurred in the hatch covers and coamings of bulkers[6,17]. It is suggested that in such structures plastic collapse should form the design criteria with a low load factor of say 1.25.

However, the possibility of local brittle fracture emanating from existing fatigue cracks also needs to be considered based upon reduction in toughness considerations arising from the gifle steep fronted pressure spike. This may be particularly relevant when mobile water is trapped locally, for example, between supports to coamings being swept by green seas.

4.   CONCLUSIONS AND RECOMMENDATIONS

Two pragmatic findings which lie behind this paper are that experience continuously shows that weather routeing does not prevent ships from encountering abnormal storm conditions. Such conditions involve non-linear waves much higher than the linear ones presently used in design. Several specific conclusions and implied recommendations have been given in the text above, but more general ones now follow.

4.1   CONCLUSIONS

• Naval Architects should look seriously at the effects of abnormal waves on their designs. Explicit survival wave design should not displace present methods but would provide essential additional checks for agreed critical scenarios.

• Various critical design and operational conditions need to be established. A preliminary list with some discussion is offered in section 1. Vulnerability of superstructure and bridge windows to wave impact is illustrated, and some guidance on the analyses and experiments required is provided.

• It is stressed that the list of critical conditions in 1.4 is far too extensive to tackle in total, even with some deletions. It is a provisional list for discussion from which it is suggested just a few real priorities are determined for initial development under a First Principles Methodology. These are uncharted waters which involve a substantial learning process for example by a team co-ordinated by the correct bodies (perhaps with IMO, IACS and Professional body representatives).

• Operability and Survivability Envelopes have been defined for northern and southern hemispheres in terms of significant wave heights H_s and most probable periods T_p.

• Guidance is provided on predicting survivability wave heights, and a range of wave periods is suggested with which to examine and establish the critical conditions in conjunction with appropriate spectra - and hopefully in time with more time-series wave data.

As a guide, abnormal survival waves for large ships, greater than 150m long say, have been provisionally defined as $H_s = 2.5H_s \geq 25m$ for wave lengths $\lambda \cong 10H$ with steep elevated crest profiles. An approximation to their probability of occurrence is offered and provisional crest elevations and steepness might follow the guidance in Ref. [6].

• Similar but smaller critical wave definitions will apply to smaller ships and their occurrence will naturally be higher than for larger waves.

• The evidence for change is substantial and IACS and IMO must be prevailed upon to take a keen interest in this subject to reduce the loss of ships and crew which is likely to be happening in wave conditions which are not catered for in present designs.

• The 1966 International Loadline Convention needs substantial updating regarding freeboard, fore-end protection, hatch cover strength, etc.

4.2   RECOMMENDATIONS

An initiative is required, for example, from the IMO and IACS in conjunction with the major professional bodies to examine more fully the survival wave concept for design and operation, and to consider a way ahead.

Clearly, validation of most of the suggestions is needed which will require some desk studies and more serious R&D. It has been suggested that the International Ship and Offshore Structures Congress, International Towing Tank Committee and the major professional bodies should take an interest in this. Three sub-headings are adopted for recommendations relating to survival wave design.

Environmental

• examine storm data to identify wind field and wave characteristics, from which to develop a better understanding of abnormal waves, their locations, profiles and incidence; use standardised HACYM analysis and provide a PC code for its wider implementation;

• seek better prediction models for abnormal waves;

- develop non-linear wave mechanics to explain the origin and propagation of these waves and their kinematics, and from these obtain suitable models for design;

- survey existing time series wave data sources, including NOAA and acquire data from storms from offshore platform operators;

- establish design wave climates;

- wave tank simulations of survival waves are regarded as essential and a first step is to provide a survey of "qualified" facilities capable of generating extreme seas and episodic waves;

- survey free-running model facilities and existing or potential test sites to determine critical loading conditions; also survey (with same objectives) full scale load and motion data.

Design and Operational Conditions

Several of the critical conditions have already been described, but these and others need to be refined in a design and operational context. In particular, time domain analyses are required in conjunction with wave tank tests. More specific R&D suggestions are given in Ref. 5 (Addendum 2) and Ref. 6 under the following headings:

- ship motion characteristics;

- primary load modelling;

- local load modelling and associated strength models, including the very important issue of water impact understanding and load criteria;

- develop adequate, but lower than normal, safety margins;

- beam on risks assessed, including defining cargo shift hazards;

- implications for main and auxiliary machinery and other ship systems.

Feedback

- improved definition of casualty data and associated sea conditions;

- measurement trials for primary and local loads using strain gauges and pressure transducers (on hatch covers, fore end and side structures, bridge fronts, etc.);

- operational implications for design with a greater dialogue between naval architects, marine engineers and mariners;

- weather routeing to be reviewed to determine its in service effectiveness.

ACKNOWLEDGEMENTS

The first author acknowledges the Department of Transport's support for the work undertaken with Lord Donaldson [Ref. 5]. The second author is indebted to the Society of Naval Architects and Marine Engineers and to the Ship Structure Committee for freedom to draw on work he has undertaken for them, including the use of the photographs for Figs. 9, 10 and 12.

REFERENCES

1. DRAPER, L: 'Freak Ocean Waves', Oceanus, 10, (4), 1964.

2. MALORY, J K: 'Abnormal Waves Off the South African Coast - a Danger to Shipping', The Naval Architect, July 1975.

3. SELLARS, F H: 'Maximum Wave Statistics for Design', SNAME T&R Bulletin no. 1-37, March 1978.

4. BUCKLEY, W H and STAVOVY, A B: 'Progress in the Development of Structural Load Criteria for Extreme Waves', SSC-SNAME Extreme Loads Response Symp., Arlington, pub. by SNAME, 1981.

5. Lord Donaldson's Assessment (DERBYSHIRE), Cm 3128, London, HMSO, December 1995.

6. FAULKNER, D and WILLIAMS, R A: 'Design for Abnormal Ocean Waves', RINA, Spring Meetings, April 1996, (Trans, Part A, Vol. 139, 1997).

7. BUCKLEY, W H: 'A Study of Extreme Waves and their Effects on Ship Structure', Report SSC-320, 1983.

8. BUCKLEY, W H: 'Analysis of Wave Characteristics in Extreme Seas', Report SSC-353, 1991.

9. FAULKNER, D: 'Safety of Ships - Risk Assessment Based Design and Operation', Greenwich and Hazards Fora, Conference on Safety of Ships, Southampton, May 1995.

10. 'The Causes of Shipwrecks', Report from the Select Committee, House of Commons, 19 August 1836.

11. Committee IV.1 Report 'Design Principles and Criteria' in Proc. 13th ISSC, Trondheim, Pergamon, vol. 1, 1997.

12. WILLIAMS, R A and FAULKNER, D: 'm.v. DERBYSHIRE - The Search, Assessment and Survey', RINA Colloquium, 15 March 1996, Proceedings with Summary Report of Discussions ed by D. Faulkner and R.A. Williams, RINA, 1996.

13. BUCKLEY, W H: 'Extreme and Climatic Wave Spectra for Use in Structural Design of Ships' - Naval Engineers Jnl, Sept. 1988.

14. BUCKLEY, W H: 'Critical Capsizing Conditions in Survivability Seaways', RINA Intl Conf. Design and Operation for Abnormal Conditions, Glasgow, 21/22 October 1997.

15. BUCKLEY, W H: 'Hull Girder Structural Design - the Case for New Loading Conditions for Extreme Waves', Nav. Engs. Jnl, February 1978.

16. NITA, A: 'Basis of IACS Unified Longitudinal Strength Standard', J. Marine Structures, vol. 5, no. 1, 1992.

17. FAULKNER, D, CORLETT, B J and ROMELING, J U: 'Design of Hatch Covers and Coamings for Abnormal Waves', RINA Intl Conf. Watertight Integrity and Ship Survivability, London, 21/22 October 1996.

18. FAULKNER, D: 'Hatch Covers - the Achilles Heel of Bulkers?', Lloyd's List, July 1, 1997.

19. MOORE, W H and BEA, R G: 'Safety Through Quality in People - A Report on the Role of the Human Element in Marine Safety', Report to the ABS, New York, 1995.

20. Specialist Panel V.1 Report 'Quality Assurance for Marine Structures', ISSC, 1997, (loc cit 11).

21. 'Climate Change Offshore N.W. Europe - An Assessment of the Impact of Changing Meteorological and Oceanographic (Metocean) Conditions on Offshore Activities', SUT Colloquium, London, 18 April 1996. Reported in SUT J. for Underwater Technology, vol. 22, no. 2, 1997.

22. COTTON, P D and CHALLENOR, P G: 'Long Term Trends in Altimeter Measured Significant wave Height, and the implications for Expected Extreme Values' (loc cit 14).

23. LYNAUGH, N: 'Weather and Climate Variability Since Prehistoric Times and Recent Indications of Continuing Fluctuations in the N.E. Atlantic', (loc cit 21).

24. OLSEN, O A: Committee I.1 Report 'Environmental Conditions' of the 7th ISSC, Paris, 1979.

25. GAYTHWAITE, John: 'The Marine Environment and Structural Design', von Nostrand Reinhold, 1981.

26. YAMANOUCHI, Y and OGAWA, A: 'Statistical Diagrams on the Winds and Waves in the North Pacific Ocean', Ship Research Institute Report, Tokyo, 1970.

27. 'How Big Can Waves Get?', Article based on interview with J. Goldman, Technical Director of the International Centre for the Solution of Environmental Problems, Ocean Industry Magazine, Houston, June 1978.

28. BUCKLEY, W H: 'Design Wave Climates for the Worldwide Operation of Ships - Part 1: Establishment of Design Wave Climates', (in publication as a SNAME T&R Report).

29. HOGBEN, N, DACUNHA, N M C and OLLIVER, G F: 'Global Wave Statistics', Unwin Brothers, 1986.

30. BUCKLEY, W H: 'Stability Criteria: Development of a First Principles Methodology', 5th Intl Conf. on Stability of Ships and Ocean Vehicles, FIT, Melbourne, FL., November 1994.

31. HOGBEN, N: in 'Long Term Wave Statistics', Ocean Engineering Science, vol. 9, Part A, Section 8, John Wiley and Sons, 1990.

32. HOGBEN, N and TUCKER, M J: 'Sea-State Development During Severe Storms: Assessment of Data and Case Histories', Underwater Technology, vol. 20, no. 3, Autumn 1994.

33. LONGUET-HIGGINS, M S: 'On the Statistical Distribution of the Heights of Sea Waves', J.Marine Research, vol. 11, no. 3, 1952.

34. CHAPLIN, J: 'The Hurricane of 1847', The Scots Magazine, vol. 146, no. 4, April 1997.

35. COLES, K. Adlard 'Heavy Weather Sailing', Adlard Coles Nautical, London, 4th edn, 1991.

36. BUCKLEY, W H et al : 'Use of the Half Cycle Analysis Method to Compare Measured Wave Height and Simulated Gaussian Data Having the Same Variance Spectrum', Ocean Engineering, vol. 11, no. 4, 1984.

37. MYRHAUG, D and KJELDSEN, S P: 'Steepness and Asymmetry of Extreme waves and the Highest Waves in Deep Water', Ocean Engineering, vol. 13, no. 6, 1986.

38. EILERSEN, C, GUDMESTAD, O T, OTTESEN HANSEN, N E and JACOBSEN, V: 'Freak Waves and their Effect on Steel Jacket Platforms', Report no. 3.12/156 Oil Industries Exploration and Production Forum, Paris, 1989.

39. BITNER-GREGERSEN et al : 'Extreme Steepness of Numerical Model and Laboratory Waves', Proc. 5th ISOPE Conf., vol. 1, 1995.

40. Committee I.1 Report 'Environment' ISSC, 1997 (loc cit 11)

41. GALLEZ, B: 'Short-Crested Wave Generation in Wave Flumes', Intl Symp.: Waves - Physical and Numerical Modelling, Vancouver, 1994.

42. van DORN, William G: 'Oceanography and Seamanship', Cornell Maritime Press, 2nd edn, 1993.

43. FAULKNER, D: 'Some Aspects of Efficient Structural Design of Future Fast Multi-Hull Ships', Plenary Session Paper, Proc. 2nd Intl Conf., FAST '93, Yokohama, December 1993.

44. WEGGEL, J R and MAXWELL, W H C: 'Experimental Study of Breaking Wave Pressures', OTC Paper 1224, vol. 2, May 1970.

45. MOGRIDGE, G R and JAMIESON, W W 'Wave Impact Pressures on Composite Breakwaters', 16th Intl Conf. on Coastal Engineering, Sydney, March 1980.

46. KAWAKAMI, M: 'On the Impact Strength of Ships Due to Shipping Green Seas', J.S.N.A., vol. 125, June 1969.

47. ZHU, Ling 'Structural Response of Ship Plates in Slamming - Drop Test Results and Analysis', University of Glasgow, Report NAOE-95-20, June 1995.

48. MIZOGUCHI, S: 'Design of Freeboard Height with the Numerical Simulation on the Shipping Water', PRADS'89, Soc. of Naval Architects of Japan, 1989.

49. TAKEZAWA, S, KOBAYASHI, K and SAWADA, K: 'On Deck Wetness and Impulsive Water Pressure Acting on the Deck in Head Seas', (in Japanese), J. Zosen Kiokai, SNAJ, vol. 141, 1977.

50. SUHARA, T, HIYAMA, H and KOGA, Y: 'Shock Pressure Due to Impact of Water Jet and Response of Elastic Plates', Trans W. Japan SNA, no. 46, 1973.

51. BUCHNER, B: 'On the Impact of Green Water Loading on Ship and Offshore Unit Design', PRADS Intl Conf., Seoul, September 1995.

52. KOROBKIN, A: Chapt. 7 'Water Impact Problems in Ship Hydrodynamics', in Marine Hydrodynamics, ed. by M. Ohkusu, Computational Mechanics Publications, 1994.

53. KVÅLVSVOLD, J, FALTINSEN, O M and AARSNES, J V: 'Effect of Structural Elasticity on Slamming Against Wetdecks of Multihull Vessels', J. Ship and Ocean Technology, (SOTECH) SNAK, Seoul, vol. 1, no. 1, 1997.

PAPER NO.7.

BEHAVIOUR OF SHIPS IN SEVERE ASTERN SEAS

by M Tsangaris and D Vassalos
Stability Research Centre, Department of Ship and Marine Technology
University of Strathclyde, Glasgow, UK

Paper presented at the

International Conference

**DESIGN AND OPERATION FOR
ABNORMAL CONDITIONS**

21 22 OCTOBER 1997 GLASGOW

BEHAVIOUR OF SHIPS IN SEVERE ASTERN SEAS

M. Tsangaris and D. Vassalos
Stability Research Centre, Department of Ship and Marine Technology,
University of Strathclyde, Glasgow, UK

SUMMARY

A time simulation model for predicting the behaviour of a vessel in severe astern seas of low encounter frequency is presented. Wave forces are validated with experimental results. Simulation results for a typical fishing vessel are presented and the exhibited wave induced capsize modes are identified. Based on these results, the behaviour of the vessel is classified for a range of operational and environmental parameters.

AUTHORS' BIOGRAPHIES

Mr. Tsangaris is a PhD student at the Ship Stability Research Centre of the University of Strathclyde, undertaking research over the past three years in the area of non-linear ship dynamics and stability with particular emphasis on transient ship behaviour in astern seas. He is a graduate of the National Technical University of Athens.

Professor Dracos Vassalos is the Director of the Ship Stability Research Centre comprising some twenty researchers working on all aspects of ship dynamics, stability and safety. He has been working for nineteen years on the stability of ships and marine vehicles and has published widely in the area. Professor Vassalos is the chairman of the ITTC Specialist Committee on Ship Stability.

1.   INTRODUCTION

Capsize in severe weather is a long-standing problem in Naval Architecture. Even though ship capsizing is an extreme event, most ships run the danger of capsize in either intact or in a damaged condition. Capsizing of vessels does not only account for material losses but also presents a great risk to human lives and depending on the nature of the cargo, considerable environmental damage.

Wave induced capsize of intact ships may be identified in several dynamic modes which occur separately or combined. For following/quartering seas, these are pure loss of transverse stability, low-cycle resonance due to parametric excitation and broaching. The latter two are physical phenomena that may or may not lead to capsize. Capsizing by broaching-to is the most dynamic mode of ship capsize, resulting from loss of control-lability in severe astern seas. Although this is a very dangerous situation especially for small vessels, a rigorous treatment of this specific mode of capsize is still awaited. More specifically, the actual capsize mechanism and the vessel behaviour at a broaching situation still defy precise definition. This situation is to be ascribed to the fact that the vessel is in a very extreme condition, which makes studies of physics, either theoretical or experimental, difficult.

Numerical studies have shed light into individual factors pertaining to the behaviour of a vessel in extreme conditions. Theoretical models and time simulation facilitated the investigation of forces and moments exerted on the ship until the event of capsize [6,3]. In studies of broaching, planar manoeuvring models [14,13] have been often used with some principles borrowed from seakeeping models.

In this work a mathematical model that realistically represents the motions of a steered vessel in severe astern seas will be used to investigate the behaviour of the vessel. Emphasis is placed on the broaching-to phenomenon and therefore the model will be simple in its description but capable to realistically describe the vessel motions during a capsize in broaching-to scenarios. It will be shown that in environmental conditions where a broaching-to situation may arise the vessel behaviour exhibits a rich dynamic behaviour.

2.   THEORETICAL MODEL

In order to study the actual ship capsize in a way that accounts fully for the ensuing coupling between longitudinal and transverse motions in a broaching-to situation [19], a non linear coupled six degrees of freedom model is used. Broaching-to is considered as a parasitic motion [2] of conventional manoeuvring and seakeeping theory. When a broaching situation arises the ship is slowly overtaken by the waves in a very low encounter frequency. It is therefore reasonable to assume that hydrostatic effects are dominant.

A conventional manoeuvring model is therefore adopted including wave excitation forces, wind and current by utilising the modular approach adopted by the Japanese Manoeuvring Group. A standard proportional-differential auto-pilot is also introduced. Two parallel co-ordinate systems are used, an inertial and one fixed to the ship with the x axis positive forward, z axis positive down-ard and y axis positive to starboard. The x-y plane coincides with the calm waterplane and the origin is located at the centreplane amidships. Assuming transverse symmetry and principal axes of inertia parallel to the system axes, the equations of motion in standard nomenclature [7], are given below [8]:

$$m\left\{\dot{u} + qw - rv - x_G\left(q^2 + r^2\right) + z_G\left(pr + \dot{q}\right)\right\} = X$$

$$m\left\{\dot{v} + ru - pw + x_G\left(pq + \dot{r}\right) + z_G\left(rq - \dot{p}\right)\right\} = Y$$

$$m\left\{\dot{w} + pv - qu + x_G\left(pr - \dot{q}\right) - z_G\left(p^2 + q^2\right)\right\} = Z$$

$$I_x\dot{p} - mz_G\left(\dot{v} + ru - pw\right) - mx_Gz_G\left(pq + \dot{r}\right) = K$$

$$I_y\dot{q} + \left(I_x - I_z\right)pr + mz_G\left(\dot{u} + qw - rv\right) - mx_G\left(\dot{w} + pv - qu\right) + mx_Gz_G\left(p^2 - r^2\right) = M$$

$$I_z\dot{r} + \left(I_y - I_x\right)pq + mx_G\left(\dot{v} + ru - pw\right) + mx_Gz_G\left(rq - \dot{p}\right) = N$$

3.   EXTERNAL FORCES AND MOMENTS

The external forces and moments are divided into the following terms depending on the source:

$$F = F_{HS} + F_{CW} + F_{WAVE} + F_{WIND}$$

where, F_{HS} denotes forces and moments of hydrostatic origin, F_{CW} conventional calm water manoeuvring terms except hydrostatics, F_{WIND} wind forces and moments and F_{WAVE} wave exciting forces and moments.

Hydrostatic forces are calculated exactly up to the instantaneous water surface as roll restoring would play a key roll in the event of capsize.

Due to the assumption of zero or very low encounter frequency and based on experimental evidence [4] calm water hydrodynamic forces represent with sufficient accuracy fluid action in a broaching situation and are used in this model. Nevertheless when the ship speed deviates from the wave celerity, the assumption of zero encounter frequency is less accurate. The assumption of calm water against that of a steady wave profile on the hull may appear "rough" but has been proven to provide good results. The model that has been adopted for these forces and moments is described in [16]. Resistance is calculated based on regression coefficients from model tests. Hydrodynamic derivatives in sway and yaw are also derived from model tests. Propeller and rudder forces are calculated based on [10] and they include both "open water" characteristics as well as interference effects with the hull.

Wind force and moments are evaluated using approximated formulae derived through experiments by Aage [1].

Wave excitation forces include Froude-Krylov and diffraction forces and are based on regular waves.

Froude-Krylov forces are obtained by integrating the undisturbed pressure field over the instantaneous wet-ed hull surface. The resulting forces and moments are:

$$F = \oiint\limits_S P\,n\,dS$$

$$M = \oiint\limits_S P\,(r \times n)\,dS$$

where P is the hydrodynamic pressure, the n is the unit normal vector of the surface element dS and r is the position vector. The vessel is divided into transverse and longitudinal sections, the points where the wave surface intersects the hull are calculated and integration over the hull is performed on body fixed co-ordinates at each time step, taking into account the ship motions.

It is assumed that linear wave theory can be extended up to the actual free surface as it has been found to provide good results [15]. This integration will provide a steady drift force resulting from a nonzero mean value of the exciting forces.

Diffraction forces have been calculated based on a strip theory method proposed by Ohkusu [11]. Wave exciting forces measured during broaching experiments [9] revealed a high discrepancy from Froude-Krylov forces. Attention is therefore drawn on other contributions and higher order terms. Under the assumption of low encountered frequency, the diffraction potential Φ_D might be approximated by the disturbance of stationary waves Φ_S [17,18] when the ship is advancing on otherwise calm water. Then the pressure terms accounting for the diffracted waves Φ_D and the interaction between incident Φ_I, diffracted Φ_D and stationary waves Φ_S are given for a section of the ship by [11]:

$$P = \rho U \frac{\partial \Phi_D}{\partial x} e^{i\omega_e t} - \rho\left(\frac{\partial \Phi_S}{\partial y}\frac{\partial \Phi_I}{\partial y} + \frac{\partial \Phi_S}{\partial z}\frac{\partial \Phi_I}{\partial z}\right)e^{i\omega_e t}$$

$$- \rho\left(\frac{\partial \Phi_S}{\partial y}\frac{\partial \Phi_{2D}^S}{\partial y} + \frac{\partial \Phi_S}{\partial z}\frac{\partial \Phi_{2D}^S}{\partial z}\right)e^{i\omega_e t} - \rho\left(\frac{\partial \Phi_S}{\partial y}\frac{\partial \Phi_{2D}^A}{\partial y} + \frac{\partial \Phi_S}{\partial z}\frac{\partial \Phi_{2D}^A}{\partial z}\right)e^{i\omega_e t}$$

The hull form of the ship is approximated with Lewis forms and the wave forces and moments are calculated on each section using expressions derived in [11] and are then integrated along the length of the ship.

4. VALIDATION OF WAVE FORCES

The calculated wave exciting forces were validated with experiments that had been performed in regular waves of small encountered frequency [20]. A 2.0m scale model of a 34.5m purse seiner fishing vessel was used, free to heave and pitch but constrained in surge, sway, yaw and roll. A range of wave conditions, model speeds and loading conditions were considered. An example of the predicted and measured forces and moments is shown in Figure 1 for a heading angle of 30°, $\lambda/L = 1.5$, $H/\lambda = 1/20$, $Fn = 0.5$ as a function of the ship position on the wave, a concept explained in Figure 10. The forces are non-dimensionalized by the vessel weight W and the wave steepness as well as the length and draught for yaw and roll moments respectively. It was found that in general the calculated values agreed well with experimental results. Diffraction terms prove to increase the accuracy of the prediction of wave forces both in amplitude and phase.

Figure 2 shows the variation of heave and pitch wave forces over the ship length for the same conditions. Unfortunately experimental data are not available for comparison. It can be seen that the effect of higher order terms on wave forces is considerable locally. However on the whole ship it is very small.

5. SIMULATION OF SHIP BEHAVIOUR

The theoretical model was used in order to simulate in time domain the wave-induced modes of capsize and the related ship behaviour in astern seas.

The equations of motion were solved algebraically for the acceleration terms and were integrated together with kinematic relationships for the position and orientation of the vessel. A Runge-Kutta numerical method was used.

The purse seiner vessel was considered in the simulation runs. Pure loss of transverse stability, parametric resonance, surf-riding and two types of broaching behaviour were realised through simulation.

Pure loss of transverse stability implies the reduction of the hydrostatic arm on a wave crest to such an extent that the vessel can not return to the upright position. The vessel becomes unstable when caught with a wave crest amidships for a sufficient length of time. With little or no preliminary rolling the ship loses all stability and capsizes. An example of this behaviour is displayed in Figure 3. The wave amplitude play an important role in determining if the vessel will capsize. This is a static mode of capsize and the hydrostatic roll moment dominate the phenomenon.

Low cycle resonance describes the phenomenon of parametrically-induced roll motion when the ratio of the encounter frequency to the roll natural frequency equals $\frac{1}{2}$, 1, $\frac{3}{2}$ and so on. Capsizing usually occurs when the vessel encounters a group of steep regular waves causing the vessel to roll at increasing amplitudes. An example is illustrated in Figure 5 at encounter frequency almost twice the natural roll frequency of the vessel (T_φ=7.47 sec).

Another extreme type of behaviour is surf-riding. When the ship travels with almost zero encounter frequency she can be trapped by a wave and be forced to move along with it. An example of this behaviour is shown on Figure 4 where the ship remains on the same relative position with respect to the wave for a considerable amount of time. Broaching-to is likely to follow and the vessel is in extreme danger of capsizing. Some transient behaviour could not be avoided, as the ship will be accelerated to the speed of the waves. The surge component of Froude-Krylov force and its variation along the ship length is significant and can be very large for following seas.

Broaching-to describes the loss of directional stability in waves induced by a large yaw moment exceeding the course keeping ability of the rudder. The sudden loss of control can turn the ship beam on to the waves. The vessel will capsize by a large roll moment created by the forward momentum and the large heading angle with her hydrostatic stability often weakened by the presence of waves. When the ship is running with the phase speed of the wave or she is very slowly overtaken by waves broaching can occur as result of a single wave action. This is refereed as "true broach" and an example of this behaviour is presented in Figure 6. The auto-pilot turns the rudder to its maximum angle, which for the purse seiner is 15 degrees but the ship capsizes while on the down slope of the wave.

In contrast the terms "cumulative yaw motion" [13] or "pseudo-broaching" [19] are used to describe the situation where the successive effect of waves cause the ship to broach. This condition will arise when the ship runs with a lower speed than the waves. The wave induced yaw causes the ship to incline from the prescribed course in a zig-zag manner and gradually shift the vessel beam to the waves. This is illustrated in Figure 7 where the ship does not capsizes but it keeps turning portside in spite of the rudder being hard over.

The relative importance of the various components of the yaw moment is demonstrated in Figure 8. The wave excited yaw moment has the greatest amplitude and a positive mean value, turning the vessel to starboard. The rudder moment on the contrary has a negative mean value and successfully counteracts the wave moment after t=30 sec. The vertical coupling component represents the effect of coupling of heave and pitch into roll and yaw and it can been seen to have a significant value.

Numerical simulations were undertaken for a range of environmental parameters corresponding to the experiments already performed for the purse seiner in regular waves [5]. The same auto-pilot was used in order to reproduce the same behaviour. Using heading angle and forward speed as control parameters, regions

3

of safe and dangerous behaviour were identified as shown in Figure 9. The graph is divided into a non-capsize region in small Froude numbers, followed by a region where capsize occurred in the simulation due to broaching-to or by pure loss of stability. At higher Froude numbers the vessel is almost always locked in surf-riding and as capsize is very likely to follow, it is considered to be a dangerous zone. Experimental results from [5] are shown to compare well with these simulations.

In Figure 11 the investigation is extended to a wider range of wave characteristics and unsafe regions are identified for the specific vessel. The apparent similarity with results from [21] is to be noted.

6.   CONCLUDING REMARKS

A non-linear six-degrees-of-freedom numerical model has been developed capable of realistically describing ship behaviour in severe astern seas with comparisons between numerical and experimental results showing encouraging agreement.

Using this model, a series of numerical experiments has been performed to identify dangerous zones of operation over a range of environmental parameters to be used as a basis for ship design and operation and for providing useful guidance to the master.

Work is currently under way aiming to compare quantitative (numerical simulation) and qualitative (geometry of behaviour) trends in an attempt to enhance understanding of ship capsize in astern seas.

ACKNOWLEDGEMENTS

The authors would like to acknowledge the support by the European Commission, RDD, Human Capital and Mobility in undertaking the research work described in the paper. Sincere thanks are also due to Dr. Naoya Umeda of NRIFE, Japan for kindly providing useful information and support and to Dr. Kostas Spyrou for building the foundations of the numerical simulation model used in this study.

REFERENCES

1.   AAGE C: 'Wind Coefficients for Nine Ship Models', Hydro-or Aerodynamisk Laboratorium Report No.A -3, 1971.

2.   BISHOP R E D & PRICE W G: 'Some Comments on Present-Day Ship Dynamics', Phil. Trans. R. Soc. Lond. A(1991), 334, 187-197.

3.   de KAT J O & PAULLING R: 'The Simulation of Ship Motions and Capsizing in Severe Seas', SNAME Transactions, Vol. 97, 1989, pp. 139-166.

4.   FUJINO *et al* (1983): 'On the derivatives for the Directional Stability of ship in following seas', Journal of the society of Naval Architects of Japan, 152, 167-179 (In Japanese).

5.   HAMAMOTO M *et al*: 'Model Experiments of Ship Capsize in Astern Seas - Second Report', Journal of The Society of Naval Architects of Japan, 1996, Vol. 179, 1-9, pp. 77-86.

6.   HAMAMOTTO M, KIM Y, UWATOKO K: 'Study on Ship Motions and Capsizing in Following Seas (Final Report)', Journal of The Society of Naval Architects of Japan, 1991, Vol.170, pp. 173-183.

7.   ABKOWITZ M A: 'Stability and Motion Control of Ocean Waves', M.I.T. Press, 1969.

8.   MCCREIGHT W R: 'Ship manoeuvring in Waves', 16th Symposium on Naval hydrodynamics, ONR, Brekeley, 1986

9.   MOTORA S, FUJINO M, FUWA T: 'On the Mechanism of Broaching-To Phenomena', Second International Conference on Stability of Ships and Ocean Vehicles, Tokyo, Oct. 1982.

10. OGAWA A & KASAI H: 'On the Mathematical Model of Manoeuvring Motion of Ships', Int. Shipbuilding Prog., Vol. 26, No. 306, 1978.

11. OKHUSU M: 'Prediction of Wave Forces on a Ship Running in Following Waves with Very Low Encountered Frequency', J. of the Society of Naval architects of Japan, 159, 129-138, 1986.

12. RENILSON M R: 'An Investigation into the Factors Affecting the Likelihood of Broaching-to in Following Seas', Second International Conference on Stability of Ships and Ocean Vehicles, Tokyo, Oct. 1982, pp.551-564.

13. RENILSON M R & DRISCOLL A: 'Broaching - An Investigation into the Loss of Directional Control in Severe Following Seas', RINA Spring Meeting, 1981.

14. RUTGERSSON O & OTTOSON P: 'Model Tests and Computer Simulations - An Effective Combination for Investigation of Broaching Phenomena', SNAME Transaction, Vol. 95, 1987, pp.263-281.

15. SOBEY R J *et al*: 'Application of stokes, Cnoidal and Fourier Wave Theories', J. of Waterways, Port, Coastal and ocean engineering, Vol. 113, No. 6, pp.565-587, 1987.

16. SPYROU K J: 'A New Approach for Assessing Ship Manoeuvrability based on Dynamical Systems Theory', PhD thesis, University of Strathclyde, 1990.

17. TUCK, E O: 'A Systematic Asymptotic Expansion Procedure for Slender Ships', J. of Ship Research, Vol. 8, No. 1, 1964.

18. TUCK, E: 'On Line Distributions of Kelvin Sources', J. of Ship Research, Vol. 8, No. 2, 1964.

19. VASSALOS D & MAIMUN A: 'Broaching-To : Thirty Years On', STAB '94

20. VASSALOS D, SPYROU K, UMEDA N: 'Captive Model Test of a purse seiner Model in Regular Astern Seas', Experimental Report, National Research Institute of Fisheries Engineering, Japan, 1994.

21. SPYROU K J: 'Surf-riding and Oscillations of a Ship in Quartering Waves', J Mar Sci Technol (1995) 1: 24-36.

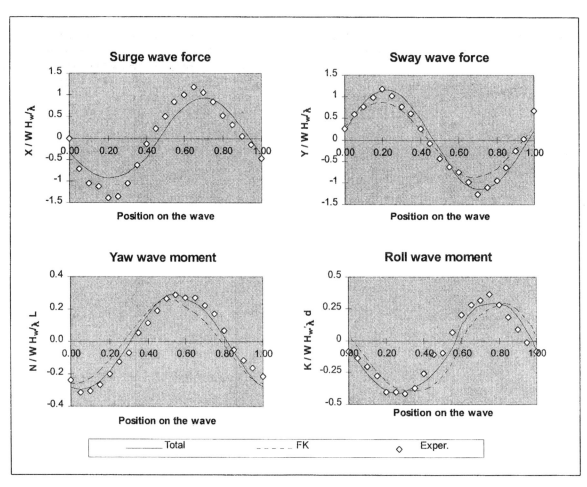

Figure 1: Wave exciting forces and moments vs.
Relative position of ship on the wave
$\lambda/L = 1.5$, $H/\lambda = 1/20$, Fn = 0.5 , Heading = 15 deg

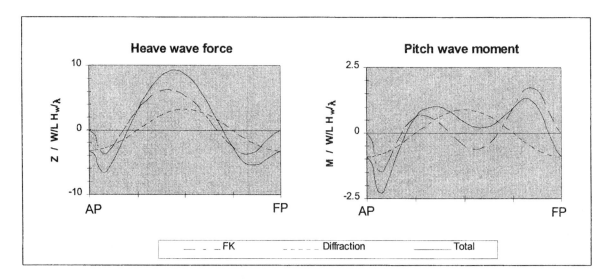

Figure 2: Wave exciting forces and moments vs. position on ship
$\lambda/L = 1.5$, $H/\lambda = 1/20$, Fn = 0.5, Heading = 15 deg

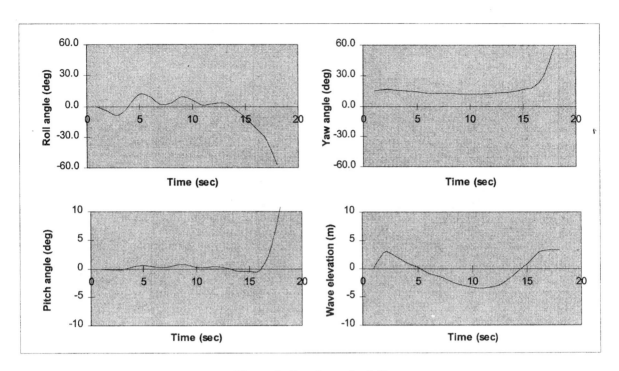

Figure 3: Pure loss of stability
Fn = 0.55, Heading = 15 deg , $\lambda/L = 1.0$, $H/\lambda = 1/10$

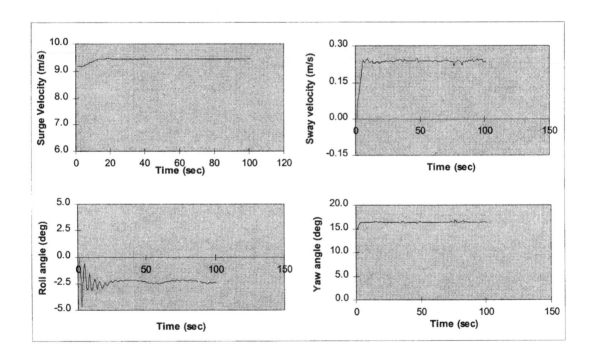

Figure 4: Surf-riding , ship positioned on a wave crest (x/λ=0.973)
Fn = 0.5, Heading = 15 deg, $\lambda/L = 1.5$, $H/\lambda = 1/20$

7

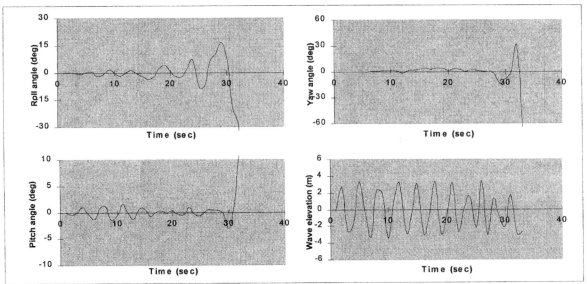

Figure 5: Low-cycle Resonance - Constant rudder at 0 deg
Fn = 0.55, Heading = 0 deg, λ/L = 1.0 , H/λ = 1/10

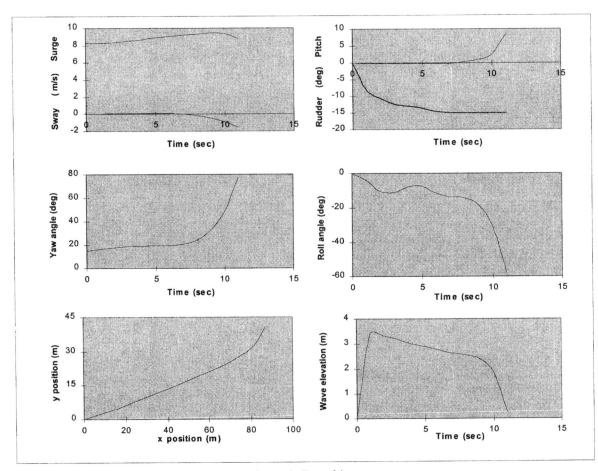

Figure 6: Broaching-to
Fn = 0.45, Heading = 15 deg, λ/L = 1.5, H/λ = 1/15

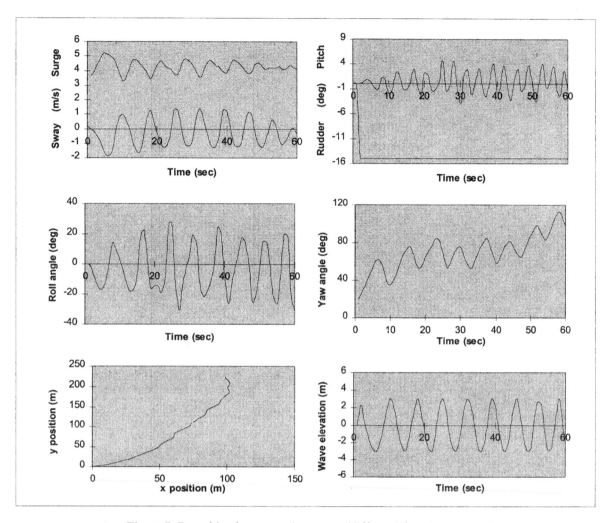

Figure 7: Broaching by successive waves (differential gain set to zero)
Fn = 0.2, Heading = 20 deg, λ/L = 1.5, H/λ = 1/17

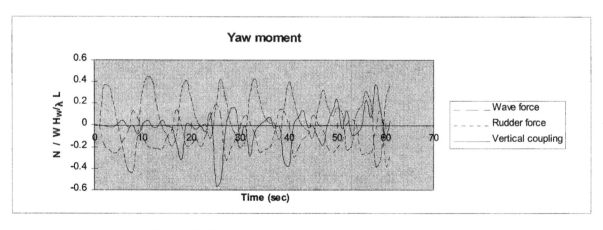

Figure 8: Relative importance of yaw moment components
Fn = 0.2, Heading = 20 deg, λ/L = 1.5, H/λ = 1/17

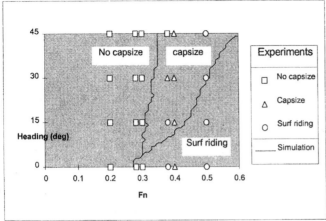

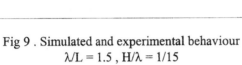

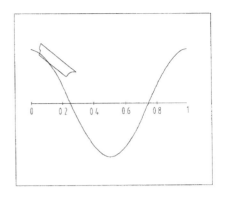

Fig 9 . Simulated and experimental behaviour
$\lambda/L = 1.5$, $H/\lambda = 1/15$

Fig 10 . Relative position of the ship on
the wave

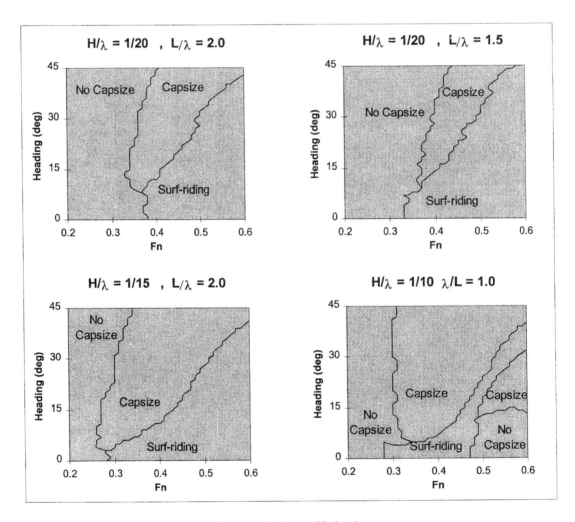

Fig 11 . Regions of behaviour

PAPER NO.8.

ON THE NONLINEAR DYNAMICS OF BROACHING-TO

by K J Spyrou
Centre for Nonlinear Dynamics and its Applications,
University College London, UK

Paper presented at the

International Conference

**DESIGN AND OPERATION FOR
ABNORMAL CONDITIONS**

21 22 OCTOBER 1997 GLASGOW

ON THE NONLINEAR DYNAMICS OF BROACHING-TO

Dr. K.J. Spyrou
Centre for Nonlinear Dynamics and its Applications
University College London

SUMMARY

The latest findings of a research project where the aim is the clarification of the dynamics of broaching are presented. A basic novelty of the approach lies in the fact that it unifies contemporary methodologies of ship controllability and transverse stability studies, within the framework of modern dynamical systems' theory. The main sources of nonlinearity are first identified. In the presence of large excitations these nonlinearities can become influential for system dynamics and the links with broaching are presented. Steady-state and transient responses are investigated and is shown how periodic motions, surf-riding, broaching and capsize are organized on a suitable parameters' plane. Different broaching mechanisms are presented concerning frequencies of encounter near to zero, where surf-riding plays the dominant role, as well as frequencies of encounter away from zero, where the instability is an intrinsic feature of yaw response due to the abnormally large waves.

AUTHOR'S BIOGRAPHY

Dr Kostas Spyrou, PhD, CEng, MRINA, is a Visiting Fellow supported by the European Union at the Centre for Nonlinear Dynamics and its Applications of University College London. He graduated in Naval Architecture and Marine Engineering from the National Technical University of Athens in 1984 and he obtained his PhD from the University of Strathclyde in 1991. Before joining UCL in 1996 he was a Fellow of the Science and Technology of Japan (STA) and of the European Union at the National Research Institute of Fisheries Engineering of Japan. At earlier stages of his career he has held managerial posts in the industry related with ship safety and the application of quality assurance in shipping. His current research interests include ship dynamics, nonlinear analysis, stability and manoeuvring, areas in which he has published several papers.

1. INTRODUCTION

Broaching can be broadly described as the sudden 'loss of heading' by an actively steered ship, that is accompanied by the quick build-up of significant deviation from the desired course. It represents thus primarily a problem of stability on the horizontal plane, although interesting post-critical behaviour is likely to arise also in roll due to energy transfer into this mode through the well known hydrodynamic coupling of sway/yaw with roll. In recent years there has been renewed interest about the broaching problem, largely inspired by some spectacular advances achieved in the analysis of nonlinear engineering systems [1], and the realization that broaching can be formulated as an escape problem of multi-degree dynamics [2], [3].

As is well known, nonlinear systems often admit multiple stable solutions. In that case, a change of value in one or more of the system's parameters, or perhaps the sudden application of a nearly impulsive external load, can create escape from the ordinary type of response and a transition towards some other type whose main characteristics are, in a physical sense, undesirable. This idea seems to be very relevant to the broaching problem; because the sudden encounter of an abnormally large wave, or group of waves, or the excess of a threshold heading angle in relation to the direction of the waves are usually the causes of the abrupt change of state that is commonly perceived as broaching. The first major challenge along this line of thinking is, to discern the system's repertoire of steady dynamic responses from the set of motion equations. It is understood of course that, practically, these equations can only represent a simplified version of the true motion equations. However what is essential here is, to retain in the model the key couplings and nonlinearities.

Furthermore, it is important to be able to predict towards which type of response a certain initial condition will lead, which is to say that the organization of the domains of attraction of these steady responses must be derived. However, unlike linear systems where the dynamics are easily found should the mathematical model be known, for nonlinear systems these tasks are, in general, far from trivial. Extra difficulties arise from the fact that in broaching one has to deal with a system of multi-dimensional nature.

A description and some earlier practical information about broaching are given in [4]. In the traditional methods of analysis one is usually content with a stability examination based on the linear sway/yaw pair [5], [6], [7] (or, surge-sway-yaw [8]) for different positions of the ship on a selected reference wave. There is a number of crucial simplifications that are innate of these approaches such as, their reliance on linearized equations of motion and their exclusive concentration on the static and steady-state problem. The ship is usually assumed to be at quasi-static equilibrium and to travel at exactly zero frequency of encounter (or momentarily 'frozen' at certain positions of the wave). With today's eyes and our easy access to vast computer power such approaches seem of course to present limited potential. Nevertheless, in the early days of ship motions' research they offered truly valuable insights into the effect of following waves on directional stability.

However, the problem with nonlinearity is that it can give rise to responses that are not deducible, even at a qualitative level, from the linear low-amplitude analysis. The significance of this matter for broaching, certainly, is not raised for the first time. In the discussion of the classic 1962 paper of Du Cane & Goodrich [9], Swaan remarked that the terms which could probably explain broaching were dropped from the equations. A similar comment was given by Weinblum in reference to the linear, yet seemingly mathematically consistent, approach of Rydill [10]. These discussions were about a Hill's type equation arising in the controlled ship motion in waves on the basis of the usual sway/yaw pair. Further research on this interesting problem has been presented very recently by the author [11].

Another source of nonlinearity which seems to have received however very limited attention within the broaching framework of analysis relates with the way the nonlinear dynamics of surge influence the other horizontal motions. In large and relatively long waves (particularly for wave length to ship length ratio between 1 and 2 where the tendency for broaching is greater) a ship does not approach 'linearly' the zero frequency of encounter but somehow 'jumps' to it once the threshold of surf-riding has been exceeded [12]. Surf-riding is that peculiar type of ship behaviour in long and steep regular waves where the ship is captured and carried forward by a single wave. It has been very recently established theoretically that if the encounter angle between the ship and the wave lies in a certain range (usually between 10 and 30°) this jump is conducive to broaching [2]. This seems however to have been empirically 'known' for long time [13].

In the rest of this paper we shall discuss in further detail the origins of instability and we shall also present some of our latest understandings about the various types of response that can exist in abnormally large, astern seas. It is hoped to make obvious that an approach rooted in nonlinear dynamics offers a powerful and arguably much more scientific framework for explaining broaching, as well as other phenomena of dynamic instability.

2. THE STATIC PROBLEM REVISITED: THE ONSET OF YAW INSTABILITY

In relatively long and steep waves many initially directionally stable ships will experience static instability of yaw when their centres of gravity lie on the down-slope of the wave and towards the trough [5], [6], [7], [8], [9], [10]. The key role is played by the wave yaw moment which in the vicinity of the trough tends to turn the ship towards a position vertical to the

direction of wave propagation $\partial N_W(x)/\partial \psi > 0$, where $N_W(x)$ is the wave-excited yaw moment, x is the relative position of the ship in respect to the wave and ψ is the heading angle, Fig. 1). To conceive the onset of this static instability one should think in terms of the well known index of directional stability that normally refers to still-water motion [14]. This index depends on the yaw and sway velocity coefficients. Suppose that a ship is initially stable in which case the index is positive. In waves the index should obviously be modified by introducing the wave force/moment derivatives in respect to the yaw angle of the ship relatively to the wave. These derivatives are of course dependent on the prevailing wave characteristics and, given the length of the wave, a critical steepness exists where in certain regions of the wave this index turns from positive to negative, see for example [6]. For such cases a steering method featuring sufficient proportional-to-heading gain will be required. One should note here however that large gains are not always desirable because they increase rudder activity and they may create rudder saturation. Also for manual steering, the required phase margins may lie beyond the capabilities of the helmsman.

3. NONLINEARITY IN SURGE RESPONSE

The above analysis is underlied by a linearity perception of surge dynamics since it is based on the notion that a ship approaches the condition of zero-encounter-frequency in a continuous and 'smooth' manner when its nominal speed is gradually increased. However, in steep and relatively long following waves this assumption does not hold. This is easily shown if one considers the balance of forces along the horizontal axis pointing in the direction of the ship's forward motion. The thrust generated by the propeller should counteract the ship's inertial and drug force, plus an alternating, position-dependent wave force. The latter pushes forward when the ship's centre is in the down-slope, while it resists the forward motion on the up-slope. The mathematical expression of this relation betrays that the system is of a pendulum-like nature [12] :

$$(m + X_{\ddot{u}})\frac{d^2 x}{dt^2} + [Res(u) - T(u; n)] + f\sin(kx) = 0$$

(1)

where m, $X_{\ddot{u}}$ are ship mass and added mass in surge respectively; x is the position of a ship on the wave measured from a system of coordinates moving with the wave celerity and fixed at a trough; $u = \dfrac{dx}{dt} + c$ is the speed of the ship measured from an earth-fixed system, where c is the wave celerity that, at first order, equals $\sqrt{\dfrac{g\lambda}{2\pi}}$; n is propeller rate; Res, T

are respectively ship resistance and propeller thrust ; k and f are respectively wave number and amplitude of wave surge force. It is noted that in (1) the wave force in surge appears to be independent of time. Of course in the representation of wave pressure there is dependency on both position and time [15]: $\zeta_p = \zeta_0 e^{-ky} \sin(k\xi - \omega t)$ (ξ is the position of a considered water particle in reference to an earth-fixed system, ω is the wave frequency, y is the distance of the water particle from the stillwater surface; ζ_p and ζ_0 are respectively the instantaneous and the amplitude of wave pressure contour depression).

$$T(u;n) = (1-t_p)\rho n^2 D^4 K_T(u;n)$$
$$K_T(u;n) = c_1 + c_2 J(u;n) + c_3 J^2(u;n) \Bigg\} \longrightarrow T(u;n) = b_1 u^2 + b_2 un + b_3 n^2 \qquad (3)$$
$$J(u;n) = \frac{u(1-w_p)}{nD}$$

where w_p , t_p are respectively the wake fraction and thrust deduction coefficients, D is the propeller diameter and a_i, b_i, c_i are appropriate coefficients. With substitution of (2) and (3) , (1) becomes:

$$(m+X_{\ddot{u}})\frac{d^2x}{dt^2} + \{[3a_3c^2 + 2(a_2 - b_1)c + a_1] - b_2n\}\frac{dx}{dt} +$$

$$+[3a_3c + (a_2 - b_1)](\frac{dx}{dt})^2 + a_3(\frac{dx}{dt})^3 + f\sin(kx) =$$

$$= b_1c^2 + b_2cn + b_3n^2 - (a_1c + a_2c^2 + a_3c^3)$$

$$= T(c;n) - Res(c)$$

$$\qquad (4)$$

If we concentrate for a while on 'locally' linearized damping , we should be able to recognize the equation of a pendulum with constant forcing:

$$\frac{d^2x}{dt^2} + \beta\frac{dx}{dt} + f\sin(kx) = d \qquad (5)$$

where the new coefficients that appear in (5) can be found by comparing with (4) (sometimes β is calculated at the wave celerity which however may be well above the average speed of the ship). Unfortunately (4), or even (5), cannot be solved analytically. When the wave steepness is low, surge velocity is described by its mean that is basically the speed in still-water, plus a cyclic term of a certain small amplitude. As the waves become steeper however, surge motion adopts an increasingly asymmetric character, Fig. 2a. The ship remains for relatively long

However, since the position of the ship centre can be expressed also as $\xi = x + ct$, we may write :

$$(k\xi - \omega t) = kx + kct - \omega t = kx + \omega t - \omega t = kx .$$

To take things slightly further, let's approximate the resistance curve with a third-order polynomial of velocity and let's write the thrust coefficient K_T as a second-order polynomial of the speed of advance $J(u;n)$) :

$$Res(u) = a_1 u + a_2 u^2 + a_3 u^3 \qquad (2)$$

time near the crest but it passes quickly from the trough (surfing on a crest [16], or large amplitude surging [12]). Such behaviour arises due to the presence of higher-order harmonics in response due to the existence of nonlinearity in the term playing the term of restoring. Explanation is possible without consideration of higher-order, non-sinusoidal wave excitation effects (of course the presence of such effects would further complicate dynamics). In Fig. 2b we demonstrate qualitatively how the inclusion of a higher-order harmonic generates the well known features of the large-amplitude surging type of response. If wave steepness is increased even further (or the equivalent, if the propeller rate is stepped up) there will be an interesting coexistence of the oscillatory motion with a pair of stationary fixed points (surf-riding condition), the one of which can be stable [17]. On the basis of (5), to achieve equilibrium there should be $f\sin(kx) = d$ (therefore $-1 \leq \frac{d}{f} \leq 1$) and by solving for x we can obtain pairs of stationary solutions:

$$x = \frac{2\mu\pi}{k} + \frac{1}{k}\arcsin(\frac{d}{f})$$

$$\qquad (6)$$

$$x = \frac{(2\mu+1)\pi}{k} - \frac{1}{k}\arcsin(\frac{d}{f})$$

where μ is an integer. The stable point appears nearer to the trough while the unstable one (saddle) nearer to the crest.

By drawing upon the parallel of the pendulum one can understand fairly easily these developments: Depending on the magnitude of the constant external torque and the initial condition, a pendulum can either perform full rotations or it can stay at the asymmetric position of equilibrium characterizing the condition of static balance [18].

Eventually, the oscillatory-type response is likely to disappear altogether due to a phenomenon of *global bifurcation* known in dynamics as *homoclinic saddle connection* [2]. This happens when a limit-cycle 'collides' with a saddle-point in state-space.

To understand the dynamics at a fundamental level, let's write (5) in the following equivalent form :

$$\frac{dx}{dt} = z$$

(7)

$$\frac{dz}{dt} = -f\sin(kx) + (d - \beta z)$$

When the damping and forcing are zero (of course in this case the physical relevance of the equation becomes superficial) the system becomes *Hamiltonian* and the solutions on the phase plane are two families of periodic orbits, one corresponding to oscillations and the other to full rotations. The line that separates the two regions is an *heteroclinic orbit*, connecting the two saddles and is given by (see Fig. 3a) :

$$H(x,z) = \frac{z^2}{2} - (\frac{f}{k})\cos(kx) \begin{cases} < \frac{f}{k} \quad \text{(oscillation)} \\ \\ > \frac{f}{k} \quad \text{(rotation)} \end{cases}$$

(8)

The introduction of constant external torque d (still without damping) destroys the symmetry in respect to the *vertical* axis and thereafter the two types of motion are separated by the homoclinic orbit of the one saddle [for positive d the right saddle with $x = \frac{\pi}{k} - \frac{1}{k}arcsin(\frac{d}{f})$], Fig. 3b. Finally, if the damping term is included, the orbits in the oscillation domain converge to the fixed point that exists within it, Fig. 3c.

A key characteristic of the homoclinic connection phenomenon is that it occurs at a nominal speed that is considerably lower than the wave celerity. During the transient towards surf-riding ship behaviour is determined to a large extent by the so-called outset of the saddle of crest. This is more conveniently shown on the phase-plane $[\cos(\frac{2\pi x}{\lambda}), u]$, Fig.3d. The saddle outset usually spirals towards the equilibrium point that exists near to the trough. However, the separatrix of the different types of behaviour is the saddle inset. The transition to surf-riding is an abrupt event featuring a momentary increase of speed before settlement at speed equal with the wave celerity. In stable surf-riding the ship appears to be locked at a specific position in the vicinity of the trough of the wave. It is interesting that stable equilibrium in surge in the vicinity of the crest cannot be achieved because this point is always unstable!

It is logical to expect, on the basis of continuity considerations, that surf-riding will be possible not only in exactly following seas, but also in quartering. On the other hand, since surf-riding at beam sea is not possible due to the immense lateral resistance of the hull at speeds comparable to the wave celerity of long waves, there should be a limiting encounter angle up to which surf-riding is possible. Indeed, through identification of the states of equilibrium for the coupled equations of motion with a *path-following* technique (also known as *continuation*) [2], it has been revealed that surf-riding can occur only within a relatively narrow range of headings [2]. When the sea is on the quarter, the wave force in surge will be reduced and (5) would become:

$$\frac{d^2x}{dt^2} + \beta\frac{dx}{dt} + f\sin(kx)\cos\psi = d$$

(9)

where ψ is the relative heading angle between the ship and the wave. This means that, other parameters being the same, higher wave steepness would be required to sustain surf-riding when $\psi \neq 0$. In Fig. 4 we show the 3-d potential energy surface, based on the idea of a ball rolling in tilted potential wells [19].

4. THE CONSEQUENCES OF COUPLING AND SOME OTHER SOURCES OF NON-LINEARITY

Yaw motion dynamics

When the relative heading angle becomes nonzero however, the other two horizontal motions, sway and yaw, begin to participate also in the dynamics. The wave loads in the sway and yaw direction depend, at least, on the position on the wave and the heading of the ship and they are usually calculated in the context of

4

potential flow theory. Consider for example the lowest order expression of the wave yaw moment which results in the familiar Froude-Krylov representation [20] :

$$N_W = \rho g a_0 k \sin\psi \int_L a(\psi, x_s) e^{-kd(x_s)} A(x_s) x_s \sin k(x + x_s \cos\psi) dx_s \qquad (10)$$

ρ is water density, g is acceleration of gravity, a_0 is wave amplitude, ψ is the ship-wave encounter angle that can be considered as the heading angle; x_s, $d(x_s)$ and $A(x_s)$ are respectively longitudinal position, local draught and area of a transverse ship section in a ship-fixed system; finally L is ship length and $a(\psi, x_s)$ is a quantity that we assume here equal to 1.0. It is common to calculate (10) assuming that the ship is in static equilibrium in the pitch and heave sense. This of course does not mean that pitch and heave motions are taken into account as has been argued in a recent paper [21]. The assumption of such equilibrium state in the vertical direction is reasonable if the natural frequencies of the ship in heave and pitch are considerably higher than the encounter frequency between the ship and the wave so that the ship finds enough time to adjust itself on the wave. It is obvious that this can easily happen in very low frequencies of encounter but it is questionable if it represents the truth for higher frequencies.

To achieve equilibrium in yaw on the other hand, the rudder yaw moment (increased by the contribution of the rudder-to hull interaction effect) should balance the hydrodynamic hull reaction in yaw as well as the moment due to the wave. From (10) is derived that the wave yaw moment depends nonlinearly on ψ although this effect may be thought as relatively weak. More influential appears to be however the dependence of the moment upon the relative position x of the ship in respect to the wave: The strongly nonlinear effects in the speed regions where large amplitude surging and surf-riding can arise will be "imported" in the lateral motions through their dependence on x. Thus through coupling mechanisms the effects of surge nonlinearity can "spread" into the other modes.

The contribution of diffraction on the total wave force when the frequency of encounter is low can be quite important and is generally twofold: Firstly, it increases the amplitude of wave forcing, although the true magnitude of this effect seems to be somehow controversial [22], [23], [24]. The effect on yaw moment seems to be more pronounced than on sway. Secondly it shifts the peak of the force/moment forward thus creating a phase lead in comparison to the Froude-Krylov excitation. The influence of diffraction on surf-riding and broaching has been discussed in [25].

A number of interesting properties accompany the surf-riding states in quartering waves [2]: The equilibria near trough that appeared stable on the basis of consideration of the uncoupled surge are now unstable in a lateral sense (owing to the fact that, as mentioned in Section 2, near trough the wave has a destabilizing effect). These points are nevertheless potentially stabilizable with active steering. Another interesting property of surf-riding in quartering seas is that, the equilibria that correspond to different settings of the rudder constitute a closed curve in state-space. This means that, the two equilibria that can exist in a directly following sea represent basically the intersection of the closed curve of surf-riding states with the $\psi = 0$ plane. It is interesting that, in addition to the stationary type of surf-riding, it has been shown that oscillatory surf-riding can exist as well [26].

At speeds below the range of surf-riding or the range of large amplitude surging, the effect of surge is equivalent with a time dependence of the yaw moment. It can easily be shown that, away from nonlinearity in terms of x, one can either express the moment as dependent on $\sin(kx)$ or he can opt for exclusive time dependence, $\sin(\omega_e t)$. As usual, by ω_e we mean the encounter frequency between the ship and the wave. In this case however, $\sin\psi$ (or ψ if it is agreed that ψ will be small) that appears outside the integral in (9) will be multiplied by a time-dependent coefficient which can lead to a Mathieu-type of instability. To prove this, let's consider the simplified version of Nomoto's equation extended to include the qualitative effect of the waves :

$$T' \frac{d^2\psi'}{dt^2} + \frac{d\psi'}{dt} = K'\delta + A'\psi \cos(\omega_e' t') \qquad (11)$$

where T' and K' are the usual system time and gain constants and A' is a wave excitation amplitude term. We couple (11) with an autopilot equation featuring gains based on heading error and yaw rate, respectively k_1 and k_2 :

$$\delta = -k_1 (\psi - \psi_r) - k_2 r' \qquad (12)$$

where δ, ψ, ψ_r, r are respectively, rudder angle, heading, desired heading, and rate of turn. By combining (11) and (12) we obtain :

5

$$\frac{d^2\psi'}{dt^2} + \frac{(1+k_2K')}{T'}\frac{d\psi'}{dt} + \frac{k_1K'}{T'}[1 - \frac{A'}{k_1K'}\cos(\omega_e't')]\psi = \frac{k_1K'}{T'}\psi_r \tag{13}$$

With $s = \omega_{0(yaw)}'t'$, where $\omega_{0(yaw)}' = \sqrt{\frac{k_1K'}{T'}}$, (13) becomes :

$$\frac{d^2\psi'}{ds^2} + 2\zeta\frac{d\psi'}{ds} + [1 - h\cos(\Omega s)]\psi = \frac{j}{\omega_{0(yaw)}'^2} \tag{14}$$

where ζ is the usual damping ratio, $2\zeta = \dfrac{1+k_2K'}{\sqrt{\dfrac{k_1K'}{T'}}}$

and also :

$$\Omega = \frac{\omega_e'}{\omega_{0(yaw)}'}, \quad h = \frac{A'}{k_1K'}, \quad j = \frac{k_1K'}{T'}\psi_r$$

Equation (14) includes a time-periodic coefficient in the stiffness term and is thus Mathieu-type. A critical parameter that determines to a large extent the behaviour is the damping ratio which for such systems is usually quite high (0.8 or even higher, see for example [27]). The range of variation of ζ is actually

very wide as can be confirmed by considering the relation between K'' and T' recommended by ITTC, $K' = 0.452 + 0.481T'$ [28]. The usual range for k_1 is between 1 and 3, for k_2 between 0 and 2 and for $\dfrac{1}{T'}$ between 0 and 2. However when damping is large, the so called instability 'tongues' that are associated with a parametrically excited system almost disappear even around the area of principal resonance (= frequency of encounter two times the natural frequency of the system). Then it is well known that the required amplitude of parametric forcing that can destabilize the system is higher than 1.0. This corresponds basically to having negative restoring at certain locations of the wave.

Nonlinearity may also reside in the hull hydrodynamic reaction terms. Let us consider Nomoto's equation once more, this time though in its full version :

$$\frac{d^2r'}{dt^2} + \frac{T_1'+T_2'}{T_1'T_2'}\frac{dr'}{dt} + \frac{1}{T_1'T_2'}r' + \frac{a'}{T_1'T_2'}r'^3 = \frac{K'}{T_1'T_2'}\delta + \frac{K'T_3'}{T_1'T_2'}\frac{d\delta'}{dt} \tag{15}$$

T_1', T_2' and T_3' are the usual time constants with $T_1' = T_1' + T_2' - T_3'$. For fixed positions of the rudder (15) is basically a Duffing-type equation. For a directionally unstable vessel it corresponds to a system with a double-well potential described by the equation:

$$\frac{d^2R}{dt^2} + b\frac{dR}{dt} - R + R^3 = F\delta \tag{16}$$

where the following variable and parameter transformations were applied:

$$t' = \sqrt{T_1'T_2'}t, \quad r' = \frac{1}{\sqrt{a'}}R, \quad b = \frac{(T_1'+T_2')}{\sqrt{T_1'T_2'}}, \quad F = K'\sqrt{a'}$$

On a steep wave the attitude of the ship, and thus the area distribution along the longitudinal axis, will vary considerably depending on the relative position of the ship centre and the relation between frequency of encounter and ship eigencharacteristics. The sensitivity of the directional stability of a ship to trim variations is

rather well known [29], [30]. Measurements of the customary manoeuvring derivatives on the basis of captive tests with the ship at various positions of equilibrium of a regular wave have been attempted by a number of researchers, see for example [13]. Theoretical studies of the same effect are however very rare [31]. It is quite obvious that the type of nonlinearity that we discuss here will become important should the rate of turn become large. At first sight, in ordinary controlled yaw motion this should not happen since the build up of yaw is suppressed. In extreme waves however the method of control (read autopilot gains) may be insufficient to cope with the highly demanding environment. Then considerable yaw oscillations are likely to accompany the forward motion of the ship resulting also in serious speed reduction [11]. Under these circumstances this type of non-linearity will become important for the dynamics.

Roll motion

In waves other than longitudinal, there will be direct forcing in roll. When the sea is on the quarter this forcing will be generally low and will be maximized at the beam sea condition. However the roll direction will be subjected to significant excitations due to drift and yaw. Considering for example a transverse section of the ship, say S, lying at a distance x_S from the centre of rotation, the local drift at that position will be $v^{(S)}(x_S) = v + x_S r$, where v and r are the drift and rate of turn in respect to the considered centre of rotation. This local drift produces the well known hydrodynamic reaction force in sway, basically a lateral resistance force. Integrating for the ship's length we obtain the total sway reaction force Y_H which acts in general at a distance z_H off the considered centre of rotation in roll. Therefore the dominant roll excitation components will be:

$$K_{roll} = K_W + K_H \tag{17}$$

with

$$K_W = \rho g a_0 k \sin\psi \int_L a(\psi, x_S) e^{-kd(x_S)} z_W(x_S) A(x_S) \sin k(x + x_S \cos\psi) dx_S \tag{18}$$

and
$$K_H = Y_H z_H \tag{19}$$

For demonstration purposes, in the above expression we kept only the Froude-Krylov component of the wave force; $z_W(x_S)$ is the vertical distance of the centre of pressure acting on a local section from the considered centre of axes (usually from the centre of gravity or from the free surface) when the motion of the ship is neglected. In the roll moment that is due to hydrodynamic reaction we avoided writing the direct contributions from the propeller and the rudder that are sometimes quite influential. The K_H moment depends generally also on the roll angle. Moreover, in steep following or quartering waves it is possible to have significant parametric variation in restoring compared to the stillwater situation. If we consider a simple cubic type restoring and an amplitude of variation due to the parametric effect ε, the dominant terms of the roll equation can be expressed with the following equation:

$$\frac{d^2\Phi}{d\tau^2} + \gamma \frac{d\Phi}{d\tau} + [1 + \varepsilon \cos(\Omega\tau)](\Phi - \Phi^3) = f_p \cos(\Omega\tau) + f_c(v, r) \tag{20}$$

where

- $\Phi = \dfrac{\phi}{\phi_v}$

- ϕ is the true roll angle,

- ϕ_v is the angle of vanishing stability,

- $\Omega = \dfrac{\omega}{\omega_{0(roll)}}$

- ω is the frequency of encounter between the ship and the wave,

- $\omega_{0(roll)}$ is the natural frequency,

- $\omega_{0(roll)} = \sqrt{\dfrac{W(GM)}{I}}$,

- W is the weight of the ship,

- (GM) is the metacentric height,

7

- I is the second moment of inertia including the added moment,

- f_p is the nondimensionalized amplitude of external periodic forcing,

$$f_p = \frac{K_w}{(I\omega_{0(roll)}^2 \phi_v)},$$

- K_w is the amplitude of the true wave excitation,

- $f_c(v,r)$ is the amplitude of the nondimensionalized excitation due to hydrodynamic reaction,

$$f_c(v,r) = \frac{K_H}{(I\omega_{0(roll)}^2 \phi_v)},$$

- K_H is the amplitude of the true hydrodynamic reaction moment,

γ is the damping coefficient,

$$\gamma = \frac{B}{\sqrt{4W(GM)I}},$$

- B is the true equivalent linear roll damping,

- τ is nondimensional time, $\tau = \omega_{0(roll)}t$

- t is real time,

The reaction related component of the roll moment should be regarded as the critical one for capsize due to broaching for the following reason: If the ship is captured in surf-riding, it attains a forward speed that is often well above its design speed. Surf-riding at non-zero angle of encounter can be followed, as explained in the next section, by escape involving turning and drifting. During this transient, considerable energy will be transferred from the surge direction into yaw and further into roll.

5. STUDIES OF GLOBAL BEHAVIOUR

Broaching at the transition towards surf-riding

Consider a steered ship in stable overtaking-wave periodic motion, with a certain non-zero encounter angle and operating near to the threshold of surf-riding.

A slight increase in either propeller thrust or wave steepness can cause the crossing of the inset of the saddle of crest and will generate the usual jump of surf-riding. However, the stability characteristics of stationary surf-riding are different from those of the previous periodic response. In other words, the autopilot gain values that guaranteed stability for the periodic motion are not necessarily sufficient for the stationary one [11]. But even if the corresponding surf-riding point is stable this still cannot guarantee that the ship will be attracted towards this point because there is, in a dynamical sense, 'competition' with turning motion. The type of motion will depend on the initial condition and in order to be able to predict the outcome one needs to understand first the global organization of the system's state space through the analysis of *transient dynamics*.

Such analysis for multi-dimensional systems is a largely unresolved matter and in order to derive some practically useful information we developed a method based on the assumption that the ship was initially in steady periodic motion. Then, as the ship passes from a trough the propeller is suddenly set at a higher rate. We should remark at this point that, it would be more relevant physically to vary a parameter linked with the wave rather than with the ship. To implement this however in a consistent way is a difficult problem and this is now under further consideration. Our new method can be much more easily demonstrated by selecting the propeller rate as the varied parameter. With repetition for a very large number of desired headings and final propeller rates (the latter represented by the corresponding nominal Froude numbers) and recording of the long-term response characteristics, a mapping is established between the points of the parameters' plane (ψ_r, Fn) and response types, Figs. 5 and 6. This mapping method produces a very clear picture of how the domains of stable surf-riding, periodic motion, broaching and capsize are organized, capturing the key information of a multi-dimensional system on a simple plane.

The ship that is taken as the basis of our study is a 34.5m purse-seiner [2]. In Fig. 5 we can compare the surf-riding domains for two different time scales, $t = 200s$ and $t = 400s$. To obtain an order of magnitude we note that the encounter period in directly following seas before the increase of Fn was 11 s. In Fig. 6 on the other hand, we present the organization of all four domains with duration of simulation $t = 400s$.

For $GM = 1.51$m broaching is mostly followed by capsize with the exception of a narrow band where capsize is avoided. The method of control influences however considerably these boundaries. Here the autopilot gains used were, in dimensional form, 3 for the proportional gain and 3 for the differential while the time constant was 1/3 [2]. Quantification of the tendency of a ship for broaching is possible, by measuring relative areas and their change under the effect of selected control parameters, in a similar fashion to the "integrity curves" concept of Thompson [32].

8

Voluntary escape from surf-riding

Here the scenario is in a sense opposite from the one presented in the last subsection. The ship is assumed caught in stable surf-riding and then some control is applied with the intention to return to the periodic mode. The possible outcomes of such control action are :

(i)   to restabilize at some other surf-riding state, that corresponds to the new control settings;

(ii)   to leave surf-riding and return to the periodic mode (the desirable outcome);

(iii)   to be engaged in forced turning motion that corresponds to broaching;

(iv)   to capsize.

Control parameter changes can be realized either in respect to the nominal Froude number, or , in respect to the desired heading of the ship. When the control change concerns Fn the boundaries have a clearly nonlinear character, Fig. 7. These boundaries are discussed in further detail in [3] and [33].

6.   CONCLUDING REMARKS

The behaviour of a ship in abnormally large astern seas has a very rich dynamical content. While interesting dynamic effects appear independently in surge, sway/yaw and roll, the existence of hydrodynamic couplings creates a very challenging multidimensional problem where energy can be transferred from one mode into another. Local and global bifurcations, instabilities of Mathieu type and phenomena of escape from a safe basin have been theoretically shown to underlie broaching behaviour. Further studies will now be needed in a number of areas, in order to enhance the theoretical foundations of the approach and in order to understand the dynamics at greater depth. For example, the frequency dependence when the encounter frequency is far from zero must be assessed.

Also, some further insights into the dynamics should be derived at more fundamental level on the basis of elementary mathematical models that capture however the key features of system response. Generally, studies based on simple and on more detailed mathematical models have their own individual merit and they should go hand-in-hand if substantial progress is to be achieved. A major advance that stems from the current work is that, in the future, experimental efforts can be much better focused since the conditions that create the instability are now fairly predictable. Indeed there is a compelling need for carrying out extensive free running model tests in order to verify the presented theoretical findings. Such experiments are however rather non-customary and they would constitute a major advance in their own right. Another challenge lying ahead is, how the new information can be brought into a form that can be effectively utilized by naval architects in the design stage of a ship as well as by ship masters during ship operation.

7.   REFERENCES

1. THOMPSON, J.M.T. and BISHOP, S.R. (eds.) (1994): 'Nonlinearity and Chaos in Engineering Dynamics'. John Wiley & Sons Ltd., Chichester, England.

2. SPYROU, K.J. (1996): 'Dynamic instability in quartering seas: The behaviour of a ship during broaching'. Journal of Ship Research, 40, 1, 46-59.

3. SPYROU, K.J. (1996): 'Dynamic instability in quartering seas - Part II: analysis of ship roll and capsize for broaching'. Journal of Ship Research, 40, 4, 326-336.

4. VOSSERS, G. (1962) 'Ships and Marine Engines. Volume IIc : Resistance, Propulsion and Steering of Ships', Section on Broaching, pp. 266-267, The Technical Publishing Company, H.Stam, N.V., Haarlem (The Netherlands).

5. WAHAB R. and SWAAN, W.A. (1964): 'Coursekeeping and broaching of ships in following seas'. Journal of Ship Research, 7, 4, 1-15.

6. MOTORA, S., FUJINO, M., KOYONAGI, M., ISHIDA, S., SHIMADA, K. and MAKI, T. (1981): 'A consideration on the mechanism of occurrence of broaching-to phenomena'. Journal of the Society of Naval Architects of Japan, 150, 84-97.

7. RENILSON, M.R. and DRISCOLL, A. (1982): 'Broaching - An investigation into the loss of directional control in severe following seas'. RINA Transactions, 124, 253-273.

8. EDA, H. (1972): 'Directional stability and control of ships in waves'. Journal of Ship Research, 16, 3, 205-218.

9. DUCANE, P. and GOODRICH, J.R. (1962): 'The following sea, broaching and surging'. RINA Transactions, 104, 109-140.

10. RYDILL, L.J. (1959): 'A linear theory for the steered motion of ships in waves'. RINA Transactions, 101, 81-112.

11. SPYROU, K.J. (1997): 'Dynamic instability in quartering seas:-Part III: Nonlinear effects on periodic motions'. Journal of Ship Research, 41, 3, 178-191.

12. KAN, M. (1990): 'Surging of large amplitude and surf-riding of ships in following seas'. Selected Papers in Naval Architecture and Ocean Engineering, The Society of Naval Architects of Japan, 28.

13. FUWA, T., SUGAI, K., YOSHINO, T. and YAMAMOTO, T. (1982): 'An experimental study on broaching-to of a small high-speed boat'. Papers of the Ship Research Institute, 66, Tokyo.

14. CLARKE, D., GEDLING, P. and HINE, G. (1983): 'Application of manoeuvring criteria in hull design using linear theory', RINA Transactions, 125, 45-68.

15. LLOYD, A.R.J.M.(1989): 'Seakeeping: Ship Behaviour in Rough Weather', Ellis Horwood Series in Marine Technology, Chichester.

16. GROCHOWALSKI, S. (1989): 'Investigation into the physics of ship capsizing by combined captive and free-running model tests'. SNAME Transactions, 97.

17. GRIM, O. (1983): 'Das Schiff in vor achtern kommendem Seegang'. Schiffstechnik, 30, 84-94 (in German).

18. STOKER, J.J. (1950): 'Nonlinear Vibrations in Mechanical and Electrical Systems', Wiley, New York.

19. THOMPSON, J.M.T. (1996): 'Global dynamics of driven oscillators: Fractal basins and indeterminate bifurcations', Chapter 1 of Nonlinear Mathematics and its Applications, P.J.Aston (ed.), Cambridge University Press, Cambridge, 1-47.

20. HAMAMOTO, M., KIM, Y. and UWATOKO, K. (1991): 'Study on ship motions and capsizing in following seas', Journal of the Society of Naval Architects of Japan, 170, 173-182.

21. TUITE, A. and RENILSON, M. (1997): 'The effect of principal design parameters on broaching-to of a small fishing vessel in following seas'. RINA Spring Meeting, London, April.

22. OHKUSU, M., (1986): 'Prediction of wave forces on a ship running in following waves with very low encounter frequency', Journal of the Society of Naval Architects of Japan, 159, 129-138.

23. YOSHINO, I., FUJINO, M. and FUKASAWA, T. (1988) : 'Wave exciting forces on a ship travelling in following waves at high speed', Journal of the Society of Naval Architects of Japan, 177, 160-172.

24. UMEDA, N., YAMAKOSHI, Y. and SUZUKI, S. (1995): 'Experimental study for wave forces on a ship running in quartering seas with very low encounter frequency. Proceedings', The Sevastianov Symposium, Ship Safety in a Seaway, Kalinigrad, May.

25. SPYROU, K. and UMEDA, N. (1995) : 'From surf-riding to loss of control and capsize: a model of dynamic behaviour of ships in following/quartering seas', Proceedings, 6th International Symposium on Practical Design of Ships and Mobile Units, PRADS'95, Seoul, September.

26. SPYROU, K.J. (1995): 'Surf-riding and oscillations of a ship in quartering waves'. Journal of Marine Science and Technology, 1, Society of Naval Architects of Japan and Springer-Verlag, 24-36.

27. FOSSEN, Th. I. (1994): 'Guidance and Control of Marine Vehicles', Wiley, New York.

28. International Towing Tank Conference (1987), Proceedings, Manoeuvrability Session, Rome.

29. BISHOP, R.E.D., PRICE, W.G., and TEMAREL, P. (1989) : 'On the dangerous of trim by the bow'. RINA Transactions, 131, 281-304.

30. SPYROU, K.J. (1990) : 'A New Approach for Assessing Ship Manoeuvrability Based on Dynamical Systems' Theory, PhD Thesis, University of Strathclyde, December 1990.

31. FUJINO, M., YAMASAKI, K. and ISHI, Y. (1983): 'On the stability derivatives of a ship travelling in the following wave', Journal of the Society of Naval Architects of Japan, 152, 167-179 (in Japanese).

32. THOMPSON, J.M.T. (1997) : 'Designing against capsize in beam seas: Recent advances and new insights'. Applied Mechanics Reviews, 50, 5, 307-325.

33. SPYROU, K.J. (1997) : 'A new method to analyze escape phenomena in multi -degree ship dynamics applied to the broaching problem'. Proceedings, 6th International Conference on Stability of Ships and Ocean Vehicles, STAB'97, Varna, September.

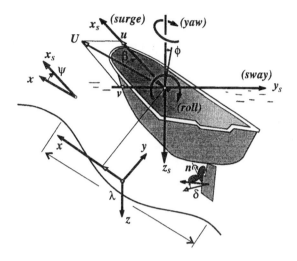

Fig. 1: Basic definitions.

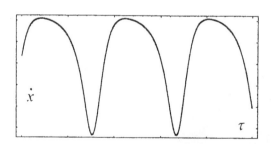

(2a)   Surge velocity versus time: Typical asymmetric
        response near to the threshold of surf-riding.

(2b)   Qualitatively similar behaviour with (2a) can be
        obtained by using the equation:

$$u = 1.4 + 0.2sin(\tau) + 0.2cos(\tau) - 0.09sin(2\tau)$$
$$+ 0.01cos(2\tau) + 0.015sin(3\tau) - 0.009sin(4\tau)$$
$$+ 0.0015sin(5\tau)$$

where $\tau = \omega_e t$.

Fig. 2: Large-amplitude surging

11

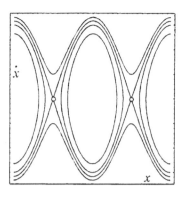

(3a)   Hamiltonian system

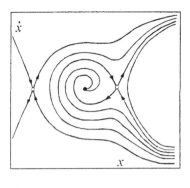

(3c)   Damped system

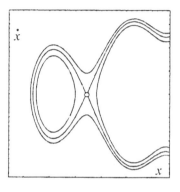

(3b)   'Break-of-symmetry' due to the introduction of external torque.

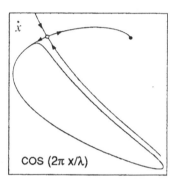

(3d)   The saddle inset separates trajectories ending either on the periodic or on the stationary attractor.

Fig. 3:   Integral curves

Fig. 4:   Ball rolling in tilted potential wells.

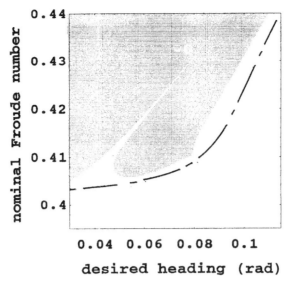

Fig. 5: The domain of surf-riding after 200s (grey area); and after 400s (higher than the dashed line).

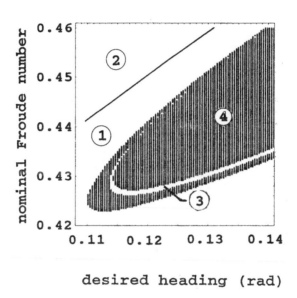

Fig. 6: The organization of the different types of response, on the plane (ψ_r, Fn).
1 periodic response, 2 surf-riding,
3 broaching without capsize, 4 broaching and capsize.

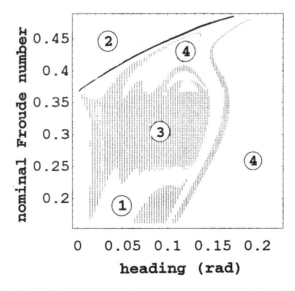

Fig. 7: Escape from surf-riding. The representation of response types is similar with Fig. 6. Also, *GM*=1.51m;
autopilot gains (dimensional): proportional 2, differential 2, time constant 1/3.

PAPER NO.9.

CRITICAL CAPSIZING CONDITIONS IN SURVIVABILITY SEAWAYS

by W H Buckley, Consultant, USA

Paper presented at the

International Conference

DESIGN AND OPERATION FOR ABNORMAL CONDITIONS

21 22 OCTOBER 1997 GLASGOW

CRITICAL CAPSIZING CONDITIONS IN SURVIVABILITY SEAWAYS

William H Buckley, Consultant

SUMMARY

This paper describes procedures for identifying and evaluating critical capsizing conditions in survivability seaways. It employs the concepts of a previously defined First Principles Methodology (FPM) which is briefly summarized. Stipulations are made upon which the approach to identifying and investigating critical capsize conditions is based. Free running model tests and full-scale operating experience are reviewed as a prelude to establishing two basic survivability design conditions: Astern Seas (powered) and Beam Seas (unpowered). These conditions are to be investigated in at least three seaway conditions on the Survivability envelope, i.e. (1) Maximum significant wave height (Hm_o) on the Seaways of Limiting Steepness boundary, (2) Maximum Hm_o on the Seaways of Extreme Hm_o boundary and (3) Maximum Modal Period (Tp) on the extreme Hm_o boundary. A structured program of model testing and computational development is proposed.. The feasibility of generating model scale seaways corresponding to survivability seaway conditions is shown to be encouraging. It is recommended that the proposed test program and its rationale be considered for adoption by capsizing researchers.

AUTHOR'S BIOGRAPHY

Mr William Buckley retired from the US Navy's David Taylor Research Center in 1992. He received a bachelor 's degree in Aeronautical Engineering in 1948 and another in Business Administration in 1949 from the Massachusetts Institute of Technology, followed by a Master of Science Degree in Ocean and Marine Engineering in 1982 from the George Washington University. He was employed for 20 years by the Bell Aerospace Company where he was responsible for structural design criteria and loads for the X-22A aircraft, SKMR-1 air cushion vehicle and SES-100B surface effect ship. He joined the US Navy's David Taylor Research Center in 1971 where he conducted hydrofoil ship loads research. In 1978 he initiated a loads research program for displacement ships with emphasis on casualty analysis, statistical analyses of non-linear random processes, extreme and climatic wave characteristics, and most recently the development of worldwide seaway criteria use in a first principles design methodology.

1. INTRODUCTION

A First Principles Methodology (FPM) is employed in the identification and evaluation of critical capsizing conditions for ships[1]. This methodology consists of five basic elements as shown in Table 1. Operational Requirements summarize information which is generally available to the ship designer. Seaway Criteria, however, have not previously been available in a form suitable for use in a first principles determination of ship loads and motions. Three developments commencing in the 1970's began to alter this situation. The first was the acquisition of continuous (at 1 hour intervals) long-term wave spectrum measurements in a variety of wave climates by the National Data Buoy Center of the National Oceanographic and Atmospheric Administration (NOAA). The second was the development of statistical methods for processing shipboard wind and wave observations so as to provide

the global wave statistics[2]. Reference 1 outlines the procedures by which these data were employed to expand the NOAA buoy data base to obtain hemispheric Operability and Survivability envelopes. The virtue of this approach is that the extreme and climatic wave spectra obtained from the NOAA data base can reasonably be applied to these envelopes.

The third element, Critical Design Condition Criteria, departs from conventional design practice in several respects. It requires consideration of seaway conditions along and within the Survivability and Operability envelopes. On the outer boundary of each envelope seaway characteristics and associated ship load and motion responses are in most cases nonlinear so that time domain analysis methods must be employed rather than linear frequency domain methods. The fourth element, Analytical Methods, is closely related to the third, i.e. analytical methods must be capable of dealing with critical nonlinear load and motion design conditions.

The last element, Response Criteria provides a basis for determining whether a ship design can be considered satisfactory under critical conditions from a motion and structural loading point of view.

2. STIPULATIONS

FPM departs significantly from empirically derived stability design criteria. Nowhere is this more evident than in regard to the establishment of critical design conditions. The recommended approach to this objective is based on certain stipulations:

(a) Seaway Criteria

The methodology requires seaway criteria which encompass all seaway conditions that may be encountered in service and in a form suitable for quantitative analysis of critical design conditions. Such seaway criteria[3] largely satisfy these requirements. Replication of design spectra at model scale in tank tests is recommended until such time as methods have been validated for use in analyzing critical design conditions.

This leaves open the question of whether or not the nonlinearity and groupiness of the full scale seaway has been replicated. Here we require measured time series wave height data from survivability seaway conditions which can be compared to model scale test tank waves. Fortunately we have such data for the upper end of the Seaways of Limiting Steepness boundary[4]. Otherwise we are mostly at a loss for data so that for the time being we must assume that replication of the design spectra in test tanks satisfies this requirement, see pp. 6-8[1]. Note: the stipulation that this seaway criteria be used should not be construed as a claim that these criteria have universal acceptance. For the moment, it is contended only that they are sufficiently comprehensive and realistic (i.e. are based upon measured data) so as to allow us to move forward with the development of FPM and critical condition identification in particular.

(b)   An Experimental Approach to the Identification of Critical Design Conditions

Because of the nonlinear character of ship motions in the extreme seas, as well as the nonlinear character of the larger waves in the seaway itself, model experiments are regarded as the most reliable basis at the present time for evaluating critical capsize conditions. Additionally, the analysis of nonlinear time domain data requires a practical basis for identifying potentially critical nonlinear events. Half-cycle matrix (HACYM) analysis[4] is one such method.

(c)   Survivability Envelope

Because empirical stability criteria are not demonstrably related to survivability conditions it is believed that testing associated with the Survivability envelope should be given first priority.

(d)   A Structured Approach to the Identification of Critical Design Conditions

The complexity of analytical treatments of ship capsizing in extreme seas is such that its development should be structured so as to progress from relatively simple situations to the level of complexity associated with extreme seas. At each level of development the following objectives are considered to be involved:

• Analytical methods which purport to account for ship responses in extreme seas should be employed in accounting for all model test results. It is implicit that predictive methods which fail to account for model behavior in the lower level tests probably cannot be trusted to account for behavior in extreme seaways.

• The identification of dominant ship design parameters should be undertaken using the best available analytical methods so as to help establish a preliminary design methodology.

(e)   Operator Comments Regarding Ship Handling Problems in Extreme Seas.

The cause and effect relationships which are inherent in a first principles methodology should be compared to operator experience in extreme seas. Obviously the opportunities for such checks are limited. Nevertheless, the rational nature of the method permits a reality check when such important information does becomes available, see below, so that an active search for first hand ship handling experience in extreme seas is an important activity.

3.   CRITICAL CAPSIZING CONDITIONS

3.1

Video tapes showing wave conditions which caused capsizing of two self propelled models are reviewed. The first model was tested in open water while the second was tested under controlled conditions in a towing tank. Following this, a brief summary is presented of comments by the master of a bulk carrier which operated in a survivability level winter storm. These findings are used in proposing critical capsize design conditions.

3.2   HIGH SPEED CONTAINER SHIP

Model tests conducted in San Francisco Bay[5] are reviewed. Here the seaway was basically wind driven with somewhat varying degrees of wave height and steepness from day to day and run to run.

Model

– 1/55th scale of an SL-7(33 knot max.) container ship. (See Fig. 1).

– Radio controlled, with an autopilot and manual override.

– Two displacements: Light and Heavy.

– Speed equivalents (full scale): 28.5 to 36 knots.

– GM set to correspond to minimum values required by Load Line regulations[6].

Test conditions of interest here are (full scale equivalents):

– Run No. 11.06; Hm_o = 35 ft (10.7m); " = 28.5 knots.

- Run No. 10.02; " = 40 ft (12.1m); " = 28.5 knots.

2

The speeds at which the model was run were very high for operation in severe stern and quartering seas. The reference states that the desired headings were not maintained because of inadequate directional control. Although not explained, one reason for this arises from the SL-7 having a single rudder located between twin screw propellers rather than in the slipstream of either one. As a result, directional control can be increased only by increasing model speed. Figure 2 presents calm water righting arm curves for each test displacement as well as for both wave crest and trough amidships. A substantial reduction in righting arm is apparent for the wave crest amidships case especially in the heavy displacement condition.

Examination of the complete test video indicates several matters of interest. For example, recovery from near capsizes appeared to occur when the water surface along the submerged deck edge following a broach was comparatively level which suggested that the model righting arm may have been similar to that for calm water. If so, this would help to explain why regulation of calm water stability characteristics can still help to assure stability in high waves.

Prior to most capsize and near-capsize occurrences, an inability to maintain heading during heavy rolls was apparent. In the case of astern seas this often lead to the model ending up at a quartering seas heading at which time broaching tended to occur. Rudder emergence also appeared to occur in several cases but with the model heavily rolled it was difficult to assess the extent of the emergence. Bow submergence was common in astern seas after a steep wave had lifted the stern.

Run 11.06 revealed a condition which found the model lifted at the stern and rolled to starboard by a relatively large, partially breaking wave on the port quarter. The crest of this wave proceeded to a midships position as the model continued to increase its starboard roll angle. At this point the model capsized. The critical nature of this sequence was apparent: the steep quartering wave caused the model to roll heavily as it moved down the hull to a position where it also reduced the model's inherent roll stability. There were relatively few white caps in evidence which suggested that the seaway was not unusually steep.

By way of contrast Run 10.02 was conducted in a seaway with numerous white caps. With the model running down seas a large, steep wave lifted the stern and then continued forward causing the rudder to emerged from the water, following which the model yawed to port and capsized in a comparatively rapid manner.

3.3   CANADIAN FISHING VESSEL

Video coverage of tank tests of a Canadian trawler operating in regular and irregular quartering seas[7] have been reviewed to identify critical operating conditions. The trawler has a full load displacement of 180 tons and an overall length of 19.75m (65 ft) with hull sections as

shown in Figure 3[8]. The tank waves and model headings were such as to create severe broaching situations in stern quartering seas. Because of the size, steepness and breaking character of the waves, the effects of water on deck, loss of stability on a wave crest, surfing on a wave front and the failure of the model to maintain its initial heading were quite evident. Combinations of these effects were shown to be involved in most of the broaching/capsize events. In the case of tests in irregular waves the existence of a substantial roll angle due to a prior wave encounter tended to cause broaching and/or capsize when a large, steep wave happened to follow.

The test conditions involved were satisfactory for the stated purpose of identifying critical elements of broaching/capsizing situations for the fishing vessel. However, for purposes of identifying critical capsizing conditions from a first principles point of view (which was not a test objective) the tests were somewhat incomplete. For example, the full scale wave spectra to which the irregular tank waves corresponded are not given[9] so that they could be plotted on or within the Survivability envelope of Figure 4. Because of the extreme steepness of the test waves it is likely that they corresponded to those on or near the Seaways of Limiting Steepness boundary. Tests in irregular seas showed that a rolled attitude existing at the time a large, steep wave was encountered could seriously effect the vessel's ability to resist capsize.

3.4   SELECTED OPERATING EXPERIENCE

SL-7 model test run No. 11.06 is of interest given the testimony of Captain Matthew, master of the M/V SELKIRK SETTLER regarding his encounter with a survivability level winter storm[1]. His testimony is excerpted here in Appendix A to provide a first hand account. Briefly, he steered dead down seas as best he could. Based upon Second Mate George Ianiev's comments[10], we learn that excursions occurred of up to ± 15 deg. from the desired course. The master held the ship's speed as low as he dared for fear of losing steerageway. Engine speed was increased to obtain steerageway in moments of necessity and then decreased to avoid increasing speed which could lead to surfing and possible broaching. His actions are understandable given the scenario of Run 11.06. Dead down seas operation avoided quartering seas as much as possible. Slow speed afforded any large, overtaking wave a minimum of time for developing a large roll angle as well as a minimum of time during which the low stability, wave crest-amidships position existed. His primary concern was for finding a successful balance between the conflicting requirements of low speed and adequate steerageway.

These observations should not be construed as suggesting that the combination of events of Run 11.06 are of greater importance than any other set which could result in capsize. On the other hand it is apparent that the ability of a ship to maintain steerageway at low speeds in extreme seas can hardly be over emphasized.

3

4. PROPOSED CRITICAL DESIGN CONDITION

4.1   The following assumptions have been made:

a) For ships in unrestricted service the southern hemisphere Survivability envelope applies together with its associated wave spectra, i.e. the modified JONSWAP formulation and the shape parameters[3]. Note: when a ship's service specifies operation only in a particular body or bodies of water, a reduced Survivability envelope should be drawn with the stipulation that the Seaways of Limiting Steepness boundary be retained up to an appropriately reduced value of Hm_o.

b) In survivability seas we assume that the master, with one exception, is able to select a heading which will minimize the potential for capsizing in overtaking seas. It will be noted that this assumption introduces a requirement for adequate steerageway under the stated conditions. The exception provides for a case in which steerageway is lost for any of a variety of reasons (e.g. engine power lost or shut down, rudder control lost, electrical system failure, etc.). Here the heading should correspond to that which a given vessel seeks in the prevailing seaway and wind conditions. (Reference 11 and Appendices VI and VII of reference 12 provide some examples of operator experience with U.S. Navy and commercial ships under survivability conditions).

c) A tolerance must be applied to any heading which a master may reasonably select so as to account for the realities of ship handling in a survivability seaway. It will be assumed for the moment that a minimum tolerance of ± 15 deg. should apply to ship heading in the absence of a rational determination of a ship's heading control in a survivability seaway.

d) Design displacements and associated GM's in calm water will be specified for a given ship by the naval architect subject to the requirement that the ship design satisfy the Response criteria associated with Survivability Conditions I and II.

e) Operation in a survivability seaway at head, bow and beam seas headings are critical mainly in regard to water tight integrity requirements. Capsize resistance requirements associated with operation within the Operability envelope (e.g. parametric resonance) will be considered separately. The effects of cargo shifting in bulk carriers, water entry and container loss are, for the moment, regarded as important matters to be addressed by the ship's designer under the heading of Response criteria.

4.2   SURVIVABILITY CONDITION I - ASTERN SEAS

Displacement and associated transverse metacentric height: As stipulated by the cognizant naval architect.

Speed: Minimum consistent with adequate directional control.

Heading: Dead down seas with a minimum tolerance of ± 15 deg.

Seaway Conditions: As defined by the wave spectra and time series wave height data associated with the Survivability envelope.

Wind: (To be defined based upon wave and wind data on hand).

Response Criteria:

• Freedom from capsize.

• No loss of directional stability and/or control resulting in broaching.

• No loss of watertight integrity or down flooding sufficient to cause loss of required lateral stability or directional control.

• No cargo shifting sufficient to produce a heel angle greater than ± (10%) of the angle of heel corresponding to the peak of the calm water lateral stability curve.

4.3   SURVIVABILITY CONDITION II- BEAM SEAS

Displacement and associated transverse metacentric height: Same as Condition I.

Speed: (No propulsion).

Heading: As results from the wind and wave conditions associated with a designated point on the Survivability envelope.

Seaway: Same as Condition I.

Wind: Same as Condition I.

Response Criteria: Same as first, third and fourth criteria of Condition I.

5.   CRITICAL CAPSIZE TEST AND EVALUATION CONDITIONS

5.1

The objective is to identify and evaluate potentially critical capsize conditions while at the same time establishing validated analytical methods suitable for demonstrating that a ship design satisfies the associated response criteria. In the case of the Survivability envelope only two design conditions have been proposed. The particular test conditions associated with the test series which follow are intended to be definitive but they should not be regarded as the last word in the matter. Discussion leading to more appropriate test conditions is solicited. Obviously the complete test program should be conducted with a single model if at all possible. In any case there are two important constraints:

a) the model must be powered in each test series and remotely controlled in certain of the tests, and

b) the model should be of such a scale that the wave making capabilities of a selected test facility can replicate Survivability seaways.

The powering requirement results from the need to determine realistic steerageway and surge characteristics of the model.

5.2   CALM WATER TEST SERIES

5.2.1   Objectives:

a) To determine the effect of hull form, displacement, speed and angle of heel on required and available directional control.

b) To determine roll/yaw coupling and directional control derivatives as a function of displacement, speed and angle of heel.

c) To determine the ability of candidate seakeeping software programs to account for the measured derivatives.

5.2.2   Towing arrangement:

Model free in heave and pitch. Measure heave and pitch angles; surge and sway forces; roll and yaw moments. Also measure rudder side force and hinge moment. Set propeller rpm so as to produce zero net drag at the desired speed.

5.2.3   Model displacement:

Light and heavy with nominal values of GM.

5.2.4   Speed range:

Zero to the larger of the maximum calm water speed or the estimated maximum surge speed in a Survivability seaway.

5.2.5   Nominal Roll Angles:

Five increments to ϕmax., where ϕmax. is the roll angle at which the righting arm is maximum in calm water. Righting arm curves are to be determined in calm water for each displacement.

5.2.6   Test Conditions (for each displacement):

- At ϕ = 0 and over the speed range, with propeller thrust equal to model drag, measure yaw moment and roll moment as a function of rudder deflection up to maximum displacement. Compare rudder effectiveness to full-scale estimates to determine the need for possible rudder modification to correct for scale effects.

- Repeat at other roll angles.

- Repeat with rudder deflection (δ_r) set to the value which results in zero yaw moment.

5.3   BREAKING WAVE TEST SERIES

5.3.1   Objectives:

a) To determine the effect of displacement, speed and heading on forces, moments and motions resulting from encounter with a large breaking wave from astern with the model restrained in surge, sway and yaw.

b) To determine the effect of displacement, speed and heading on the motions of a free running model resulting from encounter with a large breaking wave from astern.

c) To determine the ability of candidate seakeeping software programs to account for measured time domain forces, moments and motions resulting from encounter with a large breaking wave.

5.3.2   Wave Making:

This test series presumes we have the ability to generate a large, sharply breaking wave of a certain height at a predetermined location and time in a test tank. The necessary technique was demonstrated for example, in sailing yacht model capsize experiments[13]. The similarity of the test wave to a sharply breaking wave from the hurricane Camille time series data is illustrated in Figure 5[4].

5.3.3   Test Condition 1:

Towing arrangement:

Model free to heave, pitch and roll. Measure restraining surge and sway forces and yaw moments; also rudder side force and hinge moment (δ_r = 0). Use propeller rpm to produce desired speed. Grid side of model and video record it showing local wave heights from a side view together with a time code.

Model displacement:

Light and heavy ship with minimum acceptable GM per applicable Load Line criteria.

Speed and heading:

Speed (kn. -F.S.)	Heading (deg.)
0	90
5	0, 15, 45
10	0, 15, 45
15	0, 15

5.3.4   Test Condition 2:

Towing arrangement:

Free running model with autopilot for heading stabilization. Prop rpm set to achieve designated speed. Measure pitch, roll and yaw angles; speed; heading; rudder displacement, force and hinge moment.

Model displacement:

Light and heavy ship with nominal GM.

Speed and heading:

Same as Test Condition 1.

5.4   MONOCHROMATIC WAVES TEST SERIES

This test series is intended to provide a technological way point between deterministic and random wave testing. Upon reflection there appears to be limited merit in pursuing it for several reasons: (a) surging behavior can be more realistically examined in the breaking wave test series, (b) roll resonance behavior is of importance from an operator point of view, but how it might effect ship design decisions is not clear, (c) the testing already proposed would be expensive so that recommending any tests which do not offer clear relevance to the problem of achieving adequate stability and control is probably not advisable.

It is also recognized, however, that researchers developing seakeeping software programs may feel otherwise. For example, Vassalos and Maimun[8] identify a condition that they term "Pseudo-Broaching" in which pitch-heave motion couples into roll motion in successive waves which can lead to broaching. In any case it is proposed to retain this subsection heading for possible development.

5.5   RANDOM WAVE TEST SERIES

5.5.1   Objectives:

a) To simulate survivability seaway conditions and conduct model tests to identify critical motions and associated wave height vs time sequences.

b) To employ critical motion conditions and associated wave height data as input to selected seakeeping programs and to then compare measured and predicted responses.

c) To identify dominant design parameters for purposes of recommending preliminary stability and control design criteria..

5.5.2   Seaway Criteria:

Wave spectra are recommended which correspond to three points of immediate interest on the Survivability envelope, Figure 4:

a) Maximum Hm_o on the Seaways of Limiting Steepness boundary; i.e. Hm_o = 13.7m and Tp = 13.5 sec. (γ = 1.3 – 3.0).

b) Maximum Hm_o , i.e. Hm_o = 18m and Tp = 20 sec. (γ = 1.3).

c) (c) Hm_o at maximum Tp , i.e. Hm_o = 10.5m and Tp = 25 sec, (γ = 1.3).

The wave spectrum is a modified JONSWAP formulation[1]. Spectrum (a). has a range of shape parameters associated with it (1.3< γ <3). Moreover, both short crested and long crested waves should be considered. For purposes of the proposed test program it is suggested that for the moment long crested waves be generated for γ = 1.3 only to simplify the difficulties which may be encountered in relating measured and predicted model responses. Ultimately short crested, bi-directional seaways should be investigated as well as additional points along the Survivability envelope.

5.5.3   Wave Making:

Wave making for the random wave test series involves several questions. First, how closely can the wave spectra in the above section 5.5.2, (a), (b) and (c) be generated in a given tank and to what scale? Second, is there one scale at which all three spectra can be generated so that only one self powered, radio controlled model need be built? Third, could such a model also be used to investigate ship behavior in seaways corresponding to the upper boundary of the Operability envelope?

These questions will be answered in an approximate way utilizing available information[4]. The wave making experiments which were undertaken sought replication of a hurricane Camille wave spectrum, the time-series wave height data of which showed considerable nonlinearity. The objective of the wave making experiments was to determine whether the time-series wave data from two independent facilities approximated the nonlinearity of the full-scale data. The results from each showed that while the larger waves in the resulting time series data did not exhibit all of the nonlinearity of the full-scale waves, there was no question but that replication of the spectrum in question recaptured much of it as evidenced by the steep, breaking waves which were produced.

In the case of the experiments conducted at the Davidson Laboratory, the test report contained a figure defining the random wave making capabilities of their dual-flap wave maker. Answers to the above questions are suggested by Figure 6 which is a modified version of their Figure IV. Regarding the first question raised above, the figure shows that the wave maker could not quite achieve the same steep combination of Hm_o and Tp as that corresponding to the upper end of the Seaways of Limiting Steepness boundary. It should be noted here that the spectrum which was provided to each facility did not require this degree of parametric steepness because nonlinearity of the seaway was the issue at hand. The less steep one which was provided to them (Hm_o = 12.2 m, Tp = 13.6 sec) was replicated at $1/50^{th}$ scale, and at $1/30^{th}$ scale at the Arctec Offshore Corporation facility, see Appendix C[4]. The high frequency tail of the spectrum was not closely approximated at either facility. Moreover, both found that the high frequency wave energy which was generated dissipated significantly at locations removed from the wave maker. Figure 6 suggests that a slightly closer approximation to survivability spectrum (a) could have been achieved at $1/40^{th}$ scale.

Modal periods and significant wave heights for survivability spectra (b) and (c) (maximum Hm_o and maximum Tp respectively) are shown in Figure 6 for several scale factors. In this case the answer to the first question above is a qualified "yes". Tank waves corresponding to a full-scale modal period of 25 sec. would be about 64 ft. long (at $1/50^{th}$ scale) in a tank whose total length is 295 ft. This suggests that creating a random seaway corresponding to this full-scale modal period could present a problem. For the moment, Figure 6 indicates that the answer to the second question above is "yes" for a model scale of about 1/50. Wave spectra at $1/50^{th}$ scale which define the upper limit of the Operability envelope can also be accommodated within the wave making envelope shown in the figure.

Based upon these findings it appears that a seakeeping tank with a similar capability (but not necessarily at the same scale factor) could be capable of investigating critical capsizing conditions using a single self powered, radio controlled model at an appropriate scale factor. Two important qualifications apply to this generalization. First, replication of spectrum (a) might benefit from a different or more energetic wave maker. The second qualification concerns model size. If we say for the moment that a model should be at least 8 ft. in length to accommodate batteries, servos, sensors, recorders, etc., then full-scale vessels of a length less 400 ft could not be modeled at a $1/50^{th}$ scale wave making capability nor vessels of less than 240 ft. length at a $1/30^{th}$ scale wave making capability. Generation of model scale seaways which correspond to bi-directional, short crested seas has not been discussed for lack of quantitative wave making data in hand.

The fact that random wave environments are involved in this test series has a substantial effect upon the approach recommended for critical condition identification. It is important that an initial test phase be undertaken which involves tank wave generation and analysis only. Its purpose is to verify the ability of the wave maker to replicate the three wave spectra identified above and to determine if a common scale factor exists at which they can each be generated. In the case of wave spectrum (a) there is an additional requirement that the associated parametric steepness lie as close to the Seaways of Limiting Steepness boundary as possible. For this condition it is important that time series wave height data be obtained simultaneously for several wave staff locations in the vicinity of the wave maker and beyond, and that these data be analyzed in the HACYM or equivalent format (as shown in Figure 14[4]) to determine how close the nonlinearity of the wave height variable compares to that of hurricane Camille, see also Figures 14 j, k and m and Figures 18 and 22.

This type of data analysis must be supplemented by a print out of wave height vs elapsed time from start up of the wave maker so that individual wave events of interest can be identified as to elapsed time from start-up and wave staff location. This information is intended for use in specifying that the model location correspond in time and location to those wave events which are believed to be potentially critical. It is important that repeatability of major wave events be demonstrated early on for spectra (a),(b) and (c), (see section 5.5.2). For evidence of repeatability of a steep wave event see the pg. 45 and Figure 27[4].

5.5.4   Survivability Condition I

Towing arrangement:

The model is to be self propelled and steered by an autopilot. It is intended that the carriage remain positioned slightly behind and aside of the model during each test run for purposes of video taping its motion together with a time code correlated to start up of the wave maker. Measure pitch, roll and yaw angles; heave acceleration; speed; heading;   rudder displacement, force and hinge moment.

Model displacement:

Light and heavy ship with minimum GM as determined from applicable Load Line regulations.

Test Conditions I-(a), I-(b), I-(c) :

Speed (kn.)	Heading (deg.)
Minimum for adequate directional control.*	0, 15

* It is suggested that this speed be determined by operating the model at a 0 deg heading in the spectrum (a) seaway with successive increases in forward speeds until model deviations are no more then ± 15 deg. from the intended heading.

5.5.5 Survivability Condition II:

Towing arrangement:

The model is to have no propulsive power applied in this test series. With the rudder centered and locked the model is to be placed at a beam sea heading and the wave maker started. Measure time-series pitch, roll and yaw angles; heave acceleration; speed (if any); heading; rudder force and hinge moment; and local wave heights. If the model does not attain an essentially steady average heading, the test should be terminated. Note: It is recognized that this test is unrealistic insofar as it omits consideration of wind forces. The intent at this time is to provide a test condition in which wave forces predominate and to compare actual vs predicted ship responses. Clearly, the effect of wind forces on ship heading and heeling must be included if a realistic assessment of ship safety is to be conducted. Results of tank tests in which combined beam winds and seas were simulated have been reported[14].

Model displacement:

Light and heavy with minimum GM as determined from applicable Load Line regulations.

Speed and heading:

Zero forward speed with 90 deg. initial heading. Conduct runs for Spectra (a) and (b) only since waves associated with Spectrum (c) are not steep nor are they necessarily associated with wind velocities of particular significance.

5.6 COMMENTS

The foregoing test and evaluation conditions are intended to achieve objectives as stated. They have also been structured, however, to serve as a basis for coordinating individual experimental and analytical methods developments. While the particulars of the proposed towing arrangements, model speeds, angles of heel, etc. may not find general acceptance, it is hoped that those engaged in capsizing research will consider responding with counter proposals so as to ultimately produce a consensus as to required test and evaluation procedures. Such a result would be beneficial from the point of view of seaway conditions to be employed in validating analytical methods for use in preliminary and final design.

At the present time there appears to be rather limited consistency in these areas, especially in regard to the seaway criteria employed. Note: With the exception of a lack of seaway criteria, the approach[6] taken to identifying critical capsizing scenarios and critical design parameters has much in common with the first principles methodology recommended here. Moreover the authors' suggestion that ----"if the complementary expertise gained were brought together it would be possible to simulate the capsizing sequence by a ship broaching-to."-- appears to reflect sentiments similar to those expressed here.

6. RECOMMENDED ACTION

a) Survey seakeeping facility wave making capabilities to determine their ability to conduct the proposed model tests, and to generate survivability seaways and at what scales.

b) Conduct a survey of ship masters for comments regarding their ship handling experience in seaways corresponding at or above the upper boundary of the Operability envelope. This boundary is intended to correspond to seaways in which the master should be able to maintain the general heading at which he planned to proceed with weather forecasts in hand. Ship owners should also be surveyed with regard to their expectations or desires as to the ability of their ship to maintain speed and heading considering the frequency of occurrence of each of the three climatic seaways associated with the Operability envelope.

c) Investigate the availability of time series wave height data for severe storms. Such data should be obtainable from North Sea oil producing or drilling platforms. This involves the question of which activities are measuring time series wave heights during storms and at what locations and whether such information is available to the research community.

d) Obtain comments from selected individuals or agencies regarding the suitability of their seakeeping software programs for participation in the model test and analytical validation research described above. Also request comments on the acceptability of the proposed experimental/analytical development program as a standard for analytical methods development.

ACKNOWLEDGEMENTS

The author is grateful to Prof. J. Randolph Pauling for a video tape of the SL-7 model tests in San Francisco Bay and to Prof. Stefan Grochowalski for a video tape of the capsize model tests of a Canadian fishing vessel. He is also grateful to Prof. Willard J. Pierson, Jr. for copies of rare storm wave photos and related court testimony of ship masters who were caught in a survivability level storm. He is most appreciative also of the long term wave statistics research conducted by Dr. Neil Hogben without which he could not have realistically extrapolated the NOAA baseline Survivability and Operability envelopes to cover world wide wave conditions.

REFERENCES

1. BUCKLEY, W H: 'Stability Criteria: Development of a First Principles Methodology' Fifth International Conference on Stability of Ships and Ocean Vehicles, November 7-II, 1994, Volume 3 of the Proceedings.

2. HOGBEN, N, DACUNHA, N M C and OLLIVER, G F: `Global Wave Statistics', compiled and edited by British Maritime Technology Limited, England, Unwin Brothers Limited, 1986.

3. BUCKLEY, W H: 'Design Wave Climates for the World Wide Operation of Ships, Part I: Establishment of Design Wave Climates', October, 1993 (In publication)

4. BUCKLEY, W H: 'Analysis of Wave Characteristics in Extreme Seas', Ship Structure Committee Report SSC-353, 1991

5. OAKLEY, O H Jr., PAULING, J R, WOOD, P D: 'Ship Motions and Capsizing in Astern Seas', Tenth Symposium-Naval Hydrodynamics, June 24-28, 1974.

6. Personal communication with W A Cleary, Jr.

7. Video tape of SL-7 Model Capsizing Tests.

8. VASSALOS, D and MAIMUN, A: 'Broaching-To: Thirty Years On', Fifth International Conference on Stability of Ships and Ocean Vessels, November 7-11, 1994, Volume 4 of the Proceedings.

9. GROCHOWALSKI, S, ARCHIBALD, J B CONNOLLY, F J LEE, C K: 'Operational Factors in Stability Safety of Ships in Heavy Seas', Fifth International Conference on Stability of Ships and Ocean Vessels, November 7-11, 1994, Volume 4 of Proceedings.

10. Personal communication with Captain George Ianiev, then 2nd Mate of M/V SELKIRK SETTLER.

11. CALHOUN, C R: `Typhoon - The Other Enemy', The 3rd Fleet and the Pacific Storm of December 1944, Naval Institute Press, Annapolis, MD, 1981.

12. KOTSCH, W J, HENDERSON, R: Heavy Weather Guide, 2nd Ed., Naval Institute Press, 1984.

13. Capsize Study: USYRU/SNAME report on research into capsizing. (Available from U.S. Sailing, Box 209, Portsmouth, R. I. 02871-6015).

14. SHAUGHNESSY, J, NEHRLING, B C, COMPTON, R H: `Some Observations on Experimental Techniques for Modeling Ship Stability in Wind and in Waves', Fifth International Conference on Stability of Ships and Ocean Vessels, November 7-11, 1994, volume 3 of Proceedings.

APPENDIX A

EXTRACT OF CAPTAIN MATTHEW'S TESTIMONY

From: U.S. Coast Guard's Vessel Stability Symposium '93, Vols. 1 and 2, March 1993.

SHIP STABILITY IN HEAVY WEATHER: THE REAL SITUATION AND MODELS THEREOF

by Willard J. Pierson Jr.

Captain Matthew, the master of the M/V SELKIRK SETTLER, was concerned with the short distance between the waves. The M/V SELKIRK SETTLER was designed for summer operation in the Great Lakes and winter operation in the Atlantic. He ran before the waves and took the seas dead astern. The short distance between the waves increased his likelihood of capsizing. It also caused many waves to break on his stern, or in seamanship terms, to "poop" the vessel. A portion of his testimony follows.

Q. **What did you fear if you went too fast?**

A. *She would start to surf. Fall off the wind. Broach. Capsize.*

Q. **About how great a distance did you notice between the waves as compared with the length of your ship?**

A. *Approximately the same length of the ship.*

Q. **What problem if any did that fact that the waves were the same length as the ship present to you?**

A. *Between the troughs it meant that if I went over, that I'd be in the trough and I'd have problems. There would be no rise to break the sequence to help me.*

Q.	What did you fear if you went to slowly?	A.	If you went too slow, then you also fear broach. It's to keep the happy medium between the two.

The Court:	The Selkirk Settler was 700 feet?	The Witness:	730 feet.

Q.	What did you estimate the height of the seas at the height of the storm?	A.	They went up to 75 feet because we were 55 Feet above sea level. Yet I was looking up at the waves.

(Interruption)

Q.	I'd like you describe the action of your ship in these seas, in these heavy seas when you were taking them astern. When the waves first approached your stern, what happened and what did you do?	A.	When the wave approaches and it breaks, you think she is going to rise but it breaks. It doesn't break, you think she is going to rise but it breaks. It doesn't break, it comes on top of the ship, and immediately cause you, if you don't rise you get a slowing effect of the ship, and that is when the wheelman usually says "I am losing steerage way." You kick her up using your combinator from 8.5 or what you have and you kick her to give her a burst to give her extra momentum to get her out.
Q.	Then what would happen?	A.	The ship rises slowly. More often than not before the next one comes along but you get a double poop, one poop on top of the other, then you--then she will be very slow to rise. That is when you start to worry about a possible broach.
Q.	Possible broach?	A.	Yes.
Q	What happens after she starts to rise?	A.	The water, because you see the photographs here, we don't have bulwarks across the stern, we just have railings so the water can free itself pretty quickly, and it did free itself.
Q.	What would happen next then as the wave passed up the ship?	A.	It passed up, the stern rises, the water comes off, and the bow comes down and the rises up and the swell passes underneath her and then you start to fall away. Then the ship falls away the bow rises as swell goes underneath the bow.

The steep waves continually washed over the decks of the M/V SELKIRK SETTLER as shown in several photographs taken by the second mate during the storm. When the enormous wave shown in Figure B-2 of Ref.1 broke upon the M/V SELKIRK SETTLER, Captain Matthew thought she would go down.

TABLE 1   ELEMENTS OF A FIRST PRINCIPLES METHODOLOGY

Operational Requirements	which identify ocean areas and routes of operation, speeds in calm and rough water, design displacements, operational life, etc.
Seaway Criteria	which define both world-wide climatic (i.e. long-term average) and extreme wave conditions.
Critical Design Condition Criteria	which identify those particular wave and operating conditions which a designer should consider in satisfying Response Criteria. When identifying critical wave conditions the entire range of the Seaway Criteria must be considered.
Analytical Methods	which permit the establishment of ship design characteristics which satisfy Critical design Condition and Response Criteria. These methods must lead ultimately to deterministic results for both preliminary and final design, and must be suitable for analyzing linear and nonlinear responses.
Response Criteria	which define acceptable or unacceptable behavior of a ship under Critical Design Conditions for seakeeping and structural design purposes.

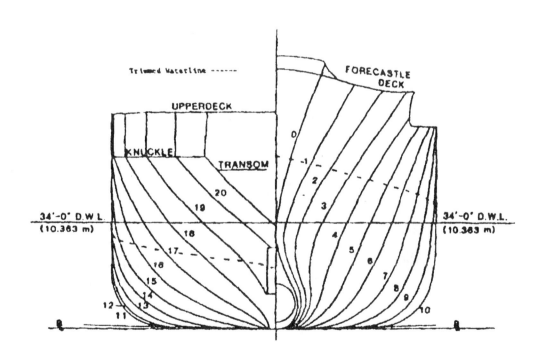

Fig. 1 Body Plan of SL-7 Containership

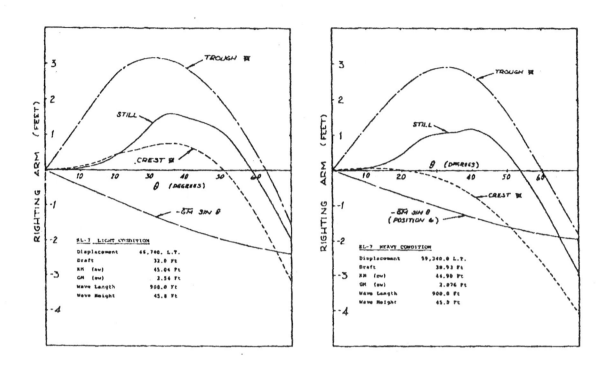

Fig. 2 Righting Arm Curves for SL-7 Containership

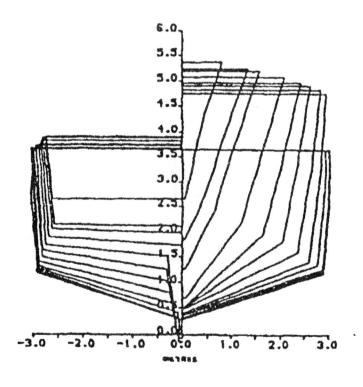

Fig. 3 Body Plan for Canadian Fishing Vessel

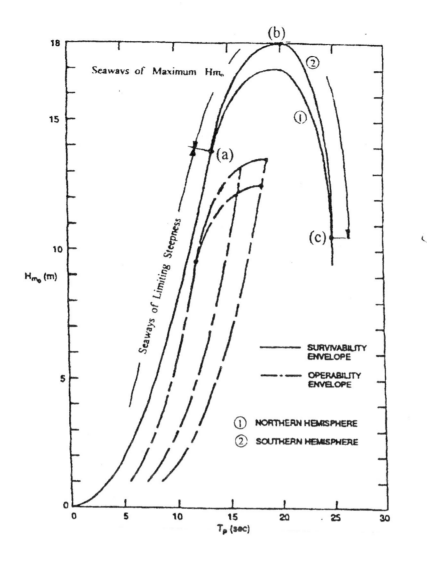

Fig. 4 Survivability Envelope Test Conditions: (a), (b) and (c)

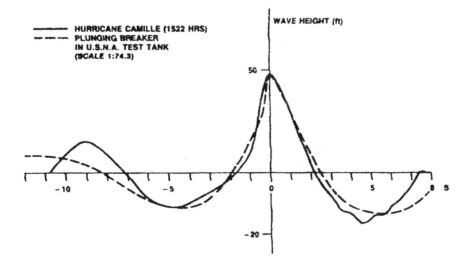

Fig. 5 Comparison of Model Scale Plunging Braker and Wave from Hurricane Camille (1522) hours)

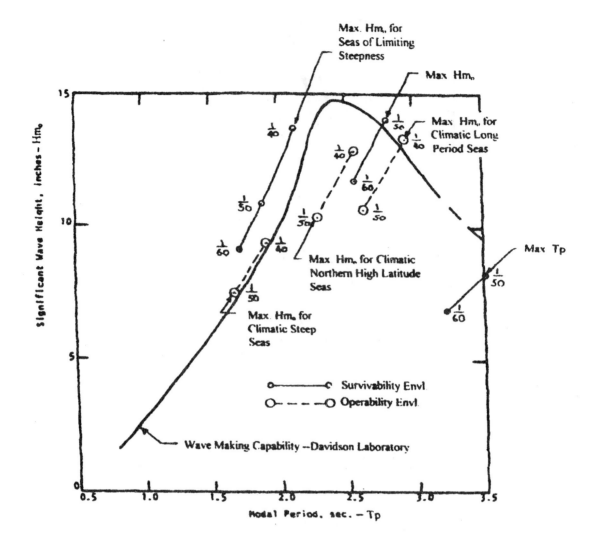

Fig. 6 Model Scales Related to Wave Making Capabilities

PAPER NO.10.

SOME CURRENT PRACTICES AND REQUIREMENTS FOR EXTREME CONDITIONS
FOR FIXED AND FLOATING PLATFORMS

by S N Smith, M T Taggart, and J W Bunce
Amerada Hess Ltd, UK

Paper presented at the

International Conference

DESIGN AND OPERATION FOR
ABNORMAL CONDITIONS

21 22 OCTOBER 1997 GLASGOW

SOME CURRENT PRACTICES AND REQUIREMENTS FOR EXTREME CONDITIONS FOR FIXED AND FLOATING PLATFORMS

S N Smith, M T Taggart, and J W Bunce
Amerada Hess Ltd

SUMMARY

This paper discusses the requirements and challenges that we see as an oil and gas operating company from the perspective of practising engineers. Thus we are looking at extreme events in existing provinces such as the North Sea and also looking at designing and operating in extremely hostile areas such as the Atlantic Margins which combines the challenges of extreme water-depth and an extreme met-ocean environment.

The paper first addresses current offshore approaches and practices for fixed offshore platforms, floating production facilities, and the Safety Case approach. It then goes on to discuss operational experience and emerging knowledge for the same range of facilities and discusses the differences in offshore and merchant marine approaches and highlights some apparently inconsistent practices.

Development in the Atlantic Margins are presented including metocean conditions and principal dimensions for FPSOs. Mooring related challenges are discussed along with some associated factors such as riser design.

A number of suggestions are made throughout the paper which could lead to benefits across the range of maritime industries.

AUTHORS' BIOGRAPHIES

Mr Stuart Smith, CEng, MRINA, has a BSc in Naval Architecture and Ocean Engineering and a PhD in Hydrodynamics both from Glasgow University.

He worked for both a Contracting Company and Operating Company before joining Amerada Hess in 1986. With Amerada Hess he has been involved in a number of capacities in all the Company's subsea and floating production developments which now include Ivanhoe/Rob Roy, Scott, Angus, Hudson, Fife, Telford and Durward/Dauntless.

He has written a number of papers on general and specific aspects of subsea and floating production systems including publications at the Offshore Technology Conference and Offshore Europe. He has received a number of awards and prizes including British Shipbuilders 'Ships for the Eighties' competition; a bronze medal from the Royal Institution of Naval Architects for a paper 'Design and Hydrodynamic Assessment of a Small Semi-submersible SWATH Ship'; and the Stanley Gray Memorial Award from the Institute of Marine Engineers for a paper 'Some Techno-Economic Considerations in the Design of North Sea Production Monohulls'.

Mr Michael Taggart, CEng, MRINA has worked in the offshore oil industry for eighteen years as a practising Naval Architect specialising in the installation of offshore structures and floating production. This has included periods with Heerema installing major structures, Midland and Scottish on the Emerald Producer and Ailsa Craig; and with Amerada Hess on a number of the Company's floating systems.

Mr J W Bunce, CEng, MRINA, is qualified as a structural engineer and naval architect and has worked for several major contractors and operating companies and was formerly lecturer in civil engineering at Imperial College. He is now Structural Engineering Supervisor with Amerada Hess.

He has been responsible for the design of a wide range of industrial and offshore structures over a thirty year period and is the author of a number of technical papers. He has been active in promoting the use of reinforced concrete for FPSO hulls.

Mr Bunce is currently Chairman of the Institution of Structural Engineers Offshore Structures Section in Aberdeen.

ABBREVIATIONS AND NOMENCLATURE

API	American Petroleum Institute
ATA	Automatic Thruster Assist
B	Breadth/Beam
C_n	Crest Elevation above still water level
D	Depth
DnV	Det norske Veritas
F	Freeboard
FPSO	Floating Production, Storage and Offtake System

F of S	Factor of Safety
fpa	fatalities per annum
GOM	Gulf of Mexico
HSE	Health and Safety Executive
H_s	Significant Wave Height
H_{s50}	Fifty Year Return Period Significant Wave Height
hp	horsepower
IR	Individual Risk
L	Length
MBL	Minimum Breaking Load
MJ	Mega - Joules
MTD	Marine Technology Directorate
m/s	metres per second
NPD	Norwegian Petroleum Directorate
NWECS	North West European Continental Shelf
PLL	Probable loss of life
Tz	Zero Crossing Period
T	Draught
T	Wave Period
T_{ass}	Associated Wave Period
TRI -	Temporary Refuge Impairment
t	tonnes
UKCS	United Kingdom Continental Shelf

1.0   INTRODUCTION

Oil and gas exploration and production is an international land and marine based industry. Many of the practices and standards have evolved from one area of the industry to another but in addition there are particular practices that have developed in a comparatively short time to meet specific requirements. This paper concerns itself primarily with activities in UK water and connected European waters.

This is broadly a practical paper which tries to draw lessons from current design practices and operational experience and looks at requirements for the frontiers of the Atlantic margins. The topics included are broadly naval architectural or structural engineering but also include related areas such as mooring and risers.

In the North Sea Oil exploration and production has now been going on for over thirty years. In the early days the metocean conditions and the response of structures in them was not properly understood. In any oil province the first substantial activity (from the naval architectural or structural point of view) is exploration drilling. Our lack of knowledge and understanding in what was then considered extreme conditions was highlighted by the fate of the Sea Gem drilling rig and more recently by the Alexander Kielland .

The first North Sea oil production was from a floating platform; the TransWorld 58 (1). Thereafter fixed platforms were widely employed and now account for by far the greatest quantities of oil and gas production. However in more recent times floating production either in the form of semi-submersible or ship shape FPSOs (Floating Production, Storage and Offtake) either new or converted have become increasingly popular. Typical fixed and floating units are illustrated in Fig. 1.

In order to aid designers with the then extreme conditions specific technical guidance was produced and refined and is now embodied in what is generally known as the Fourth Edition Guidelines (2) This contains significant sections on metocean conditions, materials, structural design, stability and damage stability. Typical metocean conditions in terms of 50 year return period significant wave height are illustrated in Fig. 2. In practice other codes and standards e.g. API RP2A - LRFD (3) for structures or Classification Society Rules for floaters are widely used as are more sophisticated analysis techniques.

In recent times the regulatory regime has changed significantly with new Goal Setting, Safety Case Legislation as a consequence of the Piper Alpha disaster (4). This has had the most impact on the topsides area. In terms of platform and floating structures the practising engineer will still be working with the same design codes and standards but will have to take much better account of the effects of fire and explosion. The overpressures resulting from some explosion simulations are a good example of another type of extreme or abnormal loads.

For frontier areas, in particular the Atlantic margin we look at some of the existing and potential trends and make various suggestions from the practising engineers point of view or perspective in particular related to the new extreme metocean conditions and water depth, these are illustrated in Fig. 3.

2.0   CURRENT OFFSHORE APPROACHES & PRACTICES

2.1   FIXED OFFSHORE PLATFORMS

There is now a broad consensus throughout the offshore oil industry on overall design principles for fixed offshore platforms. In addition to 'normal' operating conditions and 'extreme' conditions - defined as having a return period of, say, 100 years - the need to design structures to survive 'abnormal' load conditions has long been recognised, even where there was no explicit regulatory requirement for this. Two examples are the 'severed deck case' used for design of the major concrete gravity base production platforms in the North Sea where the portion of the deck structure supporting the living quarters is designed to remain intact in the event of collapse of the rest of the deck structure, and the 'redundancy analyses' now routinely carried out on steel jacket structures to demonstrate that progressive collapse does not occur if part of the primary structure is lost. This is illustrated in Fig. 4.

The main influence in this evolution of structural design philosophy in European waters was the realisation of the potential for serious structural damage resulting from ship impact, the incidence of fatigue failure on tubular members, and the potentially catastrophic consequences of fire and blast loads.

Ship impact became a major influence on development of design philosophy in the early 1980's and gave rise to improved understanding of the degree of redundancy (reserve strength) in piled steel jacket design and how to exploit this in improved designs.

The full effects of fire and blast loads are only beginning to be properly understood now, although the need for platform layout design to reduce risks and mitigate loading effects is fairly well understood.

In other parts of the world, risks of earthquake loads and hurricanes provided the impetus rather than ship impact or fire and blast but the overall conclusion for structures to be designed to be sufficiently robust was essentially the same.

As these 'abnormal' loads have become accepted as part of the 'normal' design process a rationale has become to be established and, although there is no universal 'rule', it seems generally accepted that the abnormal load offshore structures should be designed to survive has a 10,000-year return period.

This has led to the need to be able to define loads with this return period on the one hand, and the development of design and analysis techniques powerful enough to allow design without excessive cost penalties, on the other. There has thus been increased activity on the metocean front to determine appropriate wind, wave and current data and in the development of structural analyses methods to predict platform response as loads approach the maximum carrying capacity of the structure (e.g. 'push over' analysis).

It has also been realised that step changes in platform loads can occur when conditions with longer return periods than 100 years are considered and these may be severe enough to cause catastrophic failure. It is very well known, for example, that if large waves impinge on the superstructure of a platform a large increase in overall overturning moment can occur. Hence, the Ekofisk platform jacking up project to avoid this risk in the presence of the large sea floor subsidence that occurred in that field, and also the current practice of ensuring that platform superstructures are elevated sufficiently to clear the crest of a 10,000-year wave.

There are also other, less widely appreciated, phenomena which can be associated with 10,000-year waves in certain conditions, for example in which the whole sea floor can become unstable in a 'mud-slide' mechanism. While these occurrences are usually associated with a sloping sea floor near a large river estuary where sedimentation is active, or in earthquake regions, they can also be shown to be possible in flat sea floor conditions where there is no active sedimentation or seismic risk, if the wave forces are sufficiently powerful.

2.2   FLOATING PRODUCTION FACILITIES

For semi-submersibles and tension leg platforms there are some aspects of their design philosophy which have been translated from fixed platforms directly or by analogy and others refined from conventional naval architecture practice. Some obvious examples are the ballast system damage stability, and normal requirements. Semi-submersible and TLP structures are often designed using similar codes and practices to fixed structures.

For ship shaped floating facilities the majority of units, especially those in benign conditions outside the North Sea are based on converted tankers (5). These were built in compliance with Classification Society Rules. In the North Sea the first FPSO to be deployed was the Petrojarl which had considerable increase in scantlings above rule. Further units have been converted from trading tankers with addition of structural brackets to improve the fatigue performance (6) or have been purpose built (7).

This situation is clearly significantly different from fixed platform design practice.

2.3   METOCEAN CONDITIONS

Metocean conditions are clearly an important design input for fixed and floating offshore structures. Fourth Edition Guidelines give indicative values for the various parameters; for instance Fig. 2 shows the estimates of 50 year return significant wave heights, H_{s50}. In practice it is also usual to derive detailed site specific information. However the figure clearly illustrates the magnitude of the input being considered. In addition it is usual practice to consider different return periods to estimate extreme crest elevations and extreme crest heights; as detailed in Table 1.

Guidance is also given on the range of associated wave periods. This can be written as

$$2.94\sqrt{Hs50} < T_{ass} < 5.04 \sqrt{Hs50} \tag{1}$$

In addition to these extremes it is also common practice to consider a range of wave heights and periods both for fatigue analysis and in order to determine highest loads in structural members such as semi-submersible braces.

3

TABLE 1 Estimation of Extreme Crest Elevations and Extreme Wave Height

Return period, N (years)	N-year return value of crest elevation above still water level, C_N	N-year return value of individual wave height (crest to trough), H_N
5	$0.86\ H_{s50}$	$1.56\ H_{s50}$
10	$0.91\ H_{s50}$	$1.65\ H_{s50}$
100	$1.03\ H_{s50}$	$1.86\ H_{s50}$
100	$1.08\ H_{s50}$	$1.95\ H_{s50}$
1000	$1.25\ H_{s50}$	$2.25\ H_{s50}$
10,000	$1.42\ H_{s50}$	$2.57\ H_{s50}$

2.4 SAFETY CASE APPROACH AND DATA

Following the Piper Alpha disaster (4) the regulatory regime for the UKCS change from prescriptive design requirements to a Goal Setting approach. As a result every offshore installation fixed or floating has to have its safety demonstrated by the preparation of a comprehensive Safety Case.

Summaries of the overall risk levels for different major hazards for a submersible production system and a fixed production platform are given in Table 2 and 3 for illustration purposes.

TABLE 2 Semi-submersible Production Platform: Major Hazard Risk Levels

Major Hazard	PLL (fpa)	IR (fpa) Most Exposed	IR (fpa) Average	IR (fpa) Least Exposed	TRI(pa)
Loss of containment Process equipment failure	1.4×10^{-2}	1.7×10^{-4}	7.8×10^{-5}	2.3×10^{-5}	3.9×10^{-4}
Dropped Objects	3.4×10^{-3}	4.3×10^{-5}	1.9×10^{-5}	4.9×10^{-6}	9.2×10^{-5}
Marine Impacts	3.0×10^{-4}	2.2×10^{-6}	1.7×10^{-6}	1.4×10^{-6}	8.3×10^{-6}
Helicopter crash	1.2×10^{-3}	1.4×10^{-5}	6.6×10^{-6}	2.0×10^{-6}	3.8×10^{-5}
Marine System Faults	6.2×10^{-3}	3.9×10^{-5}	3.6×10^{-5}	3.4×10^{-5}	1.9×10^{-4}
Loss of Structural Integrity	-	-	-	-	-
Extreme environmental conditions	-	-	-	-	-
Helicopter transportation	1.0×10^{-2}	5.7×10^{-5}	5.8×10^{-5}	5.9×10^{-5}	-
TOTAL	3.5×10^{-2}	3.3×10^{-4}	2.0×10^{-4}	1.2×10^{-4}	7.2×10^{-4}

TABLE 3 Fixed Production Platform: Major Hazard Risk Levels

Major Hazard	PLL (fpa)	IR (fpa) Most Exposed	IR (fpa) Average	IR (fpa) Least Exposed	TRI (pa)
Loss of Containment					
- Equipment	1.9×10^{-2}	6.7×10^{-5}	4.0×10^{-5}	2.4×10^{-5}	
- Human Error	3.1×10^{-3}	1.9×10^{-5}	6.8×10^{-6}	1.2×10^{-6}	
Marine Impacts	1.8×10^{-5}	4.1×10^{-8}	3.9×10^{-8}	3.3×10^{-8}	
Structural due to Environment	1.7×10^{-4}	3.9×10^{-7}	3.7×10^{-7}	3.1×10^{-7}	
Helicopter Crash	2.4×10^{-2}	5.4×10^{-5}	5.3×10^{-5}	4.5×10^{-5}	
Dropped Objects	4.8×10^{-5}	1.5×10^{-7}	1.0×10^{-7}	1.6×10^{-8}	
TOTAL	4.5×10^{-2}	1.4×10^{-4}	1.0×10^{-4}	7.0×10^{-5}	6.1×10^{-4}

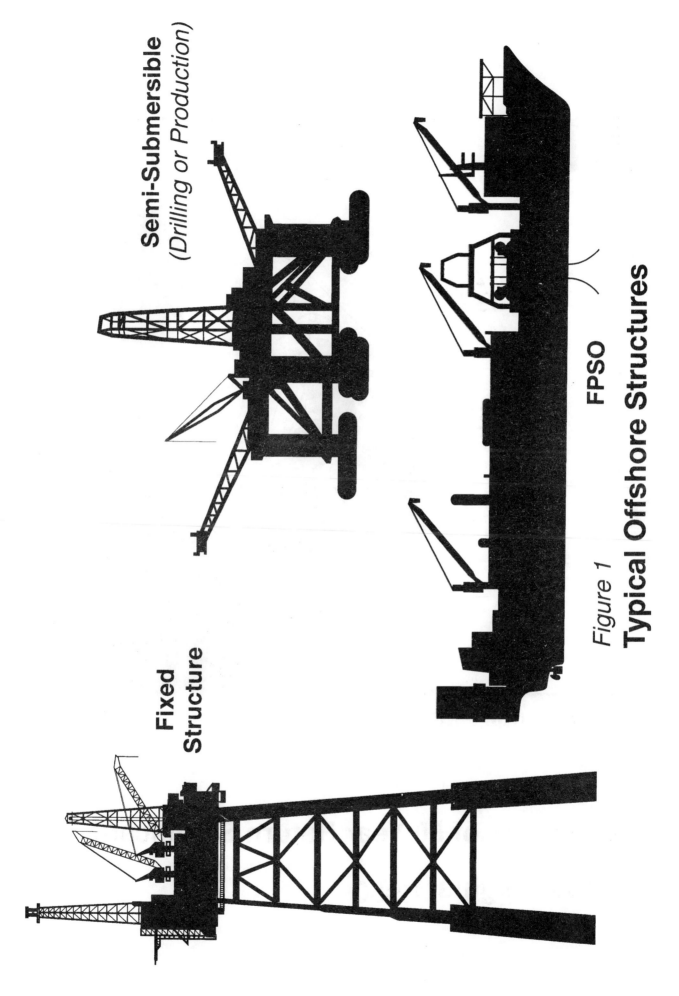

Semi-Submersible
(Drilling or Production)

Fixed Structure

FPSO

Figure 1
Typical Offshore Structures

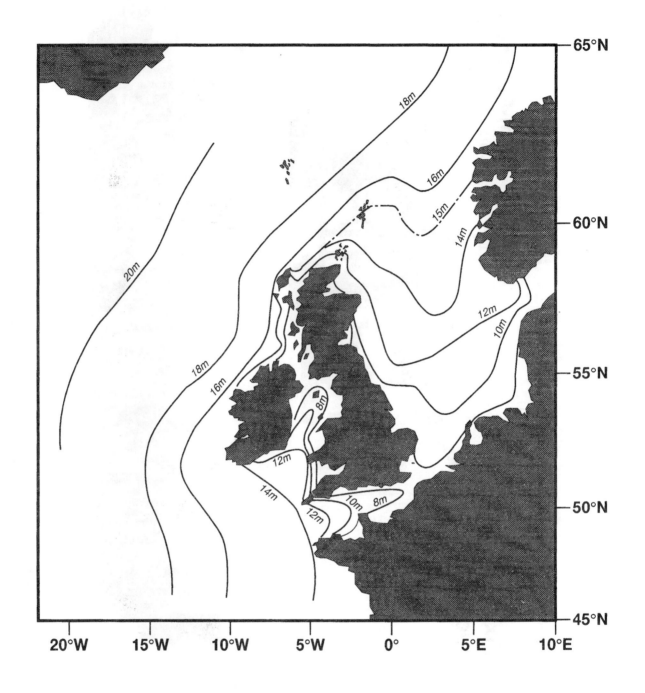

Figure 2

Estimates of 50 Year Return Significant

Wave Heights, H$_{S}$50

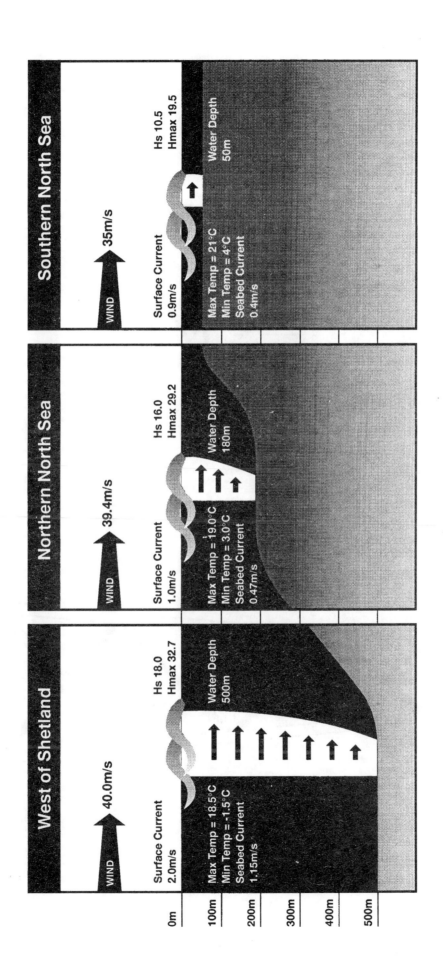

Figure 3
Metocean Conditions

7

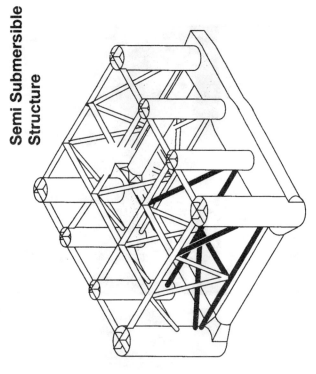

Semi Submersible Structure

Jacket Structure

Braces selected for redundancy analysis are shown in black

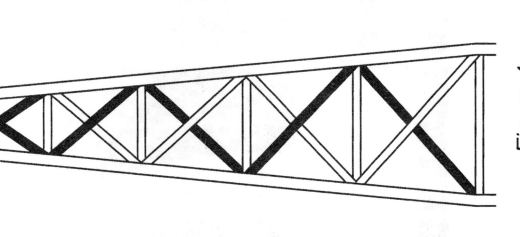

Figure 4

Illustration of Redundancy Analysis

The two sets of data are not completely comparable; however in both cases it can be seen that the calculated risks associated with loss of structural integrity due to extreme environmental conditions are significantly lower than the calculated risks from various other hazards.

Some of the other hazards also contain structural elements. For instance the risks from equipment loss of containment include consideration of the effects of a jet fire (from a postulated gas export riser failure) causing structural damage or failure of one of the main legs. Similarly the structural effects of blast over-pressures have to be considered.

3.0 OPERATIONAL EXPERIENCE AND EMERGING KNOWLEDGE

3.1 FIXED PLATFORM

Hard data on structural failures is not always readily available and it is generally believed to be under-collected if not under-reported. Some data collections are available (8) and for instance Fig. 5 shows that in 1991 there were 352 steel and 23 concrete platforms located on the NWECS (North West European Continental Shelf).

It is clear that fewer repairs per platform were undertaken in later 1980's than in the later '70's and early 80's. The data is extensively analysed by MTD but it is interesting to highlight some points:

– the number of repairs to primary structural elements has declined since 1974;

– repairs to secondary structures have stayed more or less constant;

– repairs to appurtenances have increased.

For 106 reasonably known repairs the cause of damage is listed as:-

– Fatigue	40
– Vessel Impact	37
– Dropped Objects	16
– Corrosion	13

It is interesting to note that extreme wave damage is not given as one of the causes although damage from this is known to have occurred in recent years.

It the late 70's and early 80's there was extensive research into the fatigue resistance of steel tubular joints and the data shows that structures installed since 1982 appear to have been designed adequately against fatigue. (For modern jacket designs the minimum calculated fatigue life can be as much as 90 years).

Accidental impacts are now considered as a design case as required by Fourth Edition Guidelines where it

is recommended that the total Kinetic Energy should be taken as at least 14MJ for a sideways collision which corresponds to a vessel of 5000t displacement with an impact speed of 2 m/s with the energy absorbed by the installation to be at least 4MJ.

The data above relates to the NWECS however the picture from other parts of the world is similar. It is also clear that some of the advances can be attributed to specific events. Hurricane Camille in the Gulf of Mexico during 1969 is clearly one such event.

Major changes in design loading in the GOM occurred in the early 1970's as a result of structural collapses during Hurricane Hilda 1964 and Camille in 1969 (9).

Thus in 1992 when Hurricane Andrew exposed about 100 platforms designed to post 1977 criteria to conditions with a return period of about 100 years they all survived without major damage.

Clearly the offshore industry has implemented the lessons learned from extreme events and modified fixed platform design practices accordingly.

3.2 FLOATING PRODUCTION PLATFORM

One of the most obvious manifestations of extreme waves in the design of FPSOs (and also trading ships) must be green-water on deck.

One of the early FPSOs in the North Sea is the Uisge Gorm deployed in the Fife field. It was converted from a product tanker built in 1983 and included the addition of some 1100 reinforcement brackets to provide the necessary fatigue life extension (6,10).

Elsewhere the Petrojarl 1 was used on Angus and then Hudson (11) and at that time the Operator was aware of several scores of fatigue cracks in the structure. The vessel subsequently went in for modifications and maintenance and was then re-deployed on the Blenheim field (12)).

The Uisge Gorm can be seen to have a forward deck-house around the turret but no other major bow modifications to distinguish its rough weather performance from a tanker (10, 13). In its relatively short experience to date in the Fife Field it has suffered some fairly extensive damage to walkways ladders, deck equipment, piping insulation, etc. predominately forward but also experienced water ingress to the steering flat via air intakes.

The subject of green water loading is probably considered during all FPSO projects. It has also been the subject of more academic research, for example Buchner (14) discusses a number of interesting findings including observations that in high waves the calculations over-predict motions; in short waves the moment from green water is almost equal to the wave-pitching moment; the pressure of water on the deck can be much greater than the static head of water. These factors can be influenced by choice of bow shape but he also notes that it is not sensible to optimise the bow shape solely on green water loading since this can also effect other aspects of the design such as drift forces and resultant mooring loads.

In more recent projects greater attention seems to have been paid to this aspect. For instance the "Anasuria" for Shell's Guillemot/Teal fields clearly has an elevated fore-castle and a significant breakwater (7). Similarly the FPSO Glas Dowr for Durward/Dauntless can be seen to have an enclosed fore-castle. These type of features are even more pronounced for the Schiehallion FPSO (23) which of course has to operate in even more extreme conditions.

In addition, it is normal practice on FPSOs to mount the process equipment some 3m or so above the upper deck.

The above narrative describes a fairly small sample but it suggests that while the design of FPSOs is not as mature as for fixed platform appropriate advances and features are being included in the newest designs.

However the experience base of FPSOs in severe conditions is still comparatively limited and it would be beneficial to investigate the reliability of such structures. The goal should be reliability equivalent to that of fixed structures.

3.3 METOCEAN CONDITIONS, EMERGING INFORMATION

In the Danish Sector of the Central North Sea an analysis has been made of more than 12 years of wave records (15). This found the ratio between the expected extreme crest height and extreme wave height to be 0.69. Such values are outside the range of Gaussian waves and thus also clearly more severe than 4th Edition Guidance, (i.e. "freak" waves).

However, 4th Edition Guidance recommends an air-gap between extreme crest and deck of 1.5m which can be considered as a margin for uncertainty. It is interesting to consider some more specific numbers e.g. take $H_s = 10m$.

From 4th Edition Extreme Wave Height
$$H = 1.86 \times 10 = 18.6m \qquad (2)$$

From Ref (15) Extreme Crest Height
$$C = 0.69 \times 18.6 = 12.83m \qquad (3)$$

From 4th Edition Extreme Crest Height
$$C = 1.03 \times 10 = 10.3m \qquad (4)$$

Therefore required deck elevation
(above extreme water level) $= 10.3 + 5 = 11.8m \qquad (5)$

In this example the deck elevation calculated from 4th Edition including the 1.5m margin seems to be insufficient compared with the data analysis thus supporting the practices of using (or mis-using) longer return periods.

Kjeldsen (16) presents evidence including an extreme wave at Ekofisk that damaged various items of topsides equipment providing further support for the practices.

On the loading side Kjeldsen also postulates that the under-estimation of wave-crest heights is balanced by conservatism in structural loading which seems to be borne out by the MTD data above.

It may be worth noting that the convention adopted in the North Sea of superimposing extreme wave, current and wind loads neglecting their joint probability of occurrence and the tendency to overpredict their individual extreme values has led to overall platform design loads which do approach the 10,000 year condition but the load and resistance factors for 100 year conditions are maintained.

In practice it seems that designs are sufficiently robust, however we should be able to make more cost effective structures which have both adequate strength and the necessary deck elevation if we had better understanding of the extreme wave environment.

3.4 DISCUSSIONS OF OFFSHORE AND MERCHANT MARINE PRACTICE

3.4.1 General

We do not claim any particular experience in merchant marine matters. However we were motivated by the contents of Faulkner's paper (17) to compare some experience from the offshore world with the shipping world. We also want to try to ensure that experience from the shipping world is fed into the emerging field of FPSO design.

3.4.2 Ship Losses and Structural Failure

Faulkner points out the conflicting nature of some of the data on ship losses. However, considering the range, somewhere between 30% and 70% of ship losses may have structural failure as a factor.

Clearly the regulatory regimes, the shipping industry practices, culture, commercial arrangements, the nature of ship owning and ship operating are all different from offshore but both the number of losses and the percentage attributable to structural failure seem high in the context of offshore experience and predicted risk levels such as in Tables 2 and 3 of Section 2.4. (Of course the offshore industry has also had its major disasters such as Piper Alpha so clearly all sectors have their problems).

3.4.3 Regulatory Requirements

The requirements of the different regulatory bodies in different areas is an extensive subject. The

Classification Societies however clearly have different requirements for ships and FPSOs. Some of these are detailed by Baunan (18). For instance for an FPSO hull structure, DNV rules have (in summary) the following requirements additional to shipping requirements:

− 20 year fatigue life;

− Global bending moments and shear forces to be based on 100 year return period;

− hull side to be capable of absorbing specified energy from supply vessel impact;

− turret structure to be based on the most unfavourable mooring induced forces;

− additional attention to structure detail to allow extended periods between docking.

For NPD (Norwegian Petroleum Directorate) there is a significant difference with regard to required approach that includes investigation of Ultimate Limit State (ULS), Fatigue Limit State (FLS), and Progressive Collapse Limit State (PLS).

From this it is clear that there are more stringent requirements for FPSOs than for ships but also that even for FPSOs, different bodies have different requirements.

3.4.4   Extreme Conditions

In Section 3.1 we referred to Hurricane Camille and postulated that the offshore design codes and practices had been modified to take account of such extremes.

On the other hand Hurricane Camille wave data is referred to by Buckley in 1978 on the shipping side (19) but Faulkner is still having to make a case for the new understanding to be included in ship design methodology.

He proposes (in his equation 4 and 6) that a "design abnormal wave height" should be used and a peak period where

$$H_d = 2.5\,H_s \qquad\qquad (6)$$

$$T = 3.2\,\sqrt{Hs} \qquad\qquad (7)$$

From Equation 1 and Table 1 in Section 2.3 and sections previous to this it can be seen that these proposals are very similar to offshore practice. From a philosophical point of view this is very gratifying since a merchant ship transiting through these regions may reasonably be expected to experience similar environmental conditions. It also seems reasonable that a vessel should be designed for environmental conditions that it may experience.

3.4.5   Inspection and Survey

Although not directly related to extreme conditions the differences in inspection and survey requirements for offshore structures and merchant shipping should be borne in mind. Fixed structures will remain on station for field life and be subject to an annual in-situ inspection programme. The through-life costs of such inspection and any repair work is one of the drivers to more reliable structures.

Merchant shipping on the other hand is subject to Classification Society port inspections and periodic surveys and there are greater opportunities for repair programmes if required. .

Drill rigs (which are generally classed) follow shipping practice. Production semisubmersibles and FPSO practices are closer to fixed structures again because of through life costs, resulting in a drive to more reliable structures and less tolerance of repairs.

3.4.6   Review

From the authors perspective as engineering practitioners the state of affairs seems to suggest a certain lack of consistency in the design approach to marine structures. As a body of Naval Architects or Structural Engineers it would clearly seem that we should be reviewing this situation.

We believe it would be useful to have a more scientific comparison across the Maritime industries of the reliability of the different structures and vessels and the risks to the people working on them.

3.5   MOTION RESPONSE IN WAVE GROUPS

Wave groups with particular characteristics which are not random are known to exist (as discussed above) so it will be important to know what the motion response in such groups might be, particularly if these represent extreme conditions. It has been previously proposed (20) that simplified conceptual wave groups could be used.

When looking at extreme heave motions for two examples this comparatively simple approach (although arguably not mathematically accurate) produced response ranging from about 10% less than to 15% greater than the expected frequency domain response amplitude operator solution.

These heave motion differences would also have a corresponding important effect on factors such as air gap or green-water on deck.

The wave groups considered were essentially sinusoidal but the approach could be modified to consider the type of extremely steep flat fronted waves illustrated by Faulkner.

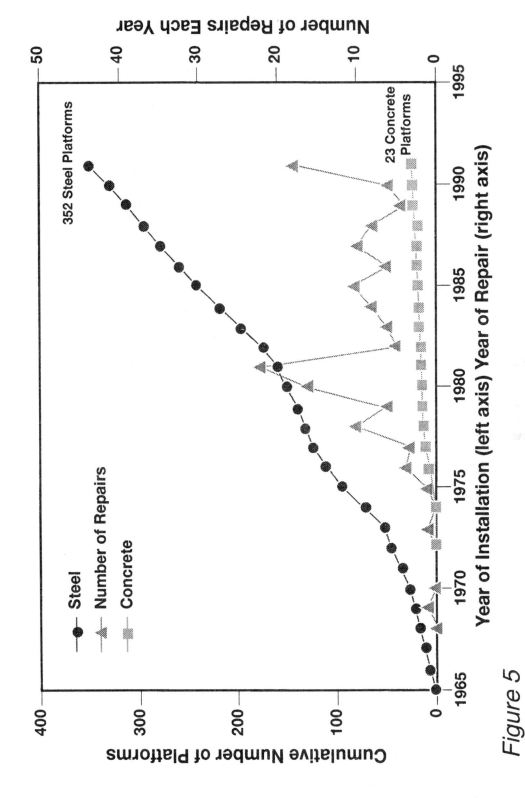

Figure 5

Cumulative Total of Platforms v Installation Year and Number of Repairs v Repair Year

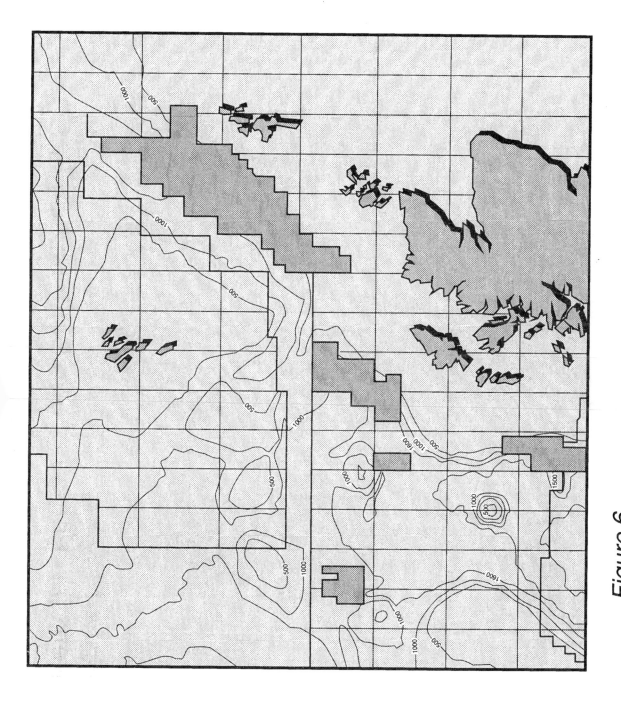

Figure 6
Atlantic Margin Deepwater Blocks

13

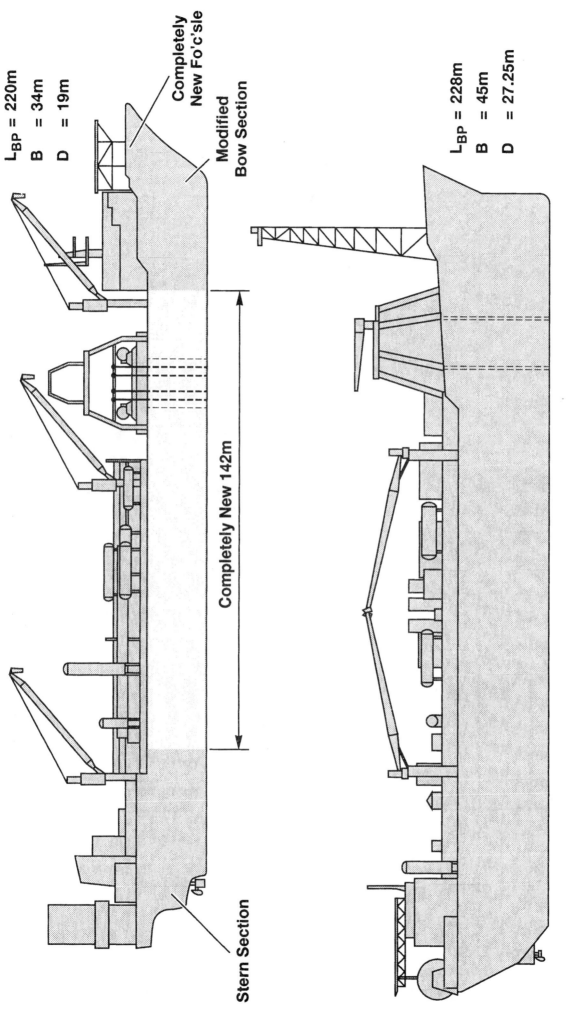

Completely New Fo'c'sle

Modified Bow Section

L_{BP} = 220m
B   = 34m
D   = 19m

Completely New 142m

Stern Section

L_{BP} = 228m
B   = 45m
D   = 27.25m

Figure 7
Petrojarl Foinaven and Schiehallion FPSOs

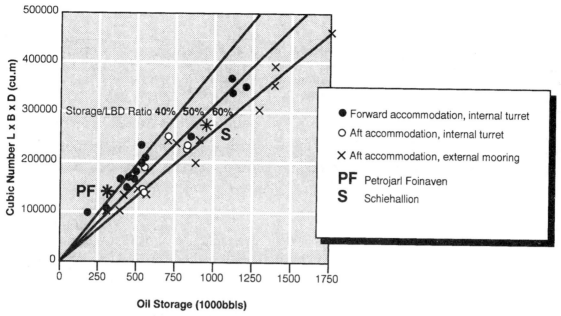

CUBIC NUMBER v OIL STORAGE

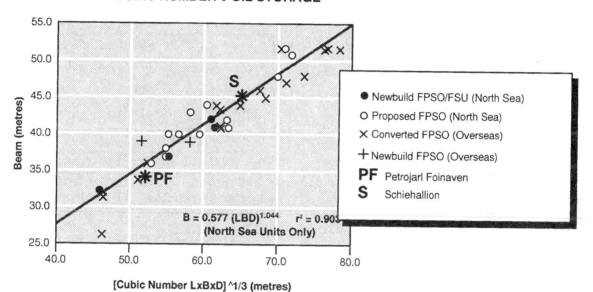

BEAM v CUBE ROOT OF CUBIC NUMBER

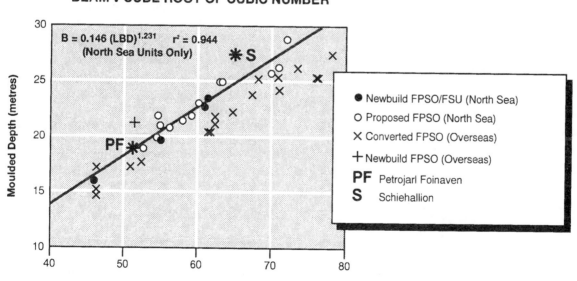

DEPTH v CUBE ROOT OF CUBIC NUMBER

Figure 8

Proportional Relationships

It can be said that the usual approach to extreme motions, loads, etc. is to first analyse and predict the environmental conditions and then to calculate the factor of interest (i.e. motion, load, green water, etc.) in those predicted conditions.

However one could also approach the problem from another angle. This is connected with the Safety Case type philosophy when we consider the effect of conditions more extreme than the design conditions.

Since we know something about the existence of wave groups and their effect but are aware that our knowledge is incomplete, it would seem to be well worthwhile to investigate a pragmatic approach in which the effect is calculated of a range of postulated wave groups with different characteristics which may exist but are not necessarily predicted by the current state of theoretical knowledge. This approach would essentially search out possible weaknesses or short comings of the design in question.

The likelihood of such an event may be extremely small (and probably unknown at this time) but if the level of the consequences are known then appropriate measures could be taken to manage the risks.

The next steps should be some academic work to investigate if there is any merit in such an approach.

4.0 FRONTIER AREAS; THE ATLANTIC MARGINS

4.1 METOCEAN CONDITIONS AND LOCATIONS

The metocean conditions associated with the Atlantic margins are extreme and illustrated in Fig. 3. Typically the maximum wave heights for design are well in excess of 30m. In addition the surface currents tend to be more extreme and the current profile is more severe with seabed currents around 1.15m/s and often in a different direction to the surface on mid-water currents.

The present development locations are West of Shetland in some 500m or so of water. However in the recent 17th licensing round further deep-water blocks were awarded in the Atlantic Margins. These are illustrated in Fig. 6 which shows that much of the acreage is over 1000m deep and extends to as deep as 2000m. It may be some years before reservoirs in such deep water extreme environments are developed but it is clearly the desire to do so.

It is important to note that development costs in such locations must be competitive with costs in more benign areas which clearly increases the challenge.

4.2 PRINCIPAL DIMENSIONS FOR FPSO's

In a previous publication (5) an extensive analysis was undertaken of a collection of basic design data for FPSOs worldwide. This included the proportional

relationships linking the four main ship dimensions of Length (L), Breadth (B), Depth (D), and Draught (T). Freeboard (F) was also discussed. This exercise looked at both conversions and purpose built units.

There is now data available for two FPSOs designed or selected for use in the extreme conditions West of Shetland and it is useful to see how these compare with previous practice to illustrate the evolution of new designs and practices.

The two units in question are the FPSOs for the Foinaven field and the Schiehallion field (21, 22, 23). The Schiehallion unit is a new build whilst the Foinaven unit (Petrojarl Foinaven) is best described as a hybrid in that it comprises the modified bow and stern from an existing ship with a new build hull in between. The principal dimensions are given in Table 4 below and the vessels are illustrated in Fig. 7.

TABLE 4 Principal Dimensions

	PETROJARL FOINAVEN	SCHIEHALLION
L_{BP}	220	228
B	34	45
D	19	27.25
T_{DESIGN}	13	20m
T_{OP}	-	16m

(It is interesting to note that the Petrojarl Foinaven hybrid is 4m broader than the original ship).

This data is plotted in Fig. 8 to compare with other FPSOs. Most obviously it can be seen that there is no real correlation between the two which is perhaps surprising considering their geographic proximity.

It can also be seen that neither unit is particularly large in comparison with the world fleet and the second point is that the hybrid approach has clearly affected the Petrojarl Foinaven's storage capacity.

Clearly for the Schiehallion unit which is purpose designed, the beam is not exceptional however the depth is significantly greater than the general data. The beam could have been expected to be larger since it should lead to a cost effective solution when there is no forward speed requirement. There may however be some limit or band when decreasing L/B will increase mooring costs disproportionately.

It should also be noted that the topsides equipment load at around 12000t on Schiehallion to cope with the production rate and other requirements is considerably greater than the 7000t or so that might be more general for production rates in the North Sea. (In the North Sea if you had such a large production rate then a fixed platform would generally be more attractive). This increased payload would also tend to suggest an increased beam.

The increased depth should also help to deal with high structural loads and give good fatigue performance.

The freeboard at the scantling draught is comparable with other FPSOs but at the quoted operating draught the freeboard is considerably increased.

Such a high operating freeboard should significantly reduce the probability of water on deck.

4.3 ALTERNATIVE DESIGNS FOR EXTREME ENVIRONMENTS

As discussed above the two units currently used or scheduled for production are FPSOs based on tanker concepts.

However in other deep-water areas increasing use is being made of concepts such as Tension Leg Platforms, SPARS, Compliant Towers etc. see Fig. 9. The reasons for selecting the different concepts are usually complex and subject to much study. Structural efficiency or motion response has a part to play but in many cases reservoir characteristics may dictate certain requirements such as surface Christmas Trees which would eliminate some of the options. Important parameters tend to be water depth and number of wells and some concepts are only attractive for fairly small ranges of these.

A major economic driver is the proximity or otherwise of existing export pipelines and other infrastructure in the area of a new field. This will determine the cost effectiveness of incorporating oil storage and determining the complexity of the topsides equipment to be incorporated.

4.4 OTHER CONSTRUCTION AND SUPPORT VESSELS

This paper has generally been concerned with FPSOs and semi-submersibles for drilling or production. However in order to develop fields in hostile regions it is also necessary to have a fleet of construction and support vessels which can cope with such conditions.

These vessels include heavy lift barges, pipelay vessels, anchor handlers, ROV support vessels, standby vessels, etc. (One notable difference related to the depth rather than the weather is that diving is not an option). In addition for off-loading and export a fleet of capable shuttle-tankers are likely to be required.

In particular it is necessary to be able to operate such vessels effectively and efficiently in conditions which might not be extreme in terms of survival but are certainly extreme in terms of operation. This will be a continuing challenge for vessel designers and project engineers alike.

5.0 MOORING RELATED CHALLENGES IN EXTREME ENVIRONMENTS

5.1 GENERAL

The present West of Shetland developments are located in areas of extreme environments with water depths of around 500m. This is clearly a considerable challenge both in terms of metocean conditions, see Fig. 2. and the water depth itself.

As exploration continues in the Atlantic Margin the water depths will become greater still and study work is now taking place for mooring in 1500m - 2000m and possibly deeper.

The challenges associated with deep water field development include a number of technical areas including drilling equipment and practices, mooring and riser design, conventional naval architecture and structural considerations, and a number of operational and logistics factors, many of which are outside the scope of this paper.

5.2 MOORING

As an example of the challenges, we present here some recent work for drilling in 580m though studies have also been performed to assess the feasibility of mooring in water depths up to 2000m. In order to moor in these water depths it has been necessary to establish the overall integrity of the mooring systems and also to ensure that the detailed design of the related equipment is appropriate.

Even for top range "Fourth Generation" drill-rigs the type of work needed to be done on equipment has included the following:-

- 8 new traction mooring winches with 300 tonnes pull and 650 tonne hold;

- buoyancy blisters for columns;

- buoyancy blisters for hulls;

- 8 new rope storage drums with a capacity each of 3500m of 92mm wire;

- modification to bolster arrangements.

These are illustrated in Fig. 10. In addition to these it has been necessary to conduct a range of modifications on the drilling related systems.

(One of the effects of these modifications combined with the increased riser requirements is the need to have a supply vessel permanently on station to assist with storage of equipment during riser handling operations).

With respect to overall mooring analysis, 50 year return period summer conditions (April - September) were used as summarised below.

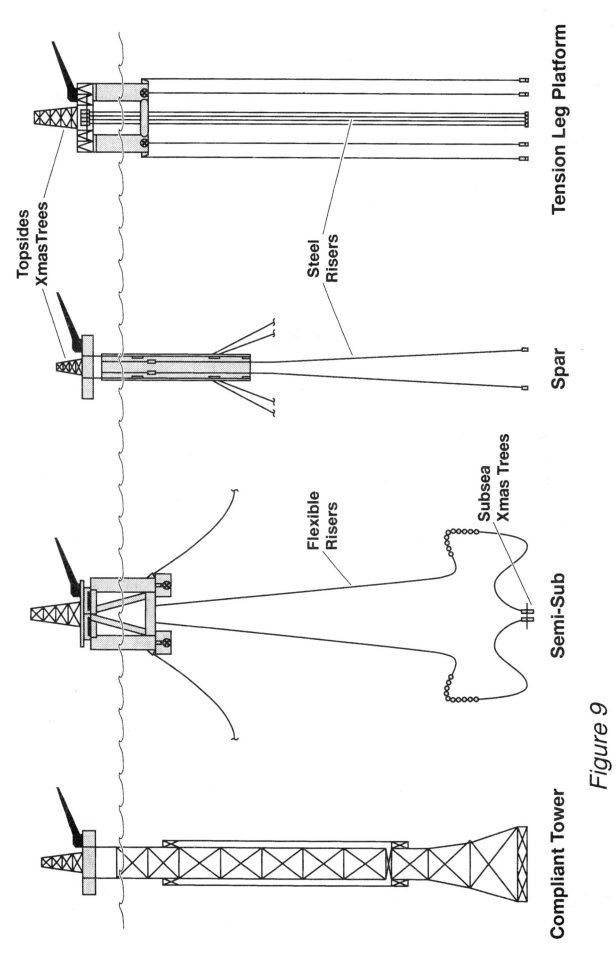

Figure 9

Some Alternative Deepwater Production Options

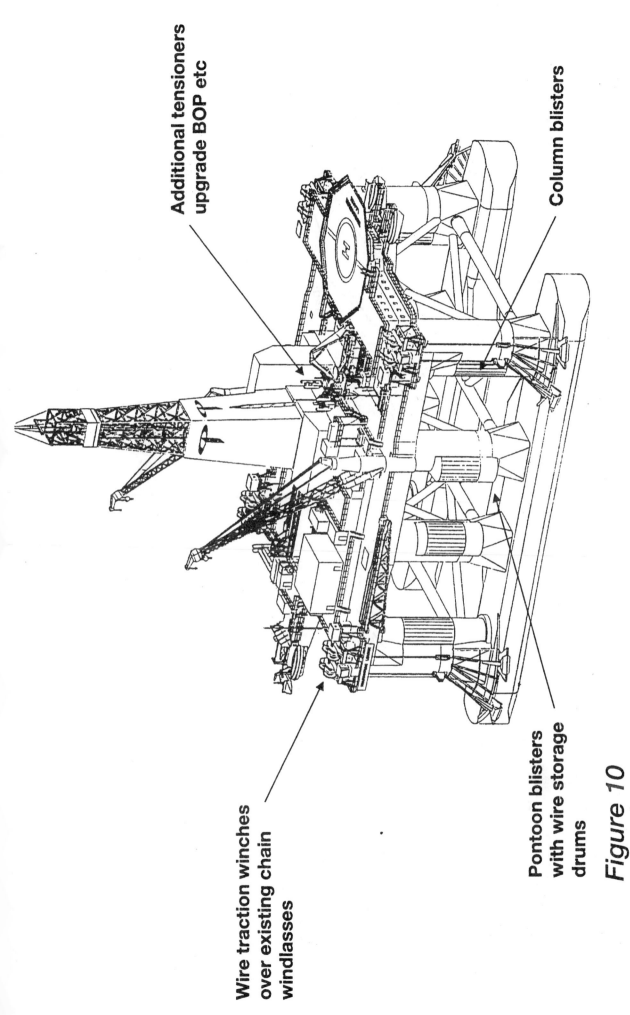

Additional tensioners
upgrade BOP etc

Column blisters

Wire traction winches
over existing chain
windlasses

Pontoon blisters
with wire storage
drums

Figure 10
Upgrade of Transocean Leader - Drydock Bergen : May/July 1997

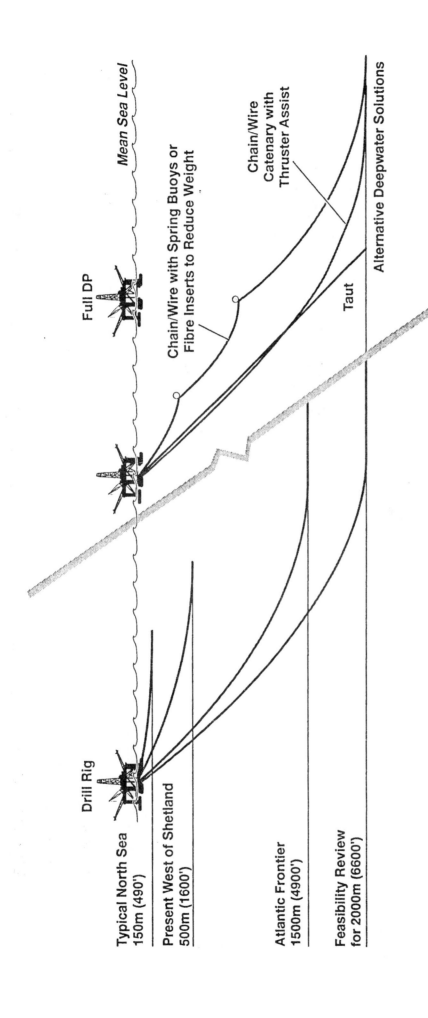

Mean Sea Level

Full DP

Chain/Wire with Spring Buoys or
Fibre Inserts to Reduce Weight

Chain/Wire
Catenary with
Thruster Assist

Taut

Alternative Deepwater Solutions

Drill Rig

Typical North Sea
150m (490')

Present West of Shetland
500m (1600')

Atlantic Frontier
1500m (4900')

Feasibility Review
for 2000m (6600')

Figure 11

Moorings for Deepwater Severe Environment

	Wind Speed (1 hour mean)	35.1m/s

Wind Speed (1 hour mean)   35.1m/s
Significant Wave Height, Hs   15.2m
Zero Crossing Period Tz   13.2s
Current at -10m   1.6m/s

The mooring spread layout consisted of 8 legs mixed wire/chain with a total length of   nearly 2 kilometres per

leg and 15t high holding power Bruce anchors. There are also four azimuthing thruster rated at 3500hp each (about 49t thrust) controlled by an automatic thruster assist system (ATA).

Further details of mooring system components are given below:

TABLE 5 Mooring Components

	Size/Grade	Length Out	MBL
Wire	92mm (6 x 48)	1500m	664t
Chain	84mm K4	1960m	737t

The code used was DnV Posmoor which has the following criteria for survival conditions:

TABLE 6 Survival Condition Criteria

Condition	Quasi-Static		Dynamic	
	Max Line Tension %MBL	Equivalent F of S	Max Line Tension %MBL	Equivalent F of S
Intact	55	1.80	67	1.5
Static Single Line Failure	80	1.25	91	1.1
Transient	19	1.1		1.0

The analysis showed that the mooring was feasible but in the survival conditions it was necessary to utilise full ATA thruster intervention and to utilise leeward line slackening in order to satisfy line tension criteria.

5.3   FUTURE ANALYSIS REFINEMENTS

If one considers mooring design and analysis as a branch of naval architecture or structural engineering then one of the obvious anachronisms is the characterisation of the strength of chain links by catalogue minimum breaking load (MBL). The environmental conditions, loads and motion responses are all analysed by sophisticated methods but we still use a comparatively crude 'MBL' for strength. In broad terms it is known that the actual breaking loads are higher than the MBL but the data available is comparatively limited (24, 25). Further work in this area would be a benefit.

5.4   ANCHOR HANDLING

The mooring problem is generally looked at by engineers from the point of view of maintaining the moored vessel on station. However in deep-water with severe environments it is also a challenge just being able to get the vessel moored in the first place.

In order to deploy anchors, pull out huge quantities of wires, and cope with the forces applied, anchor handling vessels need considerable bollard power, enormous winches, strengthened stern rollers, etc. In addition naval architects and shipowners developed new designs for deepwater work which tend to have greater beam to cope have with the forces on the stern and greater depth which helps ensure adequate immersion of propellers and side thrusters.

Some of the problems are described in articles in "Ship and Boat International" and the solutions are being developed by Contractors and Ship-Owners.

5.5   SOME FUTURE TRENDS

The mooring discussions above indicate that 'traditional' North Sea (and indeed world-wide) practices are being 'stretched' to meet the requirement of deep-water hostile environmental areas. However it is feasible that changed approaches might be more sensible.

An obvious area is the use of dynamic positioning. The current semi-submersible drill rig fleet is not generally equipped to provide this capability although there are DP (Dynamic Positioning) drill ships.

Another possibility is that drill-rig moorings may be pre-laid. This would allow the best use of good weather windows and avoid the requirement for the drill-rig to store huge quantities of wire and chain whilst in transit.

Other major trends are illustrated in Fig. 11 and include the use of:

- underwater spring buoys;
- synthetic mooring lines;
- suction anchors on vertically loaded anchors.

An 'ultra-deepwater drilling rig' has recently been ordered which will reportedly have a variable deck-load of 6000 tonnes and be capable of operating in water depth down to 8000 ft (26).

5.6 MOORING FOR FLOATING PRODUCTION UNITS

The sections above deal primarily with the mooring of drill-rigs. However the same sort of considerations will apply for more permanent floating production units (whether they be semi-subs, FPSO's, Spars, etc.)

5.7 COMBINED MOORING AND RISER DESIGN

In floating production field developments which include catenary moorings and flexible production riser systems it has been conventional practice to design the moorings and risers as separate systems but with a common interface in that the moorings allow a certain set of excursions whilst the risers have to be able to cope with the same excursions. There is a good track-record and experience of such designs (27, 28, 29).

In some conditions the wave and current forces on the risers lead to larger vessel excursions whilst in other conditions they can restrain the vessel excursions.

In a preliminary study it was shown that there was potential advantage in combining the mooring and riser design so that the whole system could be optimised. This has now been taken forward into a joint industry project.

5.8 VORTEX INDUCED VIBRATIONS

Another aspect which is important for drilling riser design in regions of high currents is vortex induced vibrations, (30). On the design side this can be overcome by the use of fairings. However this has fairly severe operational penalties because of the deck space required to accommodate the fairings and the time necessary to mount and remove the units during running and pulling the riser.

5.9 STEEL CATENARY RISERS

In the North Sea floating production units typically utilise riser systems comprised of flexible pipe. (These have superseded previous tensioned rigid riser designs).

In the Gulf of Mexico steel catenary risers are now being used in association with Compliant Towers. This is also likely to be an attractive option in areas such as the Atlantic Margins but, as for other systems, will require extensive design and analysis effort.

6.0 CONCLUSIONS

The paper has presented a collection of practices for extreme conditions and the type of oil and gas facilities used in those conditions form the early days of North Sea production through to current plans for oil development in the Atlantic Margins. Some differences between offshore and marine practices have been discussed and a number of suggestions have been made as summarised below:-

- existing offshore structure design codes lead to highly reliable platforms but better understanding of the extreme wave environment and the associated loading and response would lead to more cost-effective structures;

- it would be beneficial to investigate the overall reliability of FPSO structures and compare the results with fixed structures;

- the differences between maritime and offshore practices should be reviewed to investigate the possibilities of a rational comparison of the approaches to the different structures and vessels and risks to the people working on them;

- the motions and structural response in wave groups should be investigated further.

On a general point there is obviously a continuing challenge to design and operate a range of vessels for extreme environmental conditions and more design and engineering input will be required for a large number of years to come.

7.0 ACKNOWLEDGEMENTS

The authors would like to acknowledge all their colleagues and thank them for their help in preparing the paper and their participation in the various projects, spanning over ten years, which formed the foundations for this paper.

We would also like to thank Amerada Hess Ltd for permission to publish this paper and also the various Partners who helped make the projects possible. The opinions expressed are solely those of the authors' and not of any other body or company.

REFERENCES

1. METHVEN J O: 'The Argyll Field Life Cycle with Cost Control as the Operators Ethos' SPE 26690, Offshore Europe, Aberdeen 1993.

2. 'Offshore Installations: Guidance on Design, Construction and Certification'. Dept of Energy, Fourth Edition 1990, HSE Amendment 1995, HMSO.

3. 'Recommended Practice for Planning, Designing and Constructing Fixed Platforms - Load and Resistance Factor Design', API RP2A - LRFD, American Petroleum Institute, Washington 1993.

4. CULLEN, The Hon Lord: 'The Public Inquiry into the Piper Alpha Disaster', HMSO, London 1990.

5. MACGREGOR J R & SMITH S N: 'Some Techno-Economic Considerations in the Design of North Sea Production Monohulls'. Offshore '94, I Mar E/RINA, London, February 1994.

6. VAN VOORST O, DE BAAN J, VAN LOENHOUT A, KREKEL M: 'Conversion of Existing Tanker to North Sea FPSO Use', OTC 7724, Offshore Technology Conference, Houston, May 1995.

7. VAN BERKEL P: 'Managing Design and Construction of a Central North Sea FPSO', OTC 8074, Offshore Technology Conference, Houston 1996.

8. 'Review of Repairs to Offshore Structures and Pipelines', Marine Technology Directorate (MTD) Publication 94/102.

9. EFTHYMIOU M, VAN DE GRAAF J W, TROMANS P S: 'Reliability Based Criteria for Fixed Steel Offshore Platforms', OMAE, 1996.

10. VAN VOORST O: 'Operational Experience of FPSO Uisge Gorm', OTC 8071, Offshore Technology Conference Houston 1996.

11. 'Amerada's Hudson Turns Corner on UK subsea cost-efficiency', Offshore, April 1995.

12. 'Quick Return Blenheim', Offshore Engineer, May 1995.

13. 'Fife Conversion Enters Final Phase', Offshore Engineer April 1995.

14. BUCHNER B: 'The Influence of the Bow Shape of FPSOs on Drift Forces and Green Water', OTC 8073, Offshore Technology Conference, Houston 1996.

15. SKOURUP J, HANSEN N E O & ANDREASEN K K: 'Non-Gaussian Extreme Waves in the Central North Sea', OMAE 1996.

16. KJELDSEN S P: 'Dangerous Wave Groups', Norwegian Maritime Research, No. 2, 1984.

17. FAULKNER D, WILLIAMS R A: 'Design for Abnormal Ocean Waves', RINA Spring Meeting 1996.

18. BAUNAN T: 'FPSOs Fulfilling Shelf Requirement by the Maritime Approach', OTC 8259, Offshore Technology Conference, Houston 1996.

19. BUCKLEY W H: 'Hull Girder Structural Design - The Case for New Loading Conditions for Extreme Waves', Naval Engineers Journal, February 1978.

20. SMITH S N & ATLER M: 'On the Large Amplitude and Extreme Motions of Floating Vessels', BOSS '82 Poster Session, Massachusetts, 1982.

21. 'World's largest FPSO for Schiehallion Field', The Naval Architect, September 1996.

22. KENISON R C & HUNT C V: 'Why FPSOs for the Atlantic Frontier', OTC 8032, Offshore Technology Conference, Houston 1996.

23. LEGHORN J, BROOKES D A & SHEARMAN M G: 'The Foinaven and Schiehallion Developments', OTC 8033, Offshore Technology Conference, Houston 1996.

24. MACGREGOR J R, SMITH & PATON J E: 'Performance and Testing of Components of the Ivanhoe/Rob Roy Floating Production System Mooring', OTC 7492, Offshore Technology Conference, Houston 1994.

25. CASEY, N F & SMITH S N: 'The Evaluation of Mooring Chains Removed from AH001 Production Facility', To be published.

26. Press & Journal, 21st July 1997.

27. SMITH S N, FRASER W J, & PATON J E: 'Flexible Riser Systems: Overview of an Operator's Experience', Advances in Riser Technologies, IBC, Aberdeen, June 1996.

28. SMITH S N, FRASER W J & ALLAN P D: 'Installation and Changeout of the Ivanhoe/Rob Roy Flexible Riser System', Offshore 93 I Mar E/RINA, London February 1993.

29. SMITH S N: 'Four Years Subsea and Marine Experience with the Ivanhoe/Rob Roy Development', SPE 26686, Offshore Europe, Aberdeen 1993.

30. VANDIVER, J K: 'Vortex-Induced Vibration of Risers', Advances in Riser Technologies, IBC, Aberdeen, June 1996.

PAPER NO.11

EMERALD FIELD FSU LONGITUDINAL STRENGTH ASSESSMENT

by C A Singer, Reading & Bates, UK

Paper presented at the

International Conference

DESIGN AND OPERATION FOR ABNORMAL CONDITIONS

21 22 OCTOBER 1997 GLASGOW

EMERALD FIELD FSU LONGITUDINAL STRENGTH ASSESSMENT

C.A.Singer, Reading and Bates, UK

SUMMARY

The Emerald Field FSU was installed on location, 75 miles East of the Shetland Islands, in November 1991. By the summer of 1993 some 50-60 side shell longitudinal failures had occurred. The rate of failure continued over the next two years resulting in prolonged periods of repairs. As a result an assessment of the longitudinal strength of the vessel was commissioned to evaluate the FSU for continued operation in the North Sea and to gain a better understanding of the type and rate of the damage being experienced.

The assessment took the form of several analyses of the contributory factors affecting the longitudinal bending of the vessel while on location. These included the wave bending moments, effects of green seas and the effect of the mooring system.

A comparison with the class rule requirements was also undertaken to try to draw conclusions as to the applicability of these for this type of application where a trading tanker is converted to a FSU or FPSO.

AUTHOR'S BIOGRAPHY

Mr Alistair Singer, CEng, MRINA has worked in the offshore industry for the last eleven years with both drilling contractors and a field operator. He was responsible for the structures of both Emerald Field facilities during the life of the field while with Midland and Scottish Resources. He is presently employed with Reading and Bates (UK).

1.0   INTRODUCTION

The number of small marginal oil fields which are becoming economical to develop through stable oil prices and through improved technology is on the increase. One of the preferred options for development of these marginal fields is the FPSO (Floating Production, Storage and Offloading) type solution. The FPSO based solution for the smaller field has several benefits over the other development methods, i.e. jackets. These include cost, schedule and future value. Then the field becomes more attractive.

Converting an existing tanker reduces the time before first oil and therefore the return on the investment, and already has many of the systems required for the task. With the addition of the production plant on deck, import system, offloading systems, safety systems and a mooring system the vessel can be ready for installation on the field relatively quickly.

New build units are generally only considered for relatively long field lives, of the order of 10-20 years and for deeper water where conventional development methods are not feasible.

As a result of the boom in floating production solutions for developing smaller oil fields it is found that the age of the FPSO fleet is increasing. The average age of FPSO's in 1975-80 was 13 years, a few years ago the average age was more than 22 years which shows a

trend towards converting existing tanker tonnage into both FPSO's and FSU's (Floating Storage Units) rather than investing in specially built tonnage. The age of the fleet is governed by the age of the available tanker tonnage that is offered at an economical attractive price. (Ref. 1)

As these vessels are deployed in more harsh environments the basis of design of the hull is required to be investigated more closely, the operating philosophy for the vessel and its limitation need to be examined to ensure that the vessel is fit for the purpose intended.

Production facilities for the UK sector of the North Sea were designed in compliance with SI 289 until recently. These regulations set out the minimum environmental criteria to which all facilities should be designed. As a minimum a 50 year return period storm is to be taken into consideration, but normally designers and operators have been using the 100 year return storm for production facilities which are intended to stay on location for a longer period.

For trading tankers the main environmental design criteria of the main structure is the 'Standard Static Wave' from which the rule wave bending moment is derived. This is done by balancing the ship on wave equal in length to the length of the ship (L) and with a height equal to L/20 or $1.1 \sqrt{L}$ (ft). This method of calculating the bending moments has been developed on a trial and error basis over many years of ship operation and proved to be acceptable. However, is this applicable only for ships intended for similar types of operation?

FPSO technology is relatively young and the level of operational experience gained low, the loading exerted by the sea on the hull is mostly vertical bending of the hull girder resulting in alternating compressive and tensile stresses in the deck and bottom structure which if not kept within allowable limits will result in buckling, fracture and fatigue damage.

This paper talks only of the Emerald Field FSU and the longitudinal strength assessment that was undertaken as a result of defects discovered during its operational life and draws conclusions as to the suitability of this vessel for the FSU type of operation.

2.0   EMERALD FIELD FSU

2.1   DESCRIPTION

The Emerald field FSU, (Fig. 2) was originally built in Germany in 1974 under Germanischer Lloyd Class.

The vessel had the following main particulars.

Lbp	-	310m
B	-	49m
D	-	26m
DW	-	240,000 tonnes

She was a standard design single skin VLCC and spent a large proportion of her life in lay-up both in Scotland and in Continental Europe. The majority of her trading was carried out between the Red Sea and Europe.

As part of the conversion scope the hull was shortened by 25m, the bulbous bow removed and the bow modified to accommodate the mooring system, otherwise no other major structural modifications were carried out. The special survey was completed and the vessel was installed on location some 75 miles East of the Shetlands in November 1991. (Fig.1)

2.2   VESSEL OPERATION

The FSU was designed to remain on location for a period of 10 years without drydocking. It was permanently moored to a Tripod Mooring System (TMS) approximately 2.5km from the FPF. Oil was pumped to the FSU from the production vessel via a 10" subsea pipeline, through the mooring system which was fitted with swivels and into a reception tank, no. 2 centre tank.

The reception tank was designed to be kept at a relatively constant level and act as a separator tank with a low and high suction to allow the separation of emulsion and water from the oil. The low suction to remove water and emulsion to the slop tanks for further treatment prior to being discharged overboard at maximum 40ppm, the high suction was used to transfer the oil to the storage tanks.

The arrangement of the tanks can be seen in Fig 2. Number 2 centre was the reception tank, tanks 1,4 and 5 centre along with number 2 wing tanks being the oil storage tanks. Numbers 1,4, and 5 wing tanks were ballast tanks. At intervals, a shuttle tanker would arrive to the stern of the vessel and an export line attached.

The crude was then pumped from the storage tanks by the cargo export pumps via a metering skid to the shuttle tanker.

The vessel was restricted in draft, both minimum and maximum, leaving an operational range of around 2m. This was due to the survival capabilities of the mooring system. As a result, during oil import into the cargo tanks, ballast was necessarily discharged to maintain the vessel within its draft limits. This resulted in the wing tanks being partially filled or empty for longer periods. Conversely during offloading of the oil to a shuttle tanker the ballast tanks were filled to compensate.

During the summer months the vessel was deballasted beyond the minimum draft to allow the necessary inspections to be carried out. The vessel remained on a Continuous Hull Survey (CSH) system resulting in the inspection of the structure on a rotational basis over a five year period.

The ballast tanks were subjected to a more frequent and rigorous inspection scheme due to the absence of a complete coating system and due to the fact that they were all wing tanks and as such were subject to greater fatigue damage, particularly in way of the side shell longitudinal connections to the transverse web frames and bulkheads.

2.3   DEFECTS DISCOVERED

During the scheduled inspections of the ballast wing tanks defects were discovered . The types of defect were in themselves not a great surprise, but the extent of the defects were. In the time between the installation of the FSU in November 1991 and the summer of 1993 some 50-60 cracks were found in way of the side shell longitudinal connections to the transverse web frames and bulkheads.

The general location of the defects were as expected from the fatigue analysis carried out prior to the conversion. However the type of crack expected were in the brackets at the connections and not necessarily in the longitudinals themselves. Generally the defects found were all through thickness failures of the longitudinals adjacent to the web frame and bulkhead connection. The majority of the cracks were concentrated at the wash-bulkheads at the mid length of the tanks.

In one case in tank number 5 port, 11 consecutive longitudinal had failed at one frame, this being 42% of the total longitudinals. In some cases the longitudinal had failed in two locations within 5m of each other. Some of the defects were removed whole so that detailed analysis could be undertaken to ascertain the exact cause of the failures.

As would be expected the analysis showed that the cracks were fatigue related, initiated by multiple stress raisers at the toe of the rolled section longitudinal. The cracks grew until total failure of the stiffener was inevitable.

The majority of the cracks were found in a belt equal to about half of the ships depth with an upper boundary at or around the ships operating draft. These cracks could be explained by fatigue loading on the side shell dominated by the effect of varying pressure as waves passed the hull. However there were some defects which did not so easily fall into this category being either too close to the deck or to the bottom of the ship. In some cases cracks were found in the high tensile steel longitudinals within 2m of the tank bottom.

The defects were repaired following the recommendations set out in the 'Guidance Manual for the Inspection and Condition Assessment of Tanker Structures' (Ref. 4) using high tensile steel.

The defects within the expected band, though the reason for the cracks appearing were easily explained, the rate at which they appeared was not expected. In addition the cracks found above and below the expected mid-depth range would tend to indicate that the longitudinal bending stresses and the associated fatigue may be greater than expected.. It was therefore decided to investigate further by undertaking a dynamic analysis of the hull specifically for the Emerald Field Location. BAeSEMA were commissioned by Midland and Scottish Resources to do the analysis. (Ref. 2)

2.4   SIDE SHELL FATIGUE

A fatigue analysis was performed (Ref. 3), prior to conversion, of the side shell connections for the effects of fluctuating wave loading on the side shell. the analysis was performed for connections with and without gussets.

The results showed that the side shell connection details would be susceptible to fatigue crack propagation over the full length and depth of the vessel and up to a level of approximately 6m below the deck.

The crack propagation rates were seen to be sensitive to assumptions of residual stress within details of the connection and to whether the wing tanks were full or empty. The relative fatigue damage for residual stresses of O N/mm², 25 N/mm² and 50 N/mm² and for empty and full tanks against location from the waterline are shown in Figs 3,4 and 5.

As can be seen the static stresses within the side shell connections will have an effect on the fatigue lives. This effect cannot be precisely quantified as part of this stress is due to residual stresses associated with the welding process which is procedure dependant. It does show, however, that the tank contents do have a bearing on the fatigue life of the connections, and that these connections will last longer should the tanks remain empty whenever possible. With the tanks full, the fatigue damage is not sensitive to the varying levels

of residual stress. With the mid range residual stress of 25 N/mm² the fatigue damage is considerably reduced from a level of 4m below the waterline with an empty tank. With no residual stress within the connection details there is no fatigue damage with an empty tank.

2.5   LONGITUDINAL STRENGTH ASSESSMENT

Due to the nature of the discovered defects and the rate at which they appeared, especially in the lower regions of the hull, a preliminary review of the wave statistics for the Emerald Field Location together with recorded data from the vessel, suggested that the vessel may be experiencing wave systems greater than the design wave for the vessel.

Although the defects themselves were not a cause for great concern , a programme of inspection and repair/replacement was in place to ensure the continued integrity of the vessel, there was however a need to understand the exact cause for the cracks, whether the vessel was being operated within allowable limits for bending and shear and what the vessels remaining operational life was.

To this end a Longitudinal Strength Assessment was undertaken, (2) to clarify the above points. The analysis completed in order to understand the overall hull girder response of the FSU on the Emerald Field Location. This was achieved by carrying out a longitudinal assessment of the ship using the site specific environmental conditions together with worst case loading conditions recorded during the operation of the FSU.

Other factors, and their influence in the overall stress distributions for the ship, which were taken into account, were the effects of green seas, the effects of the mooring system and torsional loading due to the asymmetrical loading conditions encountered during the extended periods of repair and inspection.

The dynamic analysis was under taken to ascertain the expected bending moments for the site specific environmental conditions for the two worst case loading conditions. The loading conditions were taken from the loadmaster test conditions, i.e. one for maximum still water shear force and the other for maximum still water bending moment.

Four sets of environmental conditions were used for the motions and sea loads analysis. These sets of data are summarised in Table 2.5.1. below. These were the 1 year storm condition, the 10 year storm condition, the 50 year storm condition and 100 year storm conditions as complied by Marex for the Emerald Field. The data was based on measurements from Statfjord made over a five year period. The results were compared with the Stevenson data which showed a reasonable agreement between the two sets of data, although the Statfjord data showed shorter periods as would be expected as

Statfjord is further east. The analysis was carried out for three wave headings, bow on, 15° and 30° off the bow.

This was done as it was found that the FSU rarely lay head to the waves due to the currents.

The scantlings used for the analysis were taken from a thickness survey of the vessel carried out in 1992 and allowed, conservatively, for the worst level of corrosion throughout the length of the vessel.

TABLE 2.5.1

Emerald Field Environmental Data

	Return period			
	1 year	10 year	50 year	100 year
10 min mean wind (m/s)	33.4	37.5	40.0	41.0
1 hour mean wind (m/s)	30.6	34.3	36.6	37.5
Sig wave height Hs (m)	11.4	13.3	14.6	15.2
Zero crossing period- Tz (s)	11.5	12.4	13.0	13.2
Max height- Hmax (m)	21.1	24.5	26.8	27.8
Max period- Tmax (s)	14.7	15.8	16.6	16.9
Range of Tmax (s)	13.1-16.3	14.1-17.6	14.8-18.4	15.1-18.8

The maximum wave rule bending moment was calculated to the requirements of Lloyd's Register of Shipping Rules and Regulations for the Classification of Ships 1995, Part 3 Chapter 4.

This was calculated for the shortened vessel, i.e. 25m shorter than originally, giving greater allowable sagging and hogging wave bending moments that would have been calculated for the original vessel. The maximum rule wave bending moment for the vessel in its shortened state was calculated to be:

Sagging   727,217 tonne-metres
Hogging   679,104 tonne-metres

The maximum expected wave bending moments as derived using strip theory were as shown in Table 2.5.2. below for the two loading conditions and for each environmental condition. These are shown in Figs. 6 and 7.

TABLE 2.5.2

Maximum Expected Wave Bending Moments

	Maximum Expected Wave Bending Moment (tm)	
	Condition 1	Condition 2
1 year storm	686,132	610,864
10 year storm	770,858	683,555
50 year storm	792,835	702,079
100 year storm	810,485	717,270

The rule wave bending moment used here is different from that approved for the vessel due to the recent changes in the formulation of the rules following research into the non-linearities between hogging and sagging bending moments.

As can be seen, the maximum expected bending moment in one year return storm does not exceed the rule wave bending moment.

The maximum expected wave bending moment in the 10 year return storm marginally exceeds the rule wave bending moment.

For both the 50 and 100 year return storms, the maximum expected wave bending moment exceeds the rule wave bending moment.

However, exceeding the rule wave bending moment is not necessarily detrimental to the structural integrity of the vessel as it is the combined bending moments due to both the wave bending moment and the still water bending moment which are important.

The still water bending moments were taken from the FSU's 'Shipmaster' test conditions one which was for maximum bending moment, and the second for maximum shear force.

The combined total bending moments are calculated, noted that the maximum wave bending moment and maximum still water bending moment are not coincident in these cases shown in the Table 2.5.3 below for both test loading conditions, i.e. for max BM and for max SF.

TABLE 2.5.3

Maximum Combined Bending Moments

	Condition 1	Condition 2
	Bending Moment (tm)	Bending Moment (tm)
1 year storm	-980,528	971,601
10 year storm	-1,052,956	1,030,587
50 year storm	-1,072,438	1,046,290
100 year storm	-1,087,775	1,060,090

Dividing these total moments with the calculated section modules of the vessel produces the maximum bending stresses in the deck and bottom plating. The stresses are shown in Table 2.5.4. below.

The scantlings used for the calculation of the section modules were the corroded scantlings as measured during survey and not the original.

This was done to ascertain the remaining strength of the vessel.

TABLE 2.5.4

Maximum Expected Combined Bending Stresses

	Condition 1	Condition 2
	Bending stress (N/mm^2)	Bending stress (N/mm^2)
1 year storm	171	170
10 year storm	184	180
50 year storm	187	183
100 year storm	190	185

These maximum expected bending stresses are shown in Table below.

In all cases the stress is less than the maximum allowable combined bending stress for higher tensile steel of 254 N/mm^2.

The analysis was only carried out for the two given test loading conditions, where the maximum wave bending moment as calculated and the maximum still water bending moment were not coincidental.

It was therefore decided that a check should be done for a case where the maximum allowable still water bending moment and the calculated maximum wave bending moment were coincident.

The maximum still water bending moment as approved by Class for the vessel was 557,000 tonne metres, the results were shown in Table 2.5.5. below.

TABLE 2.5.5

Maximum Combined Bending Stresses

	Bending stress (N/mm^2)
1 year storm	198
10 year storm	211
50 year storm	215
100 year storm	217

In all cases the calculated maximum bending stresses are within allowable limits.

2.6   BUCKLING STRENGTH

Utilising the results from the dynamic analysis four areas were investigated in order to calculate the factors of safety against buckling. These were:

- Deck Plating.
- Bottom Shell Plating.
- Longitudinal bulkhead lower stroke.
- Under Deck centreline Girder.

The results showed that the underdeck centreline girder to have a factor of safety of only 1.01 in the 50 year storm condition using the maximum combined bending moments.

The recommended minimum factor of safety is 1.1. the centre line girder did not therefore satisfy class requirements.

2.7   BENDING MOMENTS DUE TO GREEN SEAS

An assessment of the effect of green seas on the longitudinal strength of the hull was also undertaken. The maximum expected relative motions of the bow in a 50 year storm condition was used for the wave loading.

The vessel, at the point where green water is on deck, is sitting in the trough of the wave and the bow is rising through the wave. The effect on the combined bending moments experienced by the vessel by the green seas is to reduce them. This is because the loading due to the green sea creates a hogging moment while the ship, being in the trough of the wave, is in a sagging condition.

In addition to the impulse load of the green sea there is a transient vibration response of the hull girder. The resulting bending moments, due to this relatively high frequency response, are additive to the wave bending moment.

The bending moment distribution from the effect of the green sea loading and due to the resultant transient vibration are shown in Figs. 8 and 9 respectively. It can be seen that the maximum hogging moment occurs at approximately 100m aft of the FP and the maximum vibration moment at approximately 137m aft of the FP.

The maximum bending moments due to green seas are as follows:

- Hogging moment - 360,856 tonne-metres.
- Vibration bending moment - 150,866 tonne-metres.

2.8   MOORING LOADS

In the foregoing analyses, the effect of the mooring loads have been taken into account by including them in the weight distribution while modelling the vessel and therefore, the bending moments resulting from the mooring loads are included in the maximum bending moments calculated in the dynamic analysis.

In order to separate this bending moment from the overall combined bending moment an additional analysis was carried out. Two load cases were investigated, one for the normal mooring loads and the other for the extreme condition. As would be expected, the extreme load condition resulted in the higher bending moment.

Therefore a mooring load of 2110 tonnes applied at the FP will result in a bending moment of 100,204 tonne-metres. As this load can only be applied in the downwards direction, due to the mooring system configuration, this results in a hogging moment only. The distribution of this bending moment is shown in Fig. 10.

The contribution to the overall bending moment due to the effect of the mooring system is only 8.1% for the extreme loading case. As this is a pure hogging moment it reduces the loading for the worst case sagging condition.

2.9   TORSIONAL LOADING

Due to the prolonged periods of inspection and repair found necessary during the summer months some heavily asymmetric loading conditions were experienced.

These became necessary so that oil could continue to be imported and that the vessel could be retained at as deep a draft as possible. It was therefore decided that the effect of this torsional load on the vessel should be investigated further. The analysis was done using the 1 year return environmental conditions as this tended to be done only between April and September.

The results of the analysis showed that the maximum shear stresses due to combined wave bending and torsion for both the longitudinal bulkhead and the shell were well within the Lloyds allowable shear stress for mild steel.

The same conclusion was arrived at for combined bending and torsion.

2.10   SHEAR STRENGTH

To check the shear strength of the FSU, the worst case shear force was calculated by using the absolute values of shear force due to the 100 year condition calculated in the dynamic analysis, the shear force from the loading condition 1 for maximum shear and from the green sea analysis. The shear stress was checked against Lloyds requirements and found to fall short over a considerable section of the longitudinal bulkhead. The calculated shear stresses can be seen in Table 2.10.1. below.

TABLE 2.10.1

Maximum Shear Stress in Longitudinal Bulkhead

	Condition 1 (N/mm^2)	Condition 2 (N/mm^2)
Frame 104	159.8	150.0
Frame 89	159.7	141.8

The combined bending and shear strength was then checked to see if the requirements of Lloyds could be met for combined stress. Here it was found that this also was exceeded. The level of combined stress in fact exceeded yield, therefore the buckling characteristics of the longitudinal bulkhead were checked and a factor of safety of only 0.69 calculated. It is therefore theoretically possible for the longitudinal bulkhead to buckle in the 100 year storm condition.

3.0   DISCUSSION AND CONCLUSION

The analysis described previously was initiated to confirm, or otherwise, that the Emerald Field FSU was fit for purpose and could remain on location for the duration of the field life. As such the analysis was carried out so that the results were to be conservative, thus some of the assumptions used in the assessment are also conservative. This was done to give the worst case picture with which to make a judgement on the actions which may be required to maintain the vessel in operation. The scope of the assessment also included a comparison between the class rule requirements for the ship and the calculated stresses from the analysis. Furthermore the original fatigue assessment was looked at to make conclusions as to the unexpected rate of failure of the side shell longitudinals.

The conclusion of the assessment for the Emerald Field FSU was that, although she did not meet the class requirements for the rule wave bending moment she was within the overall longitudinal bending stress limits and as such did not have an overall longitudinal strength problem. However, the stress range calculated was greater than would have been expected thus increasing fatigue damage in the deck and bottom areas of the hull. It should be remembered that had the vessel not been shortened the stress levels calculated would have been greater and possibly exceeded the allowable limits.

The mooring system contribution reduced the worst case sagging moments due to the configuration and behaviour of the system. Its contribution to the combined bending stress was between 5.2% and 8.1%.

The bending moment due to green seas was calculated to increase the overall bending stresses by between 12.2% to 15.5%. This is a relatively infrequent occurrence and the assumed wave height was conservative and therefore not considered critical to the vessel operation.

From the assessment, two main points of potential failure were identified. These were the under deck centreline girder and the longitudinal bulkhead structure. The centreline girder failed, due to buckling in the sagging condition. This was based on the worst case scantlings from the thickness survey and therefore was limited in extent. The alternatives for continued operation were: increased inspection, modification of the weakest areas or reduced operating stresses.

For the longitudinal bulkhead the failure mode was due to insufficient shear capacity. This again was based on the worst case scantlings, but showed that the bulkhead was overstressed over the majority of its height. Again the alternatives for continued operation were: increased inspection, modification or reduced operating conditions.

Neither of the above failures were of a catastrophic nature for the vessel integrity, but would certainly have been catastrophic for the viability of the field.

In reality the outcome would be a combination of all three options, with limited modification as operations would allow together with increased inspection of the most vulnerable areas and the reduction of the allowable still water bending moments during the import/export cycle.

The opportunity to reduce the SWBM for the FSU were limited due to the operating limitations imposed by the mooring system, the configuration of the vessel and the nature of the imported oil. The main consequence of which resulted in the vessel being operated to the SF and BM limits especially after cargo export.

With regard to fatigue, the assessment identified the stress range experienced by the vessel to be greater than expected, either by the rules or by the first fatigue analysis. Assuming that the rule wave bending moment will not be exceeded in a 50 year return period storm can underestimate the bending moments. This would result in an underestimate of the bending moment per unit wave height of around 50%. The difference between the dynamic analysis and the rule bending moment per unit wave height was only 7%. The fatigue life of a detail is proportional to the cube of the stress range and to the number of cycles. It is therefore concluded that the fatigue damage is not solely due to increased stress as a result of the severity of the environment.

The extent of fatigue damage is probably more attributable to the extent of exposure to the cyclic forces rather than the increase of stress range. Though for the Emerald Field location the choice of wave data does have a bearing, in particular. The relationship between the peak of the wave distribution to the peak of the bending moment transfer function. The closer the peaks are the higher the fatigue damage is likely to be, therefore using Stevenson Station data could result in lower fatigue lives compared with Statfjord data as the peak of the Stevenson data lies closer to the bending moment response peak.

For a trading tanker the exposure is limited by the fact that the ship is in port loading, unloading and tank cleaning for a substantial proportion of its life. Also the environment in which they tend to operate in less severe.

Applying the results of the analysis undertaken for the Emerald Field FSU to other vessels is not easy. Each FPSO and FSU is unique in that the design basis of the original vessel can vary depending on when it was built and for what specific task. The operating conditions also vary from field to field with different environmental extremes varying from the Atlantic Frontier to relatively benign conditions in the Persian Gulf. Also the operating philosophy for each location is governed by the rate of import and the limitations on the mooring system.

However, historically it has been realised that there are problems with the FPSO/FSU type vessel in the harsh environments of the North Sea and remedial action has been instigated, in particular for the side shell longitudinal connections. Green seas and their effects on structures have been addressed both for offshore structures and specifically for FPSO's. The effect on the longitudinal bending due to green seas will reduce as the FPSO's of the future are designed to reduce the more local effects by increasing the bow height.

To summarise, the results of the Emerald Field FSU longitudinal strength assessment identified the possible need to investigate the suitability of converting old tankers for use as FPSO's and FSU's in what are abnormal conditions compared with the original intended use. Specific location requirements will vary, the type and position of the mooring system will vary, the operating philosophy will vary, and certainly the environment will vary, but the vessel will stay on location for 365 days a year and be subjected to wave loadings greater than the original design.

4.0   ACKNOWLEDGEMENTS

The author would like to acknowledge the work done by David Yuill, David Harley and others at BAeSema in doing the assessment without which there would be no paper. Also to thank both past and present employers, *Midland and Scottish Resources* and *Reading and Bates (UK)*, for allowing me to present this paper.

5.0   REFERENCES

1.   Press and Journal May 7 1996.

2.   BAeSema report no. C4710 - Ailsa Craig Strength assessment.

3.   Emerald Field FSU, Hull Girder and Side Shell Fatigue Analysis, Atkins Oil and Gas, November 1990.

4.   Guidance Manual for the Inspection and Condition Assessment of Tanker Structures, OCIMF.

PAPER NO.12.

DESIGN OF MODERN LIGHTWEIGHT WELLHEAD PLATFORMS FOR ABNORMAL CONDITIONS UNDER THE NEW SAFETY CASE REGIME

by P R Fish, Tecnomare (UK) Ltd

Paper presented at the

International Conference

**DESIGN AND OPERATION FOR
ABNORMAL CONDITIONS**

21 22 OCTOBER 1997 GLASGOW

DESIGN OF MODERN LIGHTWEIGHT WELLHEAD PLATFORMS FOR ABNORMAL CONDITIONS UNDER THE NEW SAFETY CASE REGIME

P R Fish, Tecnomare (UK) Ltd

SUMMARY

The prescriptive requirements of former design regulations for offshore platforms are gradually being replaced by a goal-setting approach to demonstrate adequate structural redundancy under various accidental and abnormal loading conditions in order to satisfy new safety case requirements.

At the same time there is ever increasing pressure on the designer to reduce structural weight by design optimisation to minimise construction costs.

As a result, structural redundancy is reduced and more sophisticated analysis methods are required to demonstrate that a structure has adequate reserve strength to withstand specified accidental and abnormal conditions before the onset of progressive collapse.

This paper describes some of the latest lightweight platform configurations that are typical of optimised designs and details the type of abnormal loading conditions these platforms must withstand: i.e. a 10,000 year return extreme storm event as well as ship impacts, dropped objects, fires and blasts.

The paper goes on to explain the various analysis methods that are used from a simple 'missing member' approach to non-linear and progressive collapse models.

Sample results are discussed to show how load redistributes within a typical offshore structure as failures occur prior to progressive collapse. In this way the consequences of the buckling failure of a critical brace or leg member can be assessed in terms of how many more member failures are needed before overall collapse occurs.

The conclusion is that advanced analysis methods for accidental and abnormal loading conditions provide valuable insight into ultimate load structural behaviour which is required for safety case documentation.

AUTHOR'S BIOGRAPHY

Mr P R Fish, BSc, MSc, CEng, MRINA, is currently Project Manager with Tecnomare responsible for technical innovation and detailed design. He has previously held the position of Senior Project Engineer with BHP Petroleum in Melbourne, Australia where he was supervising the design, procurement, construction and installation of floating production systems.

1. INTRODUCTION

Until June 1996, all offshore installations were required by the Health and Safety Executive (HSE) Statutory Instrument No. 289 - The Offshore Installations (Construction and Survey) Regulations 1974 - to possess a Certificate of Fitness which could only be granted by one of a limited number of Certifying Authorities (CA) appointed by the HSE. The CA would have prime responsibility for performing independent assessments to ensure that an offshore installation complied with a detailed set of design procedures, such as those issued by the American Petroleum Institute (API). These requirements have become embodied in the term 'prescriptive legislation'.

However, in his report on the Piper Alpha disaster, Lord Cullen recommended the introduction of a safety case regime offshore, underpinned by complementary legislation dealing with specific aspects of safety. The Offshore Installations (Safety Case) Regulations (SI 2885) were introduced in 1992 followed in June last year by the Offshore Installations and Wells (Design and Construction, etc) Regulations (SI 913) known as DCR. Part II of these regulations contain provisions for the integrity of offshore installations which, taken together with the Provision and Use of Work Equipment Regulations introduced in 1992 (SI 2932) replace, in goal-setting form, the former requirements of SI 289. Until June 1998 a two year transition period has been agreed.

Important aspects of the SCR (Safety Case Regulations) are that major hazards should be identified and risks kept as low as reasonably possible (the ALARP principle). It is also a necessary requirement of the SCR to demonstrate that management systems are in-place to ensure compliance with relevant statutory health and safety provisions. The new verification arrangements introduced into the SCR by the DCR are an essential component of such management systems.

The new DCR place the primary responsibility for securing the integrity of an installation with its owner or operator, rather than with the CA. The regulations require safety critical elements (SCEs) to be identified and a written scheme of verification to be devised and put into effect for each. Verification is carried out by independent and competent persons. The identification of SCEs and the written scheme itself is also subject to scrutiny by independent and competent persons. Such verifying bodies are still likely to refer to the same design practice notes, such as the API code (ref. 1), as these remain applicable due to their continual development. However, there remains a need to demonstrate that the hazards for a specific installation are being effectively managed.

It is worth noting at this point that the new regulations, by promoting a goal-setting approach, have introduced a degree of subjectivity which was not present under the old system. Consequently it has been necessary for the HSE to issue guidance notes (refs. 2,3) on the new regulations to explain the new terms such as 'safety-critical elements', 'verification scheme', 'independent and competent persons', 'reasonably foreseeable' and 'as low as reasonably possible'. However, following the guidance is not compulsory and operators are free to take other action. But following the guidance will normally satisfy the law and HSE inspectors who seek to ensure compliance with the law may refer to the guidance notes as illustrating good practice.

The implications of these changes are described below with particular reference to the design of offshore installations for abnormal conditions. This paper will deal specifically with the design of steel substructures for fixed installations but similar principles can be taken to apply to topside structures and floating installations.

2.   ABNORMAL CONDITIONS FOR OFFSHORE INSTALLATIONS

The abnormal conditions which are usually considered to constitute hazards for offshore installations arise from one of the following: ship impact, dropped objects, fire and blast and abnormal waves. An extreme seismic event may also constitute an abnormal condition in some parts of the world.

The traditional approach to designing for both ship impact and dropped objects was to carry out a redundancy analysis using the 'missing member' approach; i.e. those structural members which could be damaged by a ship impact or dropped object were removed from the structural model one by one and the in-place analysis re-run using a reduced storm wave, such as the one year or ten year return wave. The aim was simply to show that there was sufficient structural redundancy to avoid overstress in the remaining structure, and this was readily achieved given the degree of basic over-design often present in early structures.

It was therefore not necessary to consider such aspects as the size or shape of the ship or object, the speed or direction of impact, the response of the structure, the structural collapse mechanism or levels of energy absorption. However, under the new SCR/DCR regime it has become necessary to consider all such aspects in order to show that the safety critical elements (or components thereof) are 'suitable' i.e. possess 'such integrity as is reasonably practical'.

The starting point is to carry out a HAZOP study which will form part of the safety case to identify the operational hazards and quantify the risks. In the case of ship impact this will entail a review of shipping lanes, and size and frequency of passing vessels. Also the size and frequency of vessels required to visit the installation will be assessed depending on its mode of operation as a manned, unmanned or normally unattended installation. Following this study it will be possible to define the size and speed of a vessel which may strike the installation and for which it is reasonably practical to design for structural integrity.

Unless a study of the collision hazards and consequences specific to the installation demonstrate that a lower value is appropriate, the HSE Offshore Guidance Notes (ref. 4) specify that structures must be capable of absorbing a minimum of 4MJ impact energy. However, this is frequently overridden by the operator's requirement to consider an impact from a 5000 tonne supply vessel drifting at up to 2 m/s. This gives rise to 14MJ of impact energy for a broadside collision or 11MJ for a bow or stern collision. Typically, not more than about one third of this energy will be absorbed by the vessel and is consequently much more onerous than the HSE minimum requirement of 4MJ.

Tecnomare's experience in the design of platforms for the North Sea has shown that ship impacts of 14MJ can give rise to base shears and overturning moments which are comparable to or even in excess of those due to the standard 100 year return design storm wave. Consequently, ship impact can be the governing design condition even for the lower part of the structure outside the ship impact zone and the foundation piles. To avoid increasing capital cost by specific strengthening of the structure (which can in turn lead to even higher impact forces), it has become necessary to employ more sophisticated design techniques to ensure integrity is maintained by avoiding progressive collapse. The application of such techniques to some recent structures is described in more detail below.

A similar approach may be adopted for dropped objects whereby a HAZOP study would consider the various lifting operations which might occur offshore and hence determine the size and weight of lifted objects, the lifting frequency and part of the installation over which the objects are lifted (e.g. transfers from supply vessels or movement on the platform). This will determine which structural members are exposed to damage from a dropped object and what the impact energy is likely to be (0.5MJ would be typical for an item of drilling equipment weighing around 5 tonnes).

Given the degree of optimisation in present day platform designs it is often not practical to consider the impacted member as totally missing and in any case this would be over-conservative considering the impact energy. Therefore a more sophisticated analysis approach has to be adopted whereby a post damage analysis is run which incorporates dented section properties at the point of impact.

With regard to design for abnormal storms, some operators will prescribe a 10,000 year return storm event which the platform must be able to withstand in addition to the usual 100 year storm event for the intact condition and either the 1 year or 10 year storm for damage conditions. The table below shows typical extreme wave heights and periods for the Central North Sea (UK sector) for a range of return periods:

TABLE 1

| Storm Return Period | Maximum Wave Height (m) | Wave | Period | T_{ass} (s) |
		Lower	Central	Upper
1 year	18.4	11.2	13.3	15.0
10 year	21.1	12.1	14.0	16.1
50 year	22.9	12.6	14.4	16.8
100 year	23.8	12.7	14.5	16.9
1000 year	26.6	14.9	16.5	18.2
10,000 year	29.9	15.6	17.5	19.1

Figure 1 shows that the wave heights for the abnormal storms lie on a linear extrapolation of the 50 year and 100 year return wave heights plotted against return period on a log-linear scale.

Other operators may require the effects of even more abnormal storms to be considered by effectively incrementing the 100 year storm loading beyond the 10,000 year load level until progressive collapse occurs.

Such a 'push-over' analysis affords useful information on the platform's reserve strength as well as establishing the ultimate collapse mechanism and hence the most critical members and joints. This information in turn will be useful to the operations group in developing a rational inspection plan based on the reliability of individual structural components. An example of an abnormal storm and reserve strength analysis recently carried out on a North Sea platform is described later in this paper.

Finally, and perhaps most importantly in view of disasters which have occurred, new regulations were introduced in 1995 for the prevention of fire and explosions and emergency response on offshore installations (PFEER), which must now be designed to be resistant to the effects of fire and blast. For topsides design this will involve a series of safety studies considering process equipment, confinement, control systems, blast walls, passive fire protection, etc. But the integrity of substructures can also be at risk in the event of pool fires in the wellbay area or if a riser ruptures and ignites.

To simulate the damage which may arise in the event of a fire or blast, one approach is to remove the leg or principal joints which are likely to be damaged and to see if overall structural integrity can be maintained. In the event that structural integrity requirements cannot be satisfied, passive fire protection measures or deluge systems may be installed to mitigate structural damage. Having estimated the extent of structural damage, section properties can be revised and the structural analysis re-run.

3.   ABNORMAL STORM DESIGN

The design of a modern lightweight wellhead platform for abnormal storm conditions (10,000 year return) is illustrated by comparison with the same platform designed for the extreme wave condition (100 year return).

The selected platform configuration, as shown in Figure 2, illustrates a recent example of structural innovation which has substantially reduced weight compared to more conventional platforms. Standing in 90m of water, the steel jacket is designed to act as a drilling template for a harsh environment jack-up in advance of deck installation. The central square tower has four vertical legs with diagonal X-bracing on all faces and diamond plan bracing connecting the face X nodes. The lower third of the tower comprises a supporting structure in which each leg has a pair of 'outrigger' braces connecting to the two nearest pile sleeves; there being six piles in total. The platform has twelve conductors and supports a topside load of 4000t including a modular work-over rig.

The platform response was analysed for abnormal storms of both 1000 year and 10,000 year return periods. Respective wave heights of 26.6m and 29.9m were used with the associated central wave periods as the minimum wave periods were considered to give rise to unrealistically steep waves.

A dynamic amplification factor (DAF) was calculated from a natural frequency run using appropriate foundation spring stiffnesses. This gave a natural period of 2.66s and an associated DAF of about 1.02.

The maximum base shear and overturning moment calculated for the 1000 year and 10,000 year return storms are shown in the table below compared with the extreme 100 year return loading:

TABLE 2

Condition	100 Year	1000 Year	10,000 Year
Base Shear (MN)	18.0	23.25	29.2
Increase	-	29%	62%
Overturning Moment (MN.m)	1342	1505	1882
Increase	-	12%	40%

Base shears and overturning moments are plotted for both the extreme and abnormal storm against the log of the return period in Figure 3, from which it may be seen that base shear has a linear relationship against log of return period whereas overturning moment shows on exponential relationship. Thus methods for predicting, say, the increase in axial pile loads with wave height based on a purely linear extrapolation from the 100 year return value will be prone to underestimation.

The platform was designed for the 10,000 year wave on the assumption that, being an abnormal condition, both the API RP2A load and resistance factors could be set to unity which effectively removes all safety factors which are normally included in the design for the 100 year storm condition. The code check program was therefore modified accordingly.

The resulting member and joint interactions ratios were only marginally (say up to 10%) higher for the 10,000 year return storm than for the 100 year storm. However, by inspection of the mill certificate material properties, it was found possible to maintain all code interaction ratios less than unity as required for the extreme storm design. Thus, despite the more stringent design requirement, it was still possible to demonstrate formal compliance with the design code for the 10,000 year return storm, and by deduction for the 1000 year return storm also.

The pile axial forces were found to be almost exactly the same for the 10,000 year storm as for the 100 year return storm after adjustment of the LRFD load factors. However, the maximum pile utilisations are generally lower for the compression piles but higher for the tension piles.

Jacket deflections along a leg have been extracted for the 10,000 year storm and are plotted against the 100 year and 1000 year return deflections in Figure 4. Top of deck deflections are shown plotted against relative base shear in Figure 5.

Unlike the requirement for a 1.5m airgap between the wave crest and underside of deck for the 100 year wave, the air gap between the crest of the 10,000 year wave and underside of cellar deck was calculated to be about 0.4m which, being greater than zero, was considered acceptable for an abnormal condition.

Although the 10,000 year wave can be considered most likely to approach from true north due to the far greater fetch, the 10,000 year wave (29.9m, 17.5s) was also considered from all eight directions to confirm whether the most probable direction was also the most critical. This is particularly important when asymmetries in topside loading are taken into consideration.

4. RESERVE STRENGTH ANALYSIS

The starting point for the reserve strength analysis was the basic structural inplace model and loading as generated for the 100 year return storm analysis described above. However, elements containing more than one cross section (i.e. stepped members) were changed to multiple prismatic elements for the software to work. Only those elements in which plastic hinges were expected to form were modified. The modifications were further limited by considering only the maximum storm wave direction for analysis. The elements to be given plastic properties were initially identified by a preliminary code check run on the results of a stiffness analysis of the original model using a load factor equal to the expected collapse load. Ten members were identified as having the potential to buckle or form plastic hinges. These increased to thirty taking account of stepped members. All of these new elements were given plastic properties.

Separate dummy pile elements were generated for each pile using the individual pile head loads taken from a full soil/pile/structure interaction run at the collapse load level, i.e. with an applied load factor equal to the calculated RSR (Reserve Strength Ratio). This ensured that the pile stiffnesses for the progressive collapse run were as accurate as possible.

As the abnormal wave (10,000 year storm) analysis showed that the NW direction was the most critical, the progressive collapse analysis concentrated on determining the reserve strength ratio (RSR) for this direction only as this could be expected to give the minimum RSR.

Figure 6 shows the flow chart for the progressive collapse analysis. The collapse runs were preceded by a stiffness analysis using unfactored loads. In the initial runs the conventional yield/plastic hinge model was specified. Also the yield strength for the maximum compression leg was specified in accordance with the mill certificate value. This resulted in apparent collapse due to the formation of a three hinge mechanism in the upper diagonal pile sleeve brace connected to the compression leg. At that point ten plastic hinges had formed as shown in Figure 7.

These runs were repeated using a more advanced version of the software which allowed collapse checks in accordance with the API buckling criteria. Non-linear properties were specified for all compression members for which buckling was the anticipated mode of failure. Also the mill certificate yield strength was again used for the compression leg. This resulted in apparent collapse at a load factor 40% less than that of the first pass run. When this occurred only three plastic hinges had formed as shown in Figure 8. Final failure was caused by the buckling of the horizontal brace on row 3 at El -67.5m. When base material values were used, progressive collapse occurred at a lower RSR when the compression leg buckled.

Finally, member code checks were carried out on the second pass progressive collapse results to identify any possible hinge formations or buckling in members other than those provided with non-linear properties. Also pile/soil/structure interaction runs were carried out with the environmental load factor set equal to the calculated RSR; however, the reported interaction ratios were adjusted to take account of the API strength resistance factors being set to unity for the ultimate collapse condition.

As column buckling was seen to be the governing failure mode at collapse, the initial collapse runs were disregarded in favour of the results obtained using the more sophisticated version of the program.

The jacket deflections at the point of progressive collapse have been extracted and are plotted against the 100 year, 1000 year and 10,000 year return deflections in Figure 4. Top of deck deflections (El +27.5) have also been plotted against load factor in Figure 5 which shows the non-linear effect of the foundation response, particularly beyond the 10,000 year load level.

It was concluded that the reserve strength of the foundations slightly exceeded the reserve strength of the jacket structure, which means that the most safety critical elements of the installation are accessible for in-service inspection.

5.   SHIP IMPACT DESIGN

This discussion will focus on designing installations for the abnormal ship impact event defined as 14 MJ for a broadside collision or 11MJ for a bow/stern collision, rather than for the operational event of 0.5MJ. Typically the ship impact zone is from about 9m below LAT to about 14m above LAT (Lowest Astronomical Tide), allowing for tidal range, platform settlement, seastate and draught/freeboard of a 5000 tonne supply vessel.

The design and analysis techniques are illustrated by application to a novel four pile wellhead jacket configuration as shown in Figure 9. This jacket differs from the one discussed above in connection with abnormal wave loading principally in the base arrangement but also by the addition of eight diagonal braces in the top bay of the jacket which are required to enable the platform to sustain the abnormally high ship impact loads.

The acceptance criteria for high energy impacts may be summarised as follows:

TABLE 3

Condition	Acceptance Criteria
Nodal impact	No punching failure or progressive collapse
Leg impact (mid-span)	One hinge allowed provided no progressive collapse
Brace impact (mid-span)	I) Ensure element failure occurs before joint failure and that the ultimate tensile forces in the brace do not result in progressive collapse of the surrounding structure; II) Ensure vessel energy is fully absorbed (i.e. vessel is brought to a standstill) without vessel intrusion causing damage to risers, wells, etc.
Post impact	Ensure that the installation in its damaged condition has sufficient residual strength to survive a 10 year return storm and satisfy code requirements.

The behaviour of the structure due to leg or nodal impacts at the moment of impact is normally evaluated using a three-dimensional finite element model. Non-linear, large deflection, elasto-plastic, finite element analyses are generally performed using programs such as the EDI SACS system, the Atkins ASAS-NL program or the USFOS program. However, for structures comprising beam elements alternative software using the virtual displacement method (VDM - see for example ref. 5), such as the Atkins APCA program, may be suitable. For the post impact analysis a linear finite element program will normally suffice.

The kinetic energy of a vessel will be absorbed through a variety of mechanisms including:

1) local denting of the impacted structural element;

2) bending of the impacted structural element;

3) axial extension of the impacted element;

4) platform global deformation;

5) joint rotation;

6) ship indentation.

The non-linear model is used to account for items 2) to 5) above. Local denting of the tube is calculated using the formulation of Ellinas and Walker (ref. 6) whereas ship indentation characteristics are generally taken from DnV (ref. 7) published data.

Non-linear analysis programs do not generally account for impact point dent formation, or the energy absorbed during the denting process, unless a detailed plate model of the impact area is generated. This level of detail is not normally necessary for a space frame structure and so the denting process is considered separately in accordance with ref. 6.

However, joint flexibility, local buckling effects, pile plasticity and strain hardening are accounted for by the software. A strain hardening ratio of 0.002 to 0.003 is normally used. Marshall and Gates criteria (ref. 8) are used to determine joint rotational limits. Rate-of-strain calculations are generally not performed due to the absence of reliable data and the assumptions which have to be made. Disregarding rate-of-strain may be considered conservative as premature brittle fracture is eliminated as a failure mechanism.

Tubular elements with 12 integration points around the circumference are used to model the jacket tubular members. Each integration point can yield independently resulting in gradual plastification of the cross-section. At least eight such elements are used per member for the final runs. Appurtenances such as conductors, risers, J-tubes, etc are not modelled as they are non-structural and increase the run time unnecessarily. A full soil-pile model is included to allow for non-linear foundation response. A deck model consisting of just the primary members is provided to model rotational stiffness at the top of the legs and to allow load transfer through the deck for impacts near the top of the jacket. For the example platform a total of twelve impact cases have to be analysed allowing for both nodal and mid-span impacts. Conservatively, only the most heavily loaded leg is considered, but impacts from both the orthogonal and diagonal directions are analysed. It is not the intention of this paper to present the results for all twelve cases but just to discuss some of the findings.

One of the more interesting cases is where a bow or stern impact occurs on the mid-side node at the intersection of four face diagonals, two perimeter plan members and two plan diagonals. The plan diagonals were found to buckle when only about 50% of the impact energy was absorbed. The remaining impact energy is absorbed through membrane tension of the face braces. The areas of plasticity are illustrated in Figure 10.

The non-linear software used for leg and node impacts as described above could not be used for analysing brace impacts following the formation of three plastic hinges in the brace. It was therefore necessary to develop an alternative approach to this particular problem as described below.

The structural models used were based upon those created for the in-place analyses, modified to include mid-span nodes on elements subjected to high compressive loads. Non-linear properties were applied to elements where plasticity was expected to develop. Other modifications to the model included the elimination of steps along all elements with non-linear (plastic) material properties, which could be achieved by inserting additional nodes at step changes in material properties.

Separate analyses were carried out for each category of brace within the ship impact zone which could be struck by the bow or stern of a supply vessel, resulting in three basic categories: upper diagonal brace, plan brace, and lower diagonal brace.

The flow chart shown in Figure 11 illustrates the analysis methodology which uses linear and progressive collapse analysis programs for global analyses of the full jacket structure, and an in-house program, IMPACT, for single member impact analyses. The methodology may be summarised as follows:

• Prepare standard structural model.

• Remove impacted brace member(s); if the loss of a single brace is insufficient to absorb all the ship impact energy then it may be necessary to consider the loss of two or more braces as the ship's hull penetrates into the structural envelope.

• Apply unit end forces and moments independently to determine brace end stiffnesses due to axial load, lateral force and joint rotations.

- Input stiffnesses into the IMPACT program to determine impact force and associated member tension at required energy level (or at failure if this occurs first).

- Apply loads obtained from IMPACT program as nodal loads to the global model, refer Figure 12. Run the global progressive collapse analysis, incrementing loads until a mechanism forms (or member tensile yield develops).

- Run member/joint code checks to confirm that no unexpected member buckling failures have occurred.

- Plot a force/displacement curve to determine the final energy and combine with the energies absorbed due to member denting, flexure and axial strain as predicted by the IMPACT program for the same axial tension.

The results of the IMPACT/progressive collapse analyses showed that sufficient capacity could be offered by the surrounding jacket members to resist the membrane forces arising from high energy ship impact on brace members. For impacts on diagonal braces, the loss of two braces was required before the 11MJ was absorbed. However, for impacts on the horizontal plan bracing above the water line, the energy could be absorbed by a single brace basically because the end connected to the jacket leg was much more flexible. This in turn allowed more lateral deformation at the centre of the brace and hence more work to be done at the point of loading. By comparison, the ends of the diagonal braces are highly restrained by the face bracing configuration and hence limit their lateral flexibility for energy absorption purposes.

Hence, the design requirement for brace impacts is a question of balancing flexibility to provide a mechanism for energy absorption against strength to prevent premature rupture prior to energy absorption.

6. CONCLUSION

The conclusion of this paper is that the new goal-setting environment for the verification of offshore installations, established through the introduction of the SCR/DCR regime, has necessitated the implementation of more sophisticated design and analysis techniques to cope with the abnormal design conditions being even more stringent. These are particularly required in the case of novel lightweight structures in order to demonstrate that, despite their apparent lack of redundancy, they still possess adequate structural integrity to ensure that the risks of collapse are kept as low as reasonably practicable for the safety of personnel offshore.

7. ACKNOWLEDGEMENTS

The author wishes to thank the management of Tecnomare (UK) Ltd for their permission to publish this paper and his colleagues for their assistance in carrying out the computing work.

8. REFERENCES

1. 'API RP2A Recommended Practice for Planning, Designing and Constructing Fixed Offshore Platforms - Load and Resistance Factor Design', 1st Edition, July 1993.

2. 'A guide to the installation verification and miscellaneous aspects of amendments by the Offshore Installations and wells (Design and Construction, etc) Regulations 1996 to the Offshore Installations (Safety case) Regulations 1992'.

3. 'A guide to the integrity, workplace environment and miscellaneous aspects of the Offshore Installations and Wells (Design and Construction, etc) Regulations 1996'.

4. 'Offshore Installations, Guidance on Design, Construction and Certification, UK Health and Safety Executive', 3rd Edition, 1990.

5. HOLNICKI-SZULC, J and GIERLINSKI, J T: 'Structural Analysis, Design and Control by the Virtual Distortion Method', John Wiley, 1995.

6. ELLINAS, C P and WALKER, A C: 'Effects of Damage on Offshore Tubular Bracing Members', IABSE; May 1983'.

7. 'Fixed Offshore Installations - Impact Loads from Boats', Det Norske Veritas; RPD 205; 1981.

8. MARSHALL, P W and GATES, W E: 'Inelastic Dynamics of Tubular Offshore Structures', OTC 2908; 1977.

Extreme Storm Return Period (Year)	Log (Year) Storm Return Period	Maximum Resultant Base Shear Fr(kN)	Max. Resultant Overturning Moment (OTM) Mr (kNM)
50	1.699	18120	1371790
100	2	18058	1341811
1000	3	23254	1.5048E+06
10,000	4	29174	1.8824E+06

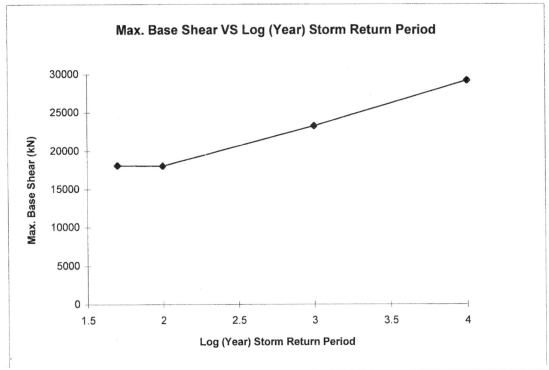

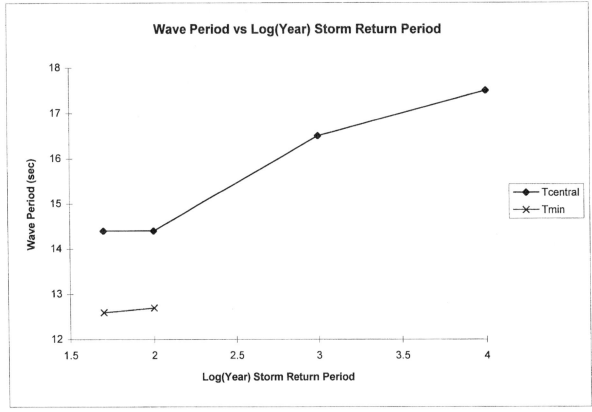

Fig. 1 Wave height and period vs return period

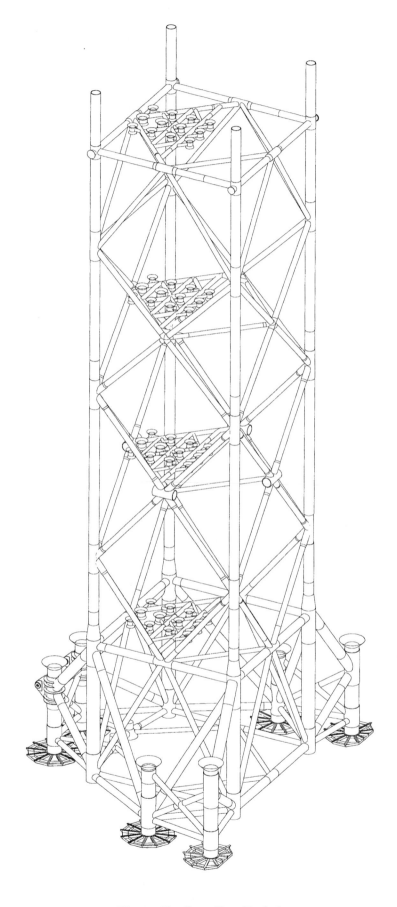

Fig. 2 Six pile wellhead jacket

9

Extreme Storm Return Period (Year)	Log (Year) Storm Return Period	Max. Wave Height Hmax (m)	Wave Period T (sec)	
			Lower	Central
50	1.699	22.9	12.6	14.4
100	2	23.8	12.7	14.4
1000	3	26.6		16.5
10,000	4	29.9		17.5

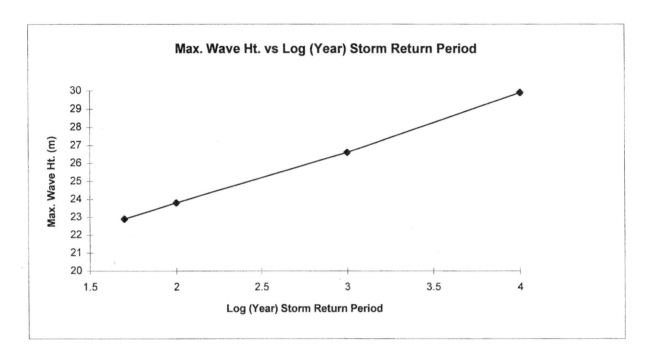

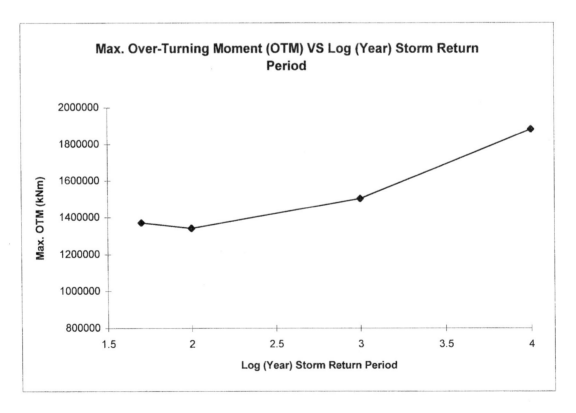

Fig. 3 Base shear and overturning moment vs return period

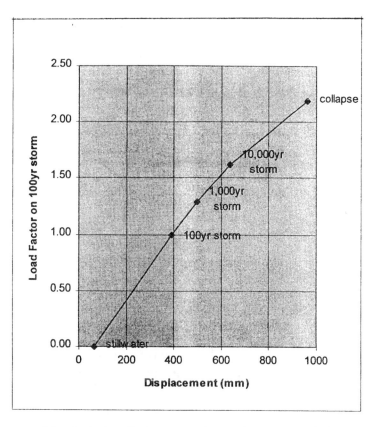

Fig. 4 Jacket displacements for varying return periods

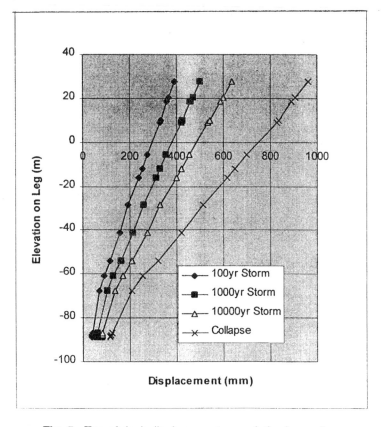

Fig. 5 Top of deck displacements vs relative base shear

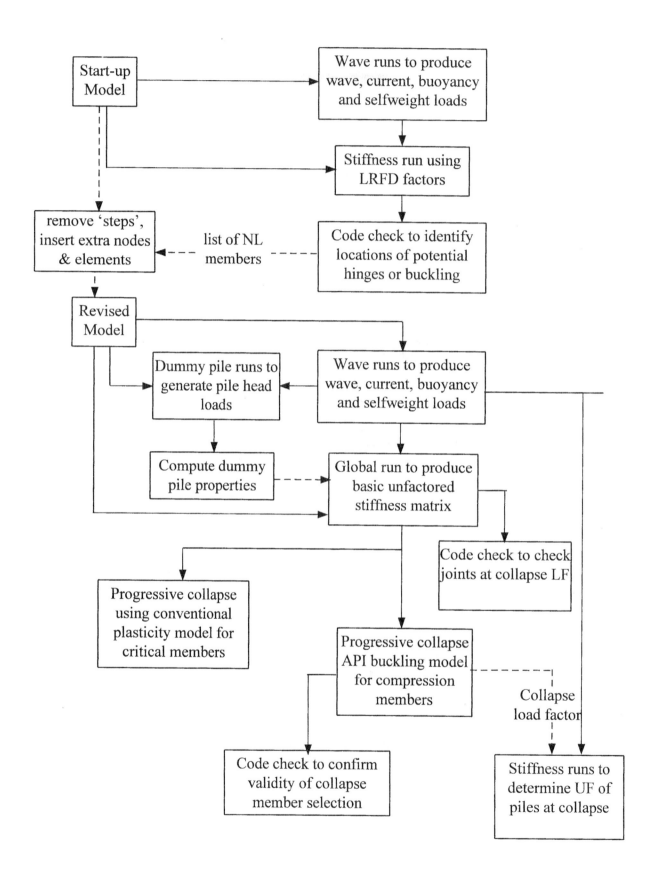

Fig. 6 Progressive collapse analysis flow chart

12

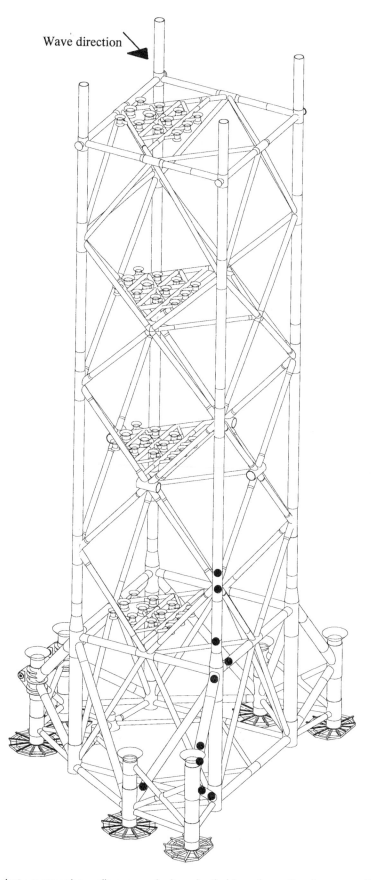

Wave direction

Fig. 7 Wellhead jacket progressive collapse analysis - plastic hinge formation for conventional plasticity model

Fig. 8 Wellhead jacket progressive collapse analysis - plastic hinge formation for buckling model in compression

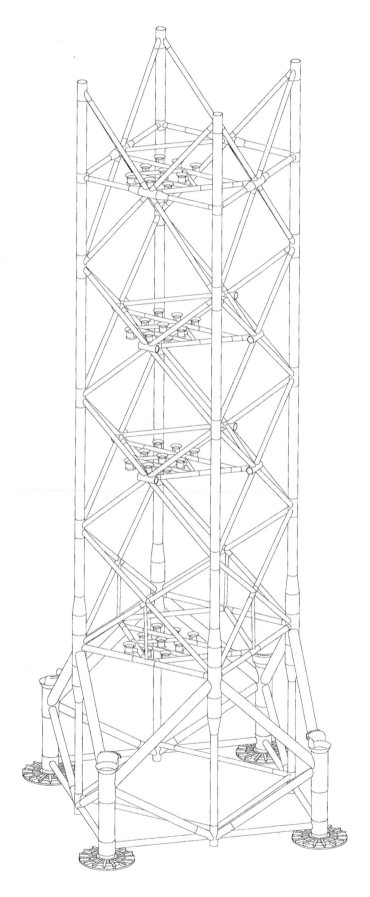

Fig. 9 Four pile wellhead jacket

PLASTICITY

■ 100.0

■ 75.0

50.0

25.0

NONE

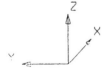

Fig. 10 Results of brace impact analysis showing areas of plasticity

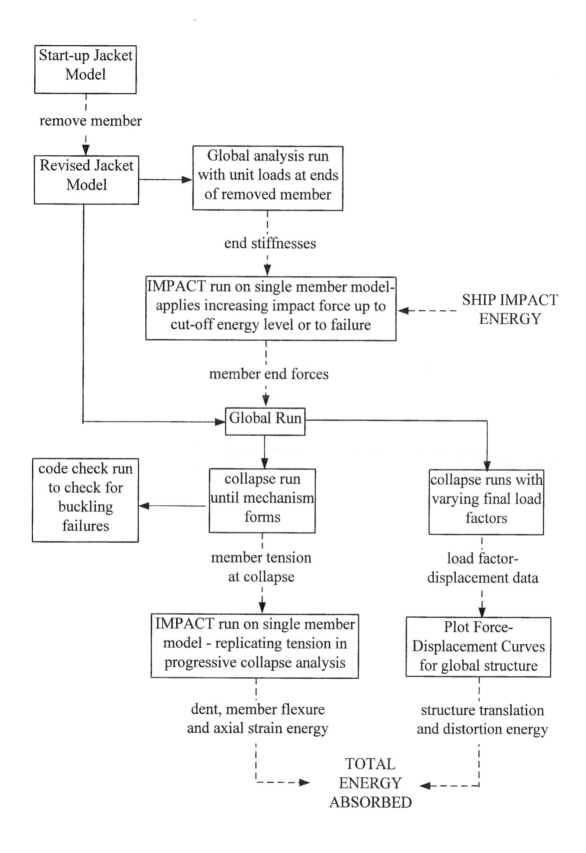

Fig. 11 Brace impact analyis flow chart

17

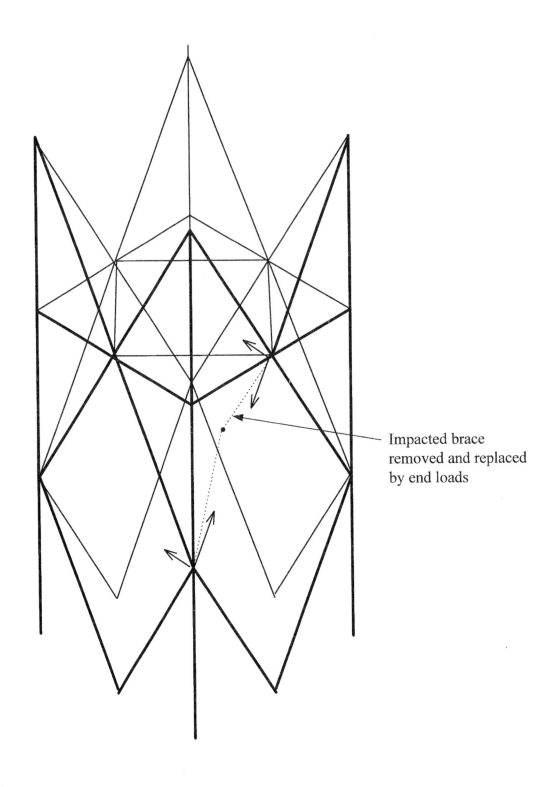

Impacted brace
removed and replaced
by end loads

Fig. 12 Typical load arrangement for ship impact on brace members

PAPER NO.13.

THE GREEN WATER HAZARD TO MOORED FLOATING OFFSHORE UNITS

by D L Yuill MRINA, and I C Smith, BAeSEMA, UK

Paper presented at the

International Conference

**DESIGN AND OPERATION FOR
ABNORMAL CONDITIONS**

21 22 OCTOBER 1997 GLASGOW

THE GREEN WATER HAZARD TO MOORED FLOATING OFFSHORE UNITS

D L Yuill MRINA and I C Smith, BAeSEMA

SUMMARY

Marine systems on barge type floating offshore units are primarily designed using ship based design techniques and the results of model testing. The design codes do not address all of the hazards due to green water on deck nor address the design of deck equipment to withstand green water loading.

As part of the ongoing Safety Case work for the ALBA FSU, a study was undertaken to identify the hazards arising from green water on deck and to assess the risk to the vessel, personnel, equipment and systems on the vessel.

A methodology has been developed for identifying the hazards due to green water and assessing the subsequent risks. The methodology has been applied to the ALBA FSU as part of the Safety Case. This paper presents the method developed for assessing the Green Water hazard to moored floating offshore units.

An initial assessment of the consequences of equipment failure due to green water was undertaken to identify those items of equipment whose integrity is paramount to the safety of the vessel and its personnel. Any items identified as presenting a hazard to the vessel, for which the risk is unacceptable and cannot be mitigated, are analysed deterministically using simplifying assumptions. These assumptions are based on our current level of understanding of the loading mechanisms and environment.

A simple representation of the sea surface, vessel motions and wave loading is used which provides an outline methodology which could be further developed for other vessel types.

AUTHORS' BIOGRAPHIES

Mr David Yuill is currently a Consultant Naval Architect at YARD Ltd. in Glasgow. He has been actively involved in assessing the risk to the ALBA FSU resulting from green water on deck and providing marine support to Chevron in the preparation of the Safety Case for the ALBA FSU. He was previously employed by a UK tanker owner where he was involved in in-service structural monitoring of the tanker fleet along with overseeing the design, construction and commissioning of new tonnage. He also has experience in the design and construction of a wide range of small vessels, having worked as a ship designer in a small UK shipyard. He has seagoing experience and holds a 2nd Mates (Foreign Going) Certificate.

Mr Ian Smith is currently a project manager within the Industry Division of *BAeSEMA* and is currently working on the Ross project as the company representative on Floating Production and Offloading Systems. He has been actively involved in several major offshore oil and gas projects and has experience in the preliminary design of monohull and semi-submersible production systems, offshore loading systems, deep water hybrid risers. He also has experience in the design, manufacture and testing of electro/hydraulic control systems for ship and offshore applications including remote underwater vehicles.

1. INTRODUCTION

Floating Storage Units (FSU's) and Floating Production, Storage and Offloading vessels (FPSO's) are still predominantly designed using ship based design codes or Classification Society Rules for the ship's structure and marine equipment. These rules do not specifically address the hazards due to extreme wave conditions and green water encroaching onto the deck of these vessels. As part of the ongoing safety case work for the ALBA FSU, Chevron (UK) commissioned *BAeSEMA* to undertake a study to identify the hazards arising from green water on deck and assess the risk to the vessel, the personnel, equipment and systems on the vessel, due to green water on deck. A methodology for identifying the hazards due to green water and assessing the subsequent risks has been developed. The methodology has been applied to the ALBA FSU as part of the ALBA Safety Case.

This paper outlines:

* the background to the study;

* the development of the methodology;

* the limitations of the methodology, and

* illustrates the application of the methodology using the ALBA FSU.

The methodology developed can also be adopted during design development phase for concept evaluation, allowing identification of sensible options prior to embarking on any model testing. Where deterministic analysis needs to be undertaken to quantify the risk then the assumptions tend to be very conservative (i.e. extreme worst case loading). It is extremely improbable that the vessel will encounter these conditions in practice but it does allow a qualitative comparison between different options.

While the current discussion is principally related to FSUs and FPSOs, the philosophy can be applied to commercial trading vessels with only minor modification.

2.   CURRENT DESIGN PRACTICE

Most of the prescriptive design codes are based on simple engineering theory with empirically derived factors of safety applied to them to account for the uncertainties in the calculation methods. It is often difficult to determine what design loading have been used and the factors of safety inherent in the formulae. These design loadings and factors of safety cannot always be explicitly defined. It is therefore difficult to apply a risk based engineering approach for a ship designed to traditional Classification Society rules.

It is important to understand that compliance with prescriptive design codes does not in itself guarantee a 'safe' vessel. Potential hazards may still exist, either due to limitations or inadequacies within the prescriptive regulations or a deviation from the design intent. Such hazards must be identified and their significance assessed.

Where the design of the structure and equipment is not specifically addressed within the design code it is incumbent on the Designer/Shipbuilder to ensure that equipment is 'fit for purpose' and designed in accordance with 'best commercial marine practice'. This approach relies on the experience of the Designer/Shipbuilder to ensure that the equipment and structure has been adequately designed. The design of such structure and equipment is usually based on previous experience, and design data may need to be extrapolated for new designs. The Design Safety Philosophy for such structure and equipment may not, therefore, be adequately developed or the risks fully evaluated.

While the use of Classification Society rules supplemented by the designer's experience have been employed successfully in marine transportation for many years, the current trends in safety management and the implementation of new safety case legislation, particularly in the Offshore sector, makes it increasingly difficult to justify the continuation of this approach. For example, it is no longer acceptable to simply argue that 'a ship is safe because it complies with Classification Society Rules'. Neither can the shipbuilder or operator rely on past practice as a safety justification. Designing, building and operating a vessel in the same manner as its predecessors does not guarantee that the risk to the vessel or personnel on board the vessel is 'As Low As Reasonably Practicable (ALARP)'. Vessels are still lost at sea and designers and operators must learn from these losses, such that the future risk to life is reduced, through the use of formal safety assessment techniques and safety management systems.

It is therefore incumbent on the operator to ensure that he has considered all of the hazards to the vessel, and to ensure that the risk to personnel, the vessel, its systems and equipment, and also the environment, are ALARP.

The guidance information on preparing an Offshore Installation Safety Case (Ref. 1) lists a number of hazards which have to be considered. These are:

- Hydrocarbon escapes, leading to fire, explosion or toxic hazard
- Vessel impact
- Structural failure
- Aircraft impact
- Dropped load
- Loss of station keeping
- Loss of stability
- Loss of buoyancy
- effects of nearby installations

These areas are covered as a matter of course in the development of an Offshore Installation Safety Case.

One of the principal hazards which requires to be addressed by the operator, which is not specifically listed in the Safety Case guidance information and which is not currently adequately addressed by the Classification Societies is the effect of wave loading on deck equipment. Vessels designed, built and operated in accordance with traditional marine practices may still encounter extreme wave loadings which exceed the design loading for the structure. Fig. 1 illustrates the damage resulting from wave loading on the superstructure front of a passenger vessel. Green water was taken over the bow, which impacted on the superstructure. The green water impact resulted in major failure of the superstructure front plating, with the consequential risk of injury to personnel. Other examples of damage and loss of life resulting from extreme environmental condition and green water on deck are given by Faulkner *et al* in Ref. 2.

3.   ADDITIONAL HAZARDS FOR FSUs AND FPSOs

When assessing the structural design of an FSU or FPSO operating in hostile areas, such as the North Sea or West of Shetland, the environment in which the vessel will operate needs to be fully considered. The environmental conditions experienced by an FSU or FPSO may be more onerous than would be experienced by a conventional trading vessel. Conventional trading vessels spend more time in port and generally operate for the greater part of their life in a more benign environment than could be expected for a permanent installation in the North Sea or West of Shetland. This does not mean that conventional trading vessels will not encounter extreme seas but the probability and frequency of encountering such weather is significantly lower than for an FSU or FPSO on continuous station.

Trading vessels have more control over their speed and direction relative to the waves. They can alter speed and heading to reduce the vessel motions, the wave loading on the vessel and the risk of green water on deck. FPSOs and FSUs on the other hand are designed to remain moored in one location for the design life of the field. The mooring system allows them to weathervane into the prevailing environmental forces and the control of heading and position is generally passive. The operator has therefore less ability to reduce the environmental loading on the vessel or the risk of shipping green water. This requires a different design methodology.

The design wave bending moment may need to be increased above normal classification requirements to ensure that the probability of the vessel encountering the design wave bending moments is not greater than for an equivalent trading tanker. Hull envelope plating and deck structure may need to be enhanced to cope with the increased hydrodynamic pressure loading associated with the increased probability of higher sea states. The structure may also need to be enhanced to cope with the higher fatigue loading which may be encountered and it is probable that the maintenance and inspection regimes on an offshore installation will need to be more rigorous and extensive than for a conventional trading tanker.

4.   RISK DUE TO GREEN WATER ON DECK

The hazards to a vessel due to wave loading can be categorised by the four main load types which can arise in a seaway. These are:

- mainhull girder wave bending and shear;

- localised wave impact loading (e.g. bottom or bow flare slamming);

- local wave pressure loading (due to hydrostatic and hydrodynamic loading on the hull structure);

- green water on deck.

While the effects of main hull girder bending and shear, wave impact loading and wave pressure loading for FPSOs are largely compatible with the traditional Classification Society Rule approach (subject to the additional risks identified above), the effect of green water on deck is not adequately addressed. Reference 2 indicates that a foredeck structural design is normally based on a uniform pressure head of only 1.75 metres, irrespective of ship size, freeboard or structural arrangement. This is considered to be inadequate as mean wave pressure heads on deck have been estimated to be an order of magnitude greater.

The design of many items of equipment and systems located on or above the upper deck, including seats and

support structure does not take into account the ability to resist green water loading since this is not specifically addressed within the Classification Society rules.

The designer/shipbuilder would normally design such equipment in accordance with 'best commercial marine practice', which will inevitably be based on previous experience. This is no longer an acceptable approach. The hazards to structure, equipment, systems and supports for these items, resulting from green water on deck, need to be identified and documented and the risk fully assessed in a systematic manner.

5.   CONSIDERATION OF GREEN WATER - ONE APPROACH

The interaction between the waves and the vessel are extremely complex. It is currently impractical to accurately mathematically model the height of green water on deck or the effect it will have on the ship's structure and deck mounted equipment. The probability of shipping green water on deck and hence the risk to the vessel is difficult to determine. Such data normally comes from model tests. Whilst model tests give some indication of the extent of green water on deck, the loading on particular items of equipment is well beyond the scope of such tests.

In order to demonstrate an acceptable level of risk due to green water loading, a different approach is required. The approach adopted in this paper is based on an initial assessment of the consequences of equipment failure due to green water in order to identify those items of equipment whose structural integrity is paramount to the safety of the vessel and its personnel.

The main steps are as follows:

1.   Identify, through primarily qualitative methods, the hazards to the vessel associated with green water on deck, consider the potential consequences of this on the vessel and distil from this any initiating events that could lead to loss of life or injury (i.e. what could green water on deck damage and what are the consequences).

2.   Identify through primarily qualitative methods the safety related risks to the vessel associated with green water on deck.

3.   Provide recommendations regarding items of equipment whose integrity must be maintained before the risk can be considered acceptable.

4.   Items which present a hazard to the vessel must then be analysed deterministically using simplifying assumptions consistent with the current level of understanding of the loading mechanisms and environment.

Should there be any hazards for which the risk remains unacceptable, then the assumptions in Step 4 may need to be reviewed and refined and additional deterministic

3

or statistical analyses undertaken to more accurately define the risks to the vessel and personnel.

To illustrate the hazards and events arising from green water, a high level event tree was prepared and is shown in Fig. 2.

6. CONSEQUENCES OF GREEN WATER ON DECK

There are two main initiating events associated with green water on deck which could cause injury or death or damage to systems or equipment. These are:

- damage to Temporary Refuge (TR) due to direct impact;

- dislodgement of systems and equipment mounted on the upper deck following wave impact.

These initiating events could lead to other consequential events. The principal consequential events and hazards identified are:

- damage to cargo or ballast tanks followed by uncontrolled flooding and a reduction in ship stability or buoyancy leading to capsize or sinking;

- a risk of structural, system or equipment failure and subsequent fire and explosions, which could have a direct consequence to the personnel on board or result in the impairment of the hull structural strength, possibly leading to sinking or capsize of the vessel;

- damage to the integrity of the TR, leading to injury of personnel within the TR.

Whilst this fault tree could be expanded and fully developed, the potential combinations of damage are limitless. A more reasonable approach is to consider a number of credible accident scenarios arising from the presence of green water on deck and to classify the risk of each one based on its perceived severity and probability, taking into account any mitigating circumtances. This can be undertaken in a primarily qualitative manner, although some analysis or modelling may be necessary to support the conclusions.

As part of the hazard identification exercise a ship visit should be arranged and a walkthrough of the vessel undertaken to identify whether the risks are credible and ensure that 'as fitted' information is used in the assessment.

As each hazard is identified, it is recorded on a standard Hazard Log. A generic Hazard Log for green water is illustrated in Table 1. The potential local damage is first identified. The potential consequences of this damage are then listed along with the mitigating factors/ safeguard and the results are summarised.

We would propose that during heavy weather, when green water on deck could be expected, access to the main deck by personnel is prohibited. This significantly reduces the number of hazard scenarios which need to be investigated.

7. RISK CLASSIFICATION

Once the hazards have been identified the risk to the vessel and personnel on board can be assessed. The risk is defined as the product of the severity of the hazard and the frequency. At this stage it is inappropriate to consider it in terms of Probable Loss of Life (PLL) which is the normal way of quantifying the risk. Instead a more general approach is adopted based on a risk matrix that allows engineering judgement to be applied.

The following judgemental scales (Tables shown on Page 5) are proposed for severity, based on Ref. 3:

If the risk is classified as **Acceptable** (i.e. 1E, 2E, 3D, 3E and 4A-4E) then no further work needs to be undertaken. If the risk is classified as **Unacceptable** or **Undesirable** then further work **must** be done to quantify the risk more accurately by undertaking some deterministic analysis to quantify the wave loading on deck structure and fittings or to provide a better understanding of the hazard, its probability of occurrence and any mitigating factors. Should the subsequent analysis indicate that there is still a significant risk to the vessel or its crew then further action will be required either to reduce or mitigate the risk or safeguard against the risk.

8. SIMPLIFIED WAVE LOADING

Where the Qualitative Risk Assessment indicated that there may be a significant risk to the vessel, the level of risk was further considered and quantified using simple analysis methods. The most difficult risk to quantify is the risk of green water impact damage to deck equipment.

As discussed previously, it is currently impractical to mathematically model the probability of green water on deck, the height of green water on deck or the effect it will have on the ship's structure and deck mounted equipment. In general, all data must come from model tests. Whilst model tests give some indication of the extent of green water on deck, the loading on particular items of equipment is normally well beyond the scope of such tests. Further, while there has been some recent research on green water loading, there is very little published data available.

A simple representation of the sea surface and vessel's motion has therefore been developed which will allow a reasonable assessment of the likelihood of shipping green water as a function of wave height and wave period.

Description	Category	Consequences
Catastrophic	I	Death or system loss
Critical	II	Severe injury, severe occupational illness or major system damage
Marginal	III	Minor injury, minor occupational illness, or minor system damage
Negligible	IV	Less than minor injury, occupational illness or system damage

The following judgemental scale is proposed for frequency:

Level	Frequency of Hazard
Frequent A (P>10^{-1})	Likely to occur frequently
Probable B (10^{-1}>P>10^{-3})	Will occur several times in the life of the FSU
Occasional C (10^{-3}>P>10^{-4})	Likely to occur within the life of the FSU
Remote D (10^{-4}>P>10^{-5})	Unlikely to occur within the life of the FSU
Improbable E (P<10^{-5})	So unlikely it can be assumed occurrence will not be experienced

By combining the above scales, the following risk matrix is formed:

Frequency of Occurrence	Hazard Categories			
	Catastrophic	Critical	Marginal	Negligible
Frequent	1A	2A	3A	4A
Probable	1B	2B	3B	4B
Occasional	1C	2C	3C	4C
Remote	1D	2D	3D	4D
Improbable	1E	2E	3E	4E

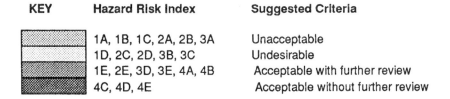

KEY	Hazard Risk Index	Suggested Criteria
	1A, 1B, 1C, 2A, 2B, 3A	Unacceptable
	1D, 2C, 2D, 3B, 3C	Undesirable
	1E, 2E, 3D, 3E, 4A, 4B	Acceptable with further review
	4C, 4D, 4E	Acceptable without further review

Such a preliminary assessment provides essential information on the response of the vessel, relative to the wave, to allow further work (either theoretical or experimental) to be more focused by identifying areas where green water on deck may be a problem.

The main simplifying assumptions used in the investigation were:

- linear analysis techniques were used to predict the occurrence and amplitude of green water along the length of the vessel in regular and irregular seas;

- the sea surface at the vessel can be represented by the undisturbed wave profile. *i.e.* the passing wave is not affected by the presence of the vessel. This is considered to be the 'worst case' assumption since the actual wave height will be less because the incident wave height will be 'squeezed out away from the vessel', see Ref. 4;

- the large amplitude motion of the vessel can be reasonably predicted by linear response amplitude operators derived using 2D - Strip Theory.

Once the wave loading on the structure or equipment has been calculated then it is a relatively simple matter of applying these loads to a structural model to calculate the stresses in the vessel's structure, equipment or seating arrangements.

8.1   WAVE HEIGHT AT DECK EDGE IN REGULAR WAVES

To obtain a better understanding of the vessel responses, a series of regular wave computer simulations in head seas, can be undertaken for a range of wave periods. The wave height associated with each of these wave periods can be calculated assuming regular waves with a limiting wave steepness of 1/10. While a wave steepness of 1/7 is theoretically possible in lower seastates, 1/13 is a more realistic limiting wave steepness during severe storm conditions. This compares favourably with the limiting steepness quoted in Ref. 2. A wave steepness of 1/10 is considered to be sufficiently conservative for calculation purposes.

The height of water on deck varies both spatially and temporally as shown in Fig. 3. Due to the phasing of the vessel's pitch and heave motion relative to the wave excitation it is improbable that a wave would come over the bow and wash down the complete length of the deck.

The distribution of the maximum height of water on deck for each regular wave period can then be calculated and superimposed onto a single diagram. The locus of maximum height of water on deck for head seas, for all regular wave periods, is illustrated in Fig. 4. The limiting water height at any location along the deck is dependent on the wave period and height. For example, the maximum height of water at the TR front bulkhead is 2.5 metres above the deck at side and occurs with a wave period of 10 seconds, whereas the maximum height of water amidships is 5.5 metres and the maximum height of water over the bow is approxi-

mately 13.5 metres occurring at a wave period of 12 seconds.

The linear wave theory can be further extended to irregular waves. Limiting Hs-Tz curves can then be developed for head seas using an appropriate wave spectra and vessel RAOs derived from strip theory analysis. These limiting Hs-Tz curves can then be imposed onto a wave scatter diagram as illustrated in Fig. 5. The probability of exceeding a defined height of water on deck is then given by the area of the scatter diagram above the limiting curves. For example, Fig. 5 indicates that there is a relatively high risk of green water both over the bow bulwark and in way of the front bulkhead of the TR with a significant wave height of only 6 metres. Fig. 5 also shows that there is a significant risk of a water height of 5 metres above the forward bulwark, whereas there is very little risk of a water height greater than 5 metres above the deck in way of the forward bulkhead of the TR.

8.2   FLUID VELOCITY IN DIRECTION OF WAVE PROPAGATION

Waves in near head seas will swell up at the bow, as shown in Fig. 6, and break inboards. It is probable that waves will also swell up along the side of the vessel and break inboard in a similar manner. As the wave breaks inboard the potential energy in the wave crest will convert to kinetic energy producing a fluid velocity in the transverse direction. The wave may also contain some residual fluid velocity in the direction of the wave propagation. The resultant fluid velocity will be some combination of the fluid velocity due to the wave breaking inboard and the residual fluid velocity vector due to the wave propagation. The residual fluid velocity in the direction of wave propagation cannot be accurately determined and hence the maximum horizontal fluid velocity determined from linear wave theory should be assumed. It is accepted that this is grossly conservative but in the absence of experimental results it is considered to be appropriate.

The maximum horizontal fluid velocity in the direction of wave propagation can be calculated from the following expression:-

$$u = \frac{\pi H}{T \tanh\left(\frac{2\pi h}{\lambda}\right)}$$

Where   u is the horizontal particle velocity (m / s)
         H is the wave height (m)
         T is the wave period (secs)
         h is the water depth (m)
         λ is the wave length (m)

For deep water this simplifies to:-

$$u = \frac{\pi H}{T}$$

From the above expression it can be seen that the highest fluid velocities result from high short waves (i.e. steep waves).

8.3 FLUID VELOCITY DUE TO INBOARD BREAKING WAVE

The fluid behaviour due to the inboard breaking wave resembles the theoretical dam breaking model. (Ref. 5). In this model it is assumed that initially there is a vertical wall of water on one side of the dam. At t=0 the dam is removed and the water flows into the empty space (Fig.7). The flow of water onto the deck is proportional to the root pressure height of water before the dam breaks:-

$$u = 2\left(\sqrt{gh} - \sqrt{gz}\right)$$

where u is the horizontal fluid velocity (m/s)

g is the acceleration due to gravity (m/s²)

h is the water height at time t = 0 seconds

$$z = \left(-\frac{y}{3\sqrt{gt}} + \frac{2}{3}\sqrt{h}\right)^2$$

where z is the height of water over the deck (m) and

y is the distance inboard from the ship's side(m)

t is the time (secs)

The resultant combined fluid velocity is the vector summation of the two components.

8.4 IMPACT PRESSURE ON TUBULAR MEMBERS

The slam loading (F) on a cylinder can be derived from the following expression (Ref. 6):

$$F = C\rho A u^2$$

where C is an empirical impact coefficient
(1.5 for smooth Circular Cylinders)

ρ is the density of water (kg / m³)

A is the Projected area of the cylinder (m²)

u is the fluid velocity (m/s)

8.5 IMPACT PRESSURE ON FLAT PLATES

The green water impact loads on flat plate panels is analogous with a jet of water impinging onto a plate (Ref. 7).

Based on experiment the peak pressure (p) is dependent on the square of the velocity as follows:

$$p = C\rho u^2$$

where C is an empirical impact coefficient

(1.0 for green seas on deck)

ρ is the density of water (kg/m³)

u is the fluid velocity (m/s)

The above wave impact pressures can then be applied to simplified structural models of the deck equipment and the stresses in the equipment, seating and bolting arrangements assessed.

9. ANALYSIS OF ALBA FSU

The above methodology for investigating the risk due to green water was applied to the Chevron ALBA FSU.

The FSU was designed by BAeSEMA and built in accordance with Lloyd's Rules and Regulations for the Classification of Ships, with some enhancements for North Sea operation. It was the first FSU to consider the impact of the 'new' safety case legislation following Lord Cullen's enquiry into the Piper Alpha disaster. The hull section modulus and plating quality was enhanced over the minimum Lloyd's values and limited use was made of higher tensile steel. These enhancements reduce the risk of brittle fracture (due to low temperatures) and increase fatigue durability.

The vessel did not have a forecastle and hence the forward bulwark height and scantlings were significantly increased to reduce the risk of green water on the fore deck and protect the forward turret area from damage.

The safety systems (e.g. fire and gas detection, monitoring and extinguishing systems and emergency shutdown systems) were designed in accordance with UK offshore engineering practice. The remaining ship systems (e.g. cargo pumping, venting and ballast systems) were designed in accordance with normal ship classification society rules.

The vessel is arranged with an internal turret mooring system at the forward end. Above the turret is a service gantry for the turret swivels. Immediately aft of the turret are the main cargo storage tanks. Cargo is stored in the centre tanks only. The wing tanks are arranged for protected location ballast in accordance with the MARPOL regulations in force at the time of construction. The accommodation and machinery spaces are located aft, as on a conventional tanker. The General Arrangement is shown in Fig. 8.

The principal dimensions of the ALBA FSU were selected to minimise the vessel motions. Minimising the vessel motions helps to improve habitability and reduce fatigue loading on moorings and risers. Minimisation of the vessel motions may, however, also increase the probability of shipping green seas in certain weather/ sea conditions. Following an incident on the 1st January 1995, whereby a large wave was shipped over the bow which resulted in some minor damage to the vessel systems, a study was initiated to identify the risk of damage to the deck mounted equipment and the consequences of such damage to the vessel and personnel on board.

10.   ACCIDENT SCENARIOS USED TO IDENTIFY INTERMEDIATE EVENTS

A number of accident scenarios were considered to identify any consequential effects from green seas which could potentially lead to a major hazard to the vessel and a Risk Register prepared. The accident scenarios assume that the vessel is in the Delayed Export Condition (fully loaded). The study assumed that at the onset of a storm the vessel would be fully loaded and unable to offload to a shuttle tanker. The vessel will be at its deepest draught/lowest freeboard and hence the probability and height of green water will be greatest. At lesser draughts the freeboard is greater and consequently the risk due to green water on deck is less.

In extreme environments likely to produce green water on the deck of the FSU, the weather vaning characteristics of the FSU will ensure that the waves will approach the vessel within a +/- 30 degree sector of the bow. Taking this factor into account the following accident scenarios were identified:

1. Toppling of the Turret gantry

2. Toppling of the LP vent mast

3. Toppling of the floodlight masts

4. Damage to main deck fore and aft walkway

5. Dislodgement of the Field Store/lab/Paint Store

6. Dislodgement of the helifuel store

7. Toppling of the crane

8. Dislodgement of the fiscal meter skid

9. Dislodgement of equipment and subsequent impact on TR.

10. Impingement of articles onto the TR front bulkhead

11. Domino effect scenarios:

- turret gantry collapses, vent mast collapses and there is damage to the forward part of the walkway;

- field store dislodged, helifuel dislodged/opened, crane collapses and aft starboard floodlight collapses.

For each of the failure scenarios defined above an assessment was made of the potential systems which could be damaged as a result of the failure. In particular, the loss of containment and the availability of safety systems (primarily the inert gas system) was evaluated. Any other mitigating factors were listed (such as protection offered by other structure, deck equipment or pipework). The most significant of these hazards (damage to the turret gantry) is presented below, to illustrate the process.

11.   TOPPLING OF THE TURRET GANTRY

The turret gantry is located at the forward end of the vessel above the turret (Fig. 9) and is used as a gantry crane for maintaining the turret components, particularly the swivel stack.

Toppling of the turret gantry may damage the deck plating and pipework on deck. This could result in some flooding of ballast tanks, loss of cargo contain-ment and loss of inert gas protection. As the turret also supports electrical lighting there is potentially a source of ignition. Generally, collapse of the structure would also put at risk items immediately below such as swivels, pig receiver and ESD valve and piping.

Toppling of the turret gantry could result in damage to main deck plating potentially leading to flooding of the forward ballast tanks. A stability mode of loss analysis was undertaken to identify the level of damage which would have to be incurred by the vessel before it would either fail to meet the IMO intact stability criteria, cap-size or sink. The mode of loss analysis indicated that the vessel could withstand damage and consequential flooding of one wing ballast tank with the reserve of stability and buoyancy exceeding the IMO **intact** stability criteria.

Additionally, flooding calculations were undertaken to estimate the probable flooding times for various size holes. The flooding calculations indicated that it would take several hours for the tank to fully flood. The ballast systems should still be operational and any water flooding into the ballast tanks can quickly be pumped out. Toppling of the turret gantry will not result in significant loss of stability.

The major risk is associated with the fracture of import and export lines along with fracture of the inert gas line. This could result in the loss of the inert gas blanket over the tank and loss of cargo containment. Further, the forward gantry supports electrical cabling which could also be damaged producing a source of ignition. The loss of inventory and the source of ignitions could result in pool fires which could ultimately lead to the impairment of the TR.

The consequences of pool fires were identified in the Quantified Risk Assessment for the ALBA Floating Storage Unit. The turret is located at the forward end of the vessel and the TR at the aft end. The TR is widely separated from the turret and this reduces the risk to the TR due to pool fires. In addition, the weather conditions and vessel motions prevalent will disperse the inventory thus reducing the probability of pool fires developing, consequently reducing the risk to the TR. Damage to the turret equipment immediately below the gantry and the subsequent loss of containment could result in a risk to the environment and have considerable implications to field production, thus the loads on the gantry needed to be quantified to ensure that any loss of field production was minimised and the risk to the environment was acceptable.

12. DISCUSSION

Green water on deck can cause damage to equipment and structure mounted on the deck and can subsequently result in risk to personnel. While we are now in a better position to quantify the effect of such damage, our current understanding of green water on deck is such that we must consider the most onerous foreseeable conditions which could occur and combine these with assumptions which are sufficiently conservative to offset any uncertainty in the applied loading. This will ensure that there is an adequate factor of safety between the applied loading and the strength of the structure or equipment to safeguard against failure.

One consideration when applying the above approach arises when the analysis indicates that there is an unacceptable risk to the vessel or its personnel. Since it is known that the approach significantly overestimates the structural loading and the risk to the vessel, it is difficult to determine whether the risk is actual or perceived. For example, if the analysis indicates that the stress in a holding down bolt is less than its yield strength then it can be concluded that the risk of failure of the bolt is negligible. However, if the calculated stress in the bolt exceeds the yield strength of the bolt then this would indicate that there may be a risk of failure of the bolt which could result in a potential risk to personnel. While we know that the results are conservative we do not know how conservative and without a better understanding of the mechanics of green water on deck we cannot justify ignoring the risk since it cannot be proved that the risk is ALARP. The risk to the vessel and personnel must then be effectively managed to ensure that the risk is ALARP. In the above example there are two alternative actions to reduce the risk. Either:

1) the consequences of the failures need to be further reviewed, or

2) the structural arrangement or seating will need to be modified to reduce the risk of failure.

There is limited scope for modifying the consequences of failure and adopting Option 2 may result in an excessive over-design of the structure or seating. Where only minor modifications to the structure are required to reduce the risk, then these modifications should be undertaken. Where major modifications are indicated then a cost/benefit analysis will need to be undertaken to determine what extent of modification is achievable and practicable to ensure that the risk is ALARP.

In undertaking the analysis the loading due to green water is still the major source of uncertainty, but the above approach allows the risk to be assessed and those hazards which result in negligible risk to be discounted. It is, however, imperative that we gain a better understanding of the mechanics of green water on deck and the resulting loading on structures and equipment on vessels. This would place the naval architect in a much better position to quantify the associated risks and design the structure and equipment to reduce the risk.

13. CONCLUSIONS AND RECOMMENDATIONS

To better understand the phenomena we need to:

*   develop better met-ocean data;

*   develop better mathematical models of the motions of a vessel in extreme waves;

*   develop probabilistic distributions of key parameters to allow a better estimate of the probability of occurrence and the risk of green water;

*   define target reliabilities/risk tolerance indices.

The recording and analysis of met-ocean data is an ongoing process, although a lot of this data is of a proprietary nature and is not readily available to the industry at large.

It is also understood that there is currently some research being undertaken to investigate the loads arising from green water on vessels, however, the results of this research is unlikely to be widely available to industry for some time.

While we are now in a better position to quantify the effect of such damage by adopting the methodology detailed above, our knowledge of the effects of green water are still limited. There remains an immediate requirement to develop better physical modelling of green water on deck and a better understanding of the probability distribution of key parameters to allow the risk due to green water on deck to be better quantified.

14. REFERENCES

1. HMSO: 'A Guide to Offshore Installations (Safety Case) Regulations 1992'.

2. FAULKNER, D and WILLIAMS, R A: 'Design for Abnormal Ocean Waves', RINA Spring Meeting 1996. Programmable.

3. DEFSTAN 56: 'Hazard Analysis and Safety Classification of the Computer and Electronic System Elements of Defence Equipment'.

4. BARRIE, D A: 'The Influence of Diffraction on the Stability Assessment of Ships', Transactions of the Royal Institute of Naval Architecture, April 1985.

5. BUCHNER, B: 'On the Impact of Green Water Loading on Ship and Offshore Unit Design', PRADS95, September 1995

6. BUCHNER, B: 'The Impact of Green Water on FPSO Design', OTC7698, Offshore Technology Conference, May 1995.

7. SUHARA et al: 'Shock Pressure due to Impact of Water Jet and Response of Elastic Plates', Transactions of the West-Japan Society of Naval Architects, No.46, 1973.

Fig. 1 Superstructure Damage on Passenger Ship due to Green Water

Reproduced from Ship Design and Construction, The Society of Naval Architects and Marine Engineers

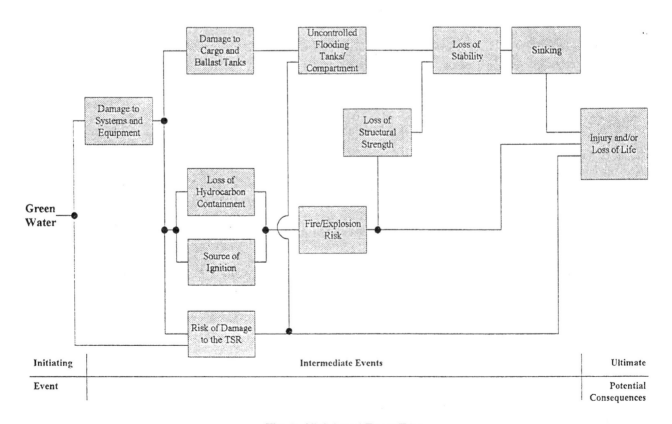

Fig. 2 High Level Event Tree

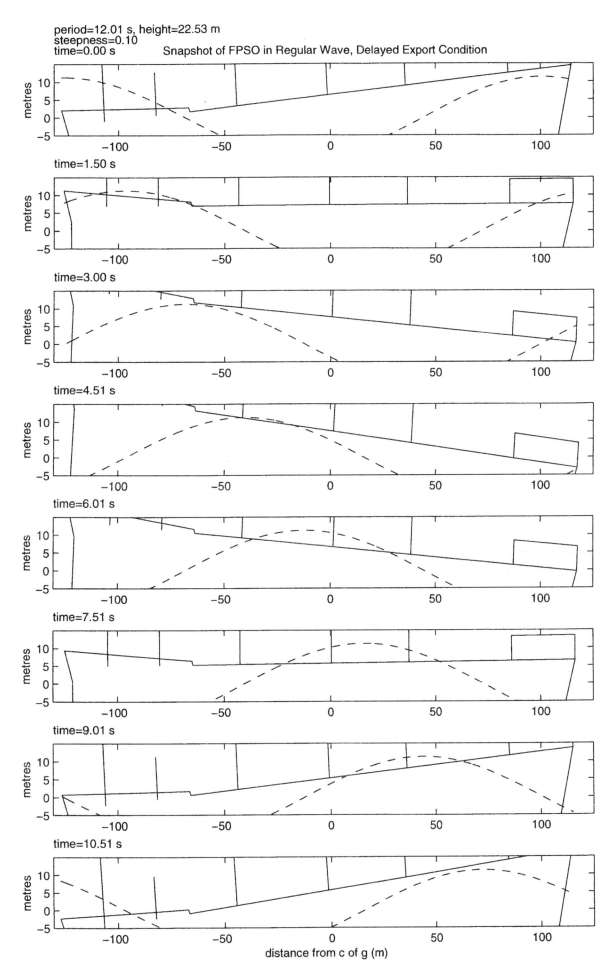

Fig. 3 Maximum height of water on deck for Regular waves with a maximum steepness of 1/10.

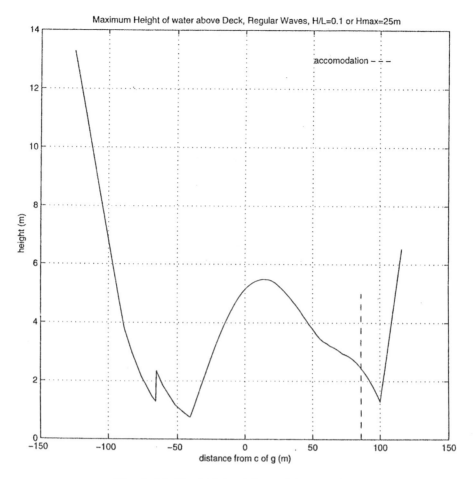

Fig. 4 Limiting Height of Green Water on Deck

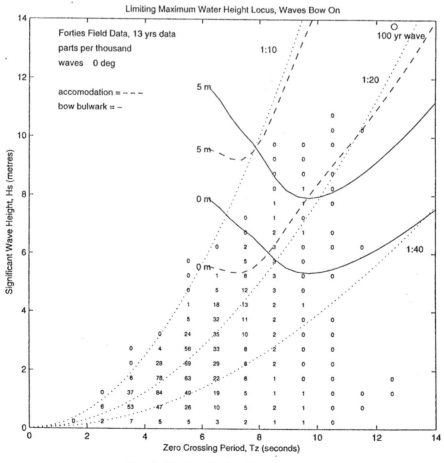

Fig. 5 Limiting Hs-Tz Diagram for Bow Waves

Fig. 6 Typical Water Elevation over the Bow in Severe Weather

Reproduced from Ship Design and Construction, The Society of Naval Architects and Marine Engineers.

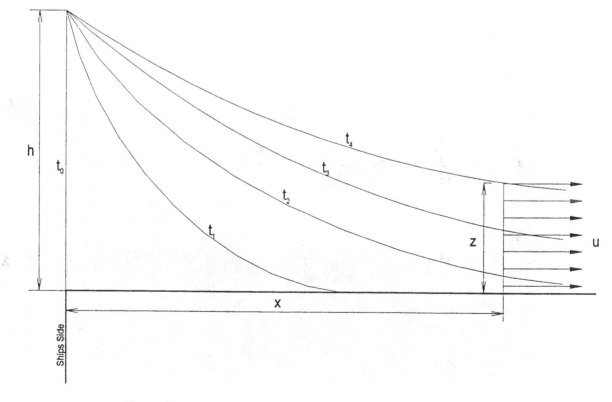

Fig. 7 Transverse Fluid Velocity due to Dam-Breaking Effect

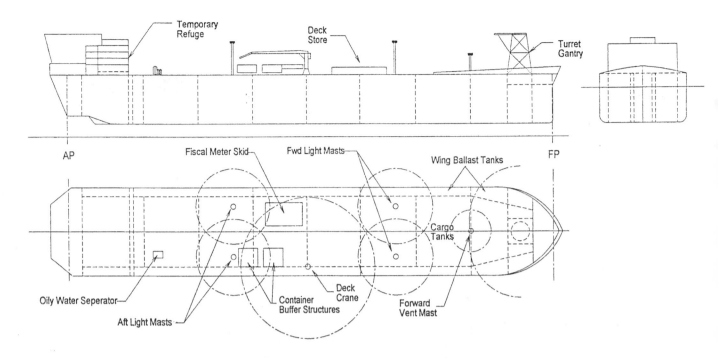

Fig. 8 Outline General Arrangement of the ALBA FSU

Fig. 9 ALBA FSU Turret Arrangement

Major Hazard	Potential Local Effect	Potential Global Effect	Mitigating Factors /Safeguards
Loss of Stability	Puncture in ballast or cargo tanks Damage to tank hatches or vent pipes Damage to Ballast Control Systems	Uncontrolled flooding of cargo/ballast tanks and loss of stability	Reserve of intact and damage stability above IMO minimum intact standards Increased freeboard
Risk of Fire and Explosion	Damage to :- ballast or cargo tank boundaries tank hatches or vent pipes Inert Gas main cargo export line cargo import lines vent mast and LP main Firemain walkway services Swivels/Pig Trap/ESD Valves	Damage to tanks, import and export lines, tank hatches or other fitting could result in loss of cargo containment. Damage to vent masts or pipework could result in gas release. Damage to Inert Gas line would result in loss of IG blanket in tanks and increase the risk of hydrocarbon release. Ignition could result from damage to electrical cables or due to sparks caused by impact of metallic objects Damage to fire and gas detection and other safety systems	Environmental conditions present at the time would rapidly disperse any flammable gas. Green water and spray would cool any pool fires that developed. No one present on deck
Loss of Hull Structural Integrity	Damage to deck plating	Loss of main hull girder strength	Enhanced factors of safety on hull section modulus Thickness of deck plating
Damage to TR	Debris from event could be projected against the house front by green water Direct green water damage	Direct injury to personnel Ingress of water Depressurisation of TR and ingress of flammable gas	The probability and consequences decrease as the distance from TR increases

TABLE 1 Generic Green Water Hazard Log

PAPER NO.14.

AN INTEGRATED APPROACH FOR A SHIP SAFETY ESTIMATION IN ABNORMAL CONDITIONS

by M Gerigk
Faculty of Ocean Engineering and Ship Technology,
Technical University, Gdansk, Poland

Paper presented at the

International Conference

DESIGN AND OPERATION FOR ABNORMAL CONDITIONS

21 22 OCTOBER 1997 GLASGOW

AN INTEGRATED APPROACH FOR A SHIP SAFETY ESTIMATION IN ABNORMAL CONDITIONS

Miroslaw Gerigk
Faculty of Ocean Engineering and Ship Technology
Technical University of Gdansk

SUMMARY

In this paper a method for a ship safety estimation at the preliminary stage of hydromechanic design is briefly presented. But it may be developed for all the project stages. Both the hydrostatic and dynamical problems are taken into account. The theoretical and computational models are described too. The safety assessment may be done for the stability, manoeuvrability, seakeeping, damage stability and survivability using the IMO regulations. The method enables the evaluation of the influence of the hull form parameters, cargo distribution and exciting forces impact on a ship safety. The impact forces may follow from many sources but the cargo and ballast shift and wave and wind are mainly taken into account. Describing the method a safety estimation algorithm is presented and some results are given for a cargo-passenger ferry in abnormal conditions.

AUTHOR'S BIOGRAPHY

Dr. Miroslaw Gerigk graduated from the Shipbuilding Research Institute, Technical University of Gdansk (TUG) in 1984. Now he is a lecturer of Naval Architecture and Ocean Engineering at the Faculty of Ocean Engineering and Ship Technology, TUG. He obtained his MSc and PhD degrees from the Technical University of Gdansk in 1984 and 1991 respectively.

The appointments in his career have been as follows: (1984-1988) Research Assistant, Division of Hydro-mechanics, Shipbuilding Research Institute TUG; (1988-1989) Lecturer, Division of Hydromechanics, Ship-building Research Institute TUG; (1989-1992) Research Assistant, Department of Marine Technology, University of Newcastle upon Tyne; (1992-1997) Senior Lecturer, Division of Hydromechanics, Faculty of Ocean Engineering and Ship Technology TUG.

1. INTRODUCTION

The safety of ships still lies between the most important aspects of modern Ocean Engineering and Ship Technology. To confirm this we may find a lot of tragic examples [1][2][3]. One which can be shortly presented is the accident of the newly built research ship RESOLUTION on the Greenland Sea in 1995 [4]. The vessel had about fifty scientists and crew on board when she met two very heavy storms acting together. There were also many icebergs in the vicinity and at that point it was not clear whether the ship could survive. The wind was up to one hundred knots. The wave height reached about twenty metres and she tried to keep the head sea course. It was too late to turn the ship because of a big drilling tower. The thrusters were used to hold the course. The speed decreased due to the power division. Finally a big wave broke the bridge windows and a lot of water got into the navigating bridge. The thrusters could not work any more because the computers were switched off. It seemed as if the ship would certainly capsize. It did not happen. The

crew and scientists managed to survive for at least fifteen hours.

The loss of the Polish ferry JAN HEWELIUSZ, which sank on the Baltic Sea very close to the Arcona Peninsula on 14th January 1993, was very tragic. It has brought about a lot of scientific and practical investigations. Twenty two Polish ships were lost between 1946 and 1993, and about one hundred and twenty eight people died during those tragedies. The most dramatic of them were the accidents of the following ships [5]:

- m/s MAZUREK, a bulk cargo ship, lost in abnormal conditions on the Baltic Sea in 1963. Six mariners died; main reason: unknown;

- m/s NYSA, a general cargo ship, lost in abnormal conditions on the North Sea in 1965. All eighteen mariners died; main reason: unknown;

- m/s KUDOWA ZDRÓJ, a general cargo ship, lost in abnormal conditions on the Mediterranean Sea in 1983. Twenty mariners died; main reason: cargo shift (?);

- m/s BUSKO ZDRÓJ, a general cargo ship, lost in abnormal conditions on the North Sea in 1985. Twenty four mariners died; main reason: cargo shift (?);

- m/f JAN HEWELIUSZ, a cargo-passenger ferry, lost in abnormal conditions on the Baltic Sea in 1993. Fifty four men died, including twenty mariners; main reason: stormy weather, cargo shift (?).

The majority of these ships met the abnormal conditions in the time of accident. But the reasons accidents happen at sea have always been very both complex and difficult to explain particularly when all the mariners and passengers lost their lives. The question mark is especially put because of doubts about the reasons. There are always complex reasons for accidents and they depend on many factors. Despite of all the efforts always undertaken to explain each accident there is a growing need to have an International Safety Code for the ships. This task is difficult and requires a lot of work.

From the general point of view the following factors may secure a ship at sea [6][7]:

- human factor;
- control systems;
- technical means, and
- legislative actions.

And these are first level factors.

There are existing interrelations between them and they play a major role for ship safety. Then we come to the conclusion that there is another group of factors which have an immediate influence on ship safety at sea and the most important are as follows [8]:

- ship characteristics including hull, propeller and rudder;

- cargo characteristics including arrangement of internal spaces, cargo and ballast distribution and loading condition;

- environment characteristics including wind, waves and current;

- operational characteristics connected mainly with the integrated ship management system if available; if not then both the navigational aids and information available on board are very important (ship speed and course?);

- human factors including both the psychological and physical predispositions, character, morale, integrity, knowledge, experience and training degree.

And these are the second level factors.

The ship safety domains as stability, survivability or manoeuvrability depend on a complex set of parameters which belong to the different factors from either the first or second levels. For example the stability safety depends on the following factors: ship dimensions, main dimensions ratios, hull form, form coefficients, hydrostatics, cargo and ballast distribution, loading condition, ship centre of gravity, etc. But it also depends on the environment characteristics as the wind, waves and current parameters. More, it depends on the human factor and all the control systems, technical means and legislative actions such as existing regulations for example.

Next there are interrelations between the safety domains as between both the stability and manoeuvr-

ability, stability and survivability, stability and sea-keeping or stability, manoeuvrability and seakeeping. All of them often depend on the same factors of the second level for example. The interrelations between the safety domains and the interrelations between certain hydromechanic characteristics/parameters are the reason why a common set of parameters they depend on should be created.

And these parameters should be the third level factors.

Taking into account the interrelations between the factors at different levels and the interrelations between the factors at the same level we come to the conclusion that the system approach applied for the ship safety estimation is both very complicated to create and difficult tool in using it. But the first step is done and a structure of the levels of factors affecting a ship safety may be as presented in Fig. 1.

When a ship encounters abnormal conditions all the factors discussed are very important for the safety of the ship but the interrelations between them have the biggest influence on the dynamical ship characteristics. They are taken into consideration when both the manoeuvrability and seakeeping models are in use.

The major sources of information on hazards and risks involved in shipping are both the statistics and investigations into serious casualties [5][18][19][20]. Studying this information it becomes clear that the safety of life at sea and the pollution of the environment are a function of the actual ship's design, operation and maintenance conditions. Therefore an integrated rational framework is necessary. Such a framework should apply an approach based on risk acceptance criteria (if available) combining both the designs features and operational, ageing, safety and pollution prevention aspects.

Taking all the above into account a method for safety estimation has been worked out. The method is associated with the ship safety problems concerning the naval architecture and ship hydromechanics.

2. INTEGRATED SHIP SAFETY ESTIMATION METHOD

A proposal of Integrated Ship Safety Estimation Method (ISSEM) has been prepared including the theoretical and computational models. The theoretical model describes both the global and technical approaches. The computational model uses these approaches in the form of a dynamical data base.

The global approach adopts the idea of the Formal Safety Assessment method together with the integrated system approach briefly described in Section 1 [9][10][11][12].

The basic assumptions when applying the global approach were as follows:

- ship operation is associated with a risk from the safety point of view;

- safety measures should be quantified as without this you can not manage the safety;

- ISSEM method should be applicable.

The global approach has enabled the preparation of the ISSEM method framework as follows [13][14]:

- method philosophy development including reviewing literature, existing vessels, regulations, etc.;

- ship and environment definition;

- hazard and scenario identification;

- hazard and risk assessment;

- hazard resolving and risk reduction;

- cost/benefit analysis;

- decisions made on ship safety (selection of optimal design, operational and mitigation measures).

Finally the ISSEM method should enable a Safety Code proposal to be prepared. The technical approach is connected with developing the following [13] [14]:

- logical structure of ISSEM design system;

- logical structure of ISSEM computational model;

- both analytical and numerical methods for ISSEM;

- application methods for ISSEM.

The links between the global and technical approaches are incorporated by the computational model. The structure of the ISSEM design system combines both the global and technical approaches. The logical structure of the ISSEM design system is presented in Fig. 2.

The most important features of the ISSEM system are as follows:

- the system is open;

- the structure is hybrid-modular;

- the system has a common library of analytical and numerical methods;

- the system has a common library of application methods (direct geometry-based methods are preferable);

- the system should enable the analysis to be done at a few project stages.

The computational model is based on the DYNAMICAL HYDROMECHANIC DATA BASE (DHDB) concept and it is original. The basic information concerning the DHDB was published a few years ago when a computer program for the preliminary ship design of operational stability was discussed [15]. The structure of DHDB data base is presented in Fig. 3.

The DHDB data base enables the safety analysis to be done when the ship hydromechanic characteristics can be obtained using either hydronumerical calculations (direct methods), model tests results, results from the full scale trials, empirical and hydronumerical calculations (semi direct methods) or empirical calculations (indirect methods).

Both the ship and environment are defined as hydromechanic objects described by a set of parameters. The methods using both the functions and procedures associated with solving particular hydromechanic problems are called safety domains ("Hydromechanic Analysis"). The "Risk Assessment" module includes the methods which combine both the "hydromechanic" and "risk assessment" functions and procedures. Currently this module applies not too many methods. The DHDB data base has a lot of advantages and a few disadvantages. In fact another paper could be written on the DHDB data base concept details.

3.   SHIP AND ENVIRONMENT DEFINITION

This is the first step in a risk assessment approach to the safety problems. As the ISSEM method is prepared to deal with the safety problems (including partial risk assessment approaches, too) from the ship hydromechanic point of view, the following elements describe a ship: hull, propeller and rudder.

The hull is defined by:

- Hull form representation - consisting of main dimensions, form coefficients and a changeable number of waterlines at each section. The dynamically interpolated sections have been introduced to increase the accuracy of numerical calculations. Some singularities of the hull form are taken into account, too. During the calculations the hull form is mainly represented by the network of cubic splines or b-splines.

- Arrangement of internal spaces - generated according to both the existing classification and operational rules. It can be evaluated by the survivability analysis, too. The watertight compartments' form is interpolated from the hull form representation.

- Hydrostatic characteristics - include the Bonjean scale and ship hydrostatics. The compartments' hydrostatic characteristics are attached as well.

- Cargo distribution - done according to the arrangement of internal spaces. Both the centre of gravity

3

and trim can be estimated using the iterative process.

The propeller and rudder are currently defined separately by both their geometry and hydrodynamic coefficients. The direct methods to calculate their hydrodynamic characteristics will be applied as well. Some examples concerning a ship definition are presented in Fig. 4.

The environment description consists of the wave and wind definitions. Because a few safety domains are considered and different application methods used by the ISSEM method, the regular wave theory and pseudo spectrum approach (similar to the St. Denis & Pierson method) are used [16]. The main idea of this approach is to substitute the real frequency for the encounter one:

$$\omega_E = \omega - (\omega^2/g) \cdot v_S \cdot \cos \gamma \qquad (3.1)$$

where: ω_E - encounter frequency;

ω real frequency;

v_S heading speed;

γ ship course angle according to the wave propagation direction.

Using the pseudo spectrum approach the irregular waves are presented as a Fourier series expansion by the encounter frequencies:

$$\zeta_W (t) = \zeta_{Wi} \cdot \sin (\omega_{Ei} t + \varepsilon_1) \qquad (3.2)$$

where: ε_1 random number with constant distribution in range $[0, 2\pi]$;

ζ_{Wi} amplitudes of harmonics calculated using the JONSWAP spectrum or another [16] [21];

$\zeta_W (t)$ wave amplitude.

The wind is defined by the apparent wind speed v_A used for the wind resistance calculation [17]. It depends on the ship speed v_S, real wind speed v_W and ship course angle according to wind β_W as follows:

$$v_A = v_S^2 + v_W^2 - 2 \cdot v_S + v_W \cdot \cos \beta_W \qquad (3.3)$$

4. HAZARD AND SCENARIO IDENTIFICATION

The major hazards on board ship include [18]: ship casualties, human casualties, failures, pollution and unlawful acts. In this work we have mainly been interested in the ship casualties from the hydro-mechanic point of view and the hazard identification is closely connected with the system approach applied by the ISSEM method. The following methods can be used to identify the hazards [18]: casualty statistics, failure rates, failure mode and effect analysis, hazard and operability studies (HAZOP). Up to now the casualty statistics have been applied by the ISSEM method. The statistics were taken from the publications: [5][18][19][20]. All the statistics have been put into the DHDB data base briefly described in Section 2.

Considering the potential hazards and initiating events it is possible to identify the significant accidental scenarios. Such an analysis needs a lot of model test and full scale trials data as well as numerical simulations. This is in order to identify the consequences of initiating events. The event tree analysis, fault tree analysis, cause consequence analysis and escape, evacuation and rescue analysis may enable us to assess how the initiating event arises and what the consequences will be.

A simple ISSEM event tree analysis in the case of a cargo-passenger ferry accident is presented in Fig. 5.

Analysing the factors of the first, second and third levels it has been decided that the exciting forces may follow from:

– external sources: wind, wave and current defined as the environment;

– internal sources: cargo and ballast shift.

Other exciting forces as the rudder hydrodynamic force are taken into account, too.

5. HAZARD AND RISK ASSESSMENT

For the risk assessment both the hydromechanic and risk assessment application methods are applied. So far, the risk assessment techniques have been used for the stability, survivability and seakeeping analysis.

The buoyancy condition calculation for both the undamaged and damaged ship can be done according to the hydrostatic data and direct calculations for any ship trim. The stability analysis can be done using the cross curves or constant displacement method. The stability is evaluated according to the current loading condition. The loading calculations are based on the arrangement of internal spaces and cargo, stores and ballast distribution, using the iterative approach. When the full loading condition is achieved for example and the centre of gravity known, the stability righting arms can be obtained. Then the stability parameters are checked against the IMO stability criteria [22].

The probabilistic concept has been adopted for the ISSEM survivability assessment and the algorithm was presented in the following papers for example [7][23].

4

The resistance and propulsion analysis is mainly needed for the manoeuvrability assessment. The exciting beam forces generated by both the rudder and propeller may be taken into account when the stability is evaluated [24]. The resistance and propulsion algorithms are taken from [25].

The manoeuvrability characteristics are very important from the safety point of view. The very well known modular approach has been applied for the manoeuvrability calculation and the algorithm applied is from [26]:

$$m \cdot (u - r \cdot \dot{v}) = X_H + X_P + X_R + X_E$$
$$m \cdot (u + r \cdot \dot{v}) = Y_H + Y_P + Y_R + Y_E \qquad (5.1)$$
$$I_z \cdot \dot{r} = M_H + M_P + M_R + M_E$$

where indices H,P,R describe the Hull, Propeller and Rudder generated exciting hydrodynamic forces. The index E represents the environment exciting forces from both the wind, waves and current.

When the seakeeping is under consideration then the following degrees of freedom are taken into account [16]: rolling, pitching, heaving, surging and swaying. The system of differential equations describing a ship motion in waves is as follows:

$$(m + m_{11}) \ddot{\xi}_G + \lambda_{11} \dot{\xi}_G = F_\lambda(t) \qquad (5.2)$$
$$(m + m_{22}) \ddot{\eta}_G + \lambda_{22} \dot{\eta}_G = F_\eta(t)$$
$$(m + m_{33}) \ddot{\zeta}_G + \lambda_{33} \dot{\zeta}_G + \gamma S_{WL} \zeta_G + m_{35} \ddot{\psi} +$$
$$(\lambda_{35} + vm_{33}) \dot{\psi} + (\lambda_{33} - \gamma S_{WL}(x_f - x_g)) \psi = F_\zeta(t)$$
$$(I_X + m_{44}) \ddot{\phi} + R(\dot{\phi}) + D \, GM \, \phi = M_\phi(t)$$
$$(I_X + m_{55}) \ddot{\psi} + (\lambda_{55} + (v^2/\omega_E) \lambda_{33}) \dot{\psi} + (\gamma I_{WL} - vm_{33}) \psi +$$
$$m_{35} \ddot{\zeta}_G + \lambda_{35} \cdot vm_{33}) \dot{\zeta}_G + (- \gamma S_{WL}(x_f - x_g) - v\lambda_{33}) \zeta_G = M_\psi(t)$$

where: m - ship mass;

$m_{11}, m_{22}, m_{33}, m_{44}, m_{55}$	corresponding added masses;
$\lambda_{11}, \lambda_{22}, \lambda_{33}, \lambda_{44}, \lambda_{55}$	corresponding wave damping coefficients;
$\xi_G, \eta_G, \zeta_G, \phi, \psi$	surging, swaying, heaving, rolling and pitching motions;
$F_\lambda(t), F_\eta(t), F_\zeta(t)$	corresponding exciting forces;
$M_\phi(t), M_\psi(t)$	corresponding exciting moments;
x_f	abscissa of the centre of waterplane area;
x_g	abscissa of the centre of gravity;
I_{WL}, S_{WL}	inertia moment of the waterplane area.

The coupling between pitching and heaving is taken into account, too. The hydrodynamic components of exciting forces are ignored in rolling and heaving where the restoring terms exist. The seakeeping computational model enables us to obtain the significant values of roll, pitch, surge, sway and heave accelerations and compare them with the officially adopted seakeeping standards. The yaw motion is fully undertaken by the manoeuvrability computational model. To get the full information for the safety decision process it is necessary to know the contribution of each motion to the full acceleration vector at a given ship point. The roll contribution should be considered as the most significant when ship at the beam position. In the ISSEM method the importance of each motion contribution depends mainly on the following seakeeping factors:

- ship hull form (parameters: main dimensions, coefficients, body form, ...);

- technical devices such as thrusters and foils (parameters: ...);

- sea environment: wind, wave, current (parameters: direction, speed, wind pressure; amplitude, ...);

- loading condition (parameters: arrangement of internal spaces, cargo distribution, centre of gravity, centre of buoyancy, heel, trim, metacentric height, ...);

- heading speed and course angle;

- human factor (experience, physical abilities, mental abilities,...).

This model gives a possibility to trace the changes of accelerations according to the changes of both the ship hull form and environment parameters.

6. FIRST RESULTS FOR ABNORMAL CONDITIONS

The analysis was done to verify the ISSEM computational modules and both the data and results were taken from [17][24] for this purpose. Some data from the Shipbuilding Research Centre in Gdansk and Polish Register of Shipping were used for verification. As the ISSEM method is still under construction it is not yet possible to obtain some safety characteristics.

According to the event tree presented in Fig. 5 the stability, manoeuvrability, seakeeping and survivability analysis has been done for a cargo-passenger ferry with the following parameters [17][24]:

Length:	125.65 m;
Length BP:	114.0 m;
Breadth:	17.0 m;
Height to main deck:	6.00 m;

Height to car deck: 12.00 m;
Draught: 4.31 m;
Capacity: 3014.66 BRT;
c_B: 0.63

The following loading condition was chosen for the safety evaluation:

Displacement: 5160 t;
draught: 31 m;
trim: 4.55 m at AP and 4.13 m at FP;
KG: 8.14 m;
x_G: 54.20 m;
GM: 0.74 m.

TABLE 1 Example

Angle [deg]	0	10	20	30	40	50	60
Heeling arms [m]	0.306	0.304	0.301	0.438	0.456	0.439	0.419

These are the averaged values but both the maximum and minimum values evaluated were as shown in Fig. 8.

The seakeeping analysis gave the following mean ("1/10") values:

rolling: 10.19 deg.
pitching: 0.81 deg.
swaying: 10.10 m.

Verifying the results obtained from the ISSEM modules with those published in [17][24] the differences are acceptable. The main conclusion following from the analysis was that the ship could capsize only due to the common action of factors. Each factor separately could not.

7. HAZARD RESOLVING/RISK REDUCTION

The risk reduction decisions should be made by designers, operators and safety managers. And they can be very different depending on the stage of the project. Table 2 presents an example from the ISSEM computational model where the risk reduction decisions depend on the intolerable risk values.

The knowledge base on both the intolerable risk values and risk reduction decisions is rather complicated mainly because of the number of project stages, loading conditions, environment loads, ship speed and course. Therefore the decision-making process should be controlled by both the designer, operator or safety manager and knowledge-based system.

8. REQUIREMENTS, CRITERIA AND CONSTRAINTS

The main ISSEM requirements may be as follows: general requirements, IMO regulations, requirements of classification societies and requirements of conventions.

The cargo distribution (which was kept fixed during the analysis) at the midship section is presented in Fig. 6.

The changes concerning the ballast distribution were taken into account as shown in Fig. 7.

Taking into account the wind (speed up to 90 knots) and waves (significant wave height up to 5m) the common averaged heeling arms were as follows:

The current set of requirements used by the ISSEM method consists of the IMO regulations. For example the manoeuvrability requirements are based on the resolution A.751(18) from 1993.

The results of risk assessment (scientific calculations) should be compared with the assigned risk targets. And there are a few methods to show the acceptable risks in comparison with the intolerable one and they are as follows [18]:

- ALARP (As Low As Reasonably Possible) concept;
- F-N curve;
- Risk acceptance matrix.

The third one has been accepted for the ISSEM method. The following division of risk levels was introduced according to the frequency and consequence categor-ies: broadly acceptable, acceptable with controls, undesirable and unacceptable. An example of the risk acceptance matrix in the case of survivability analysis will be presented during the conference.

9. DECISIONS MADE ON SHIP SAFETY SAFETY OBJECTIVES

Having established the risk acceptance criteria we may identify the safety and environmental protection object-ives which should be known for a given operation to avoid hazardous situations and accidents. The safety objectives could be as follows: avoidance of injuries, death, ship's loss or spillage of oil. And they may be introduced in the form of a ISSEM safety code shown in Table 3.

The above code is still under the development and there are no numbers in the second last row. This is mainly because of lack of completed risk assessment methods and risk acceptance criteria for a few safety domains, represented in the ISSEM method.

6

CONCLUSION

The idea of the Integrated Ship Safety Estimation Method has been worked out. Currently, the method is a kind of Integrated Formal Safety Assessment (IFSA) partially risk-based method. The ISSEM method should be a tool used on a case by case basis and for rule development purposes. A few safety levels are introduced in the ISSEM method because of lack of risk assessment algorithms for some ship hydromechanic domains. Generally both the stochastic and deterministic safety measure techniques are used. As the human factor is the cause of almost 80% of accidents at sea it should be taken into account by the ISSEM method. Probably the new International Safety Management Code (ISM Code) should be used.

ACKNOWLEDGEMENTS

The author would like to thank both the Polish Scientific Research Council (KBN), Faculty of Ocean Engineering and Ship Technology and Division of Hydromechanics for sponsoring his research, very good research facilities and friendly help.

REFERENCES

1. BISHOP R.E.D., PRICE W.G: 'On the loss of the Herald of Free Enterprise". The Naval Architect, January 1988.

2. 'Passenger and crew safety on board ship'. World Maritime Day 1991, MER, January 1991.

3. 'Improving ship safety: the means, the handicaps', MER, January 1992.

4. SCHNEIDER D: 'A storm at sea' (in Polish: 'Burza na morzu'). Scientific American (Polish edition), No. 2 (54), February 1996.

5. GERIGK M: 'Safety at sea. Statistics for the parametric method for ships safety estimation', Internal report of the Faculty of Ocean Engineering and Ship Technology, Technical University of Gdañsk, No 15/97, Gdañsk 1997.

6. KOBYLINSKI L, GERIGK M: 'System Approach to Ship-Handling Problems', Seminar `Shipbuilding 2000 Maritime Conference - BALTEXPO'88', Gdansk, 5-9 September 1988.

7. GERIGK M: 'Expert System for Preliminary Ships Design for Stability and Survivability', Technical University of Gdansk, Bryza Publisher, Gdansk 1995.

8. GERIGK M: 'A Knowledge-Based System for Preliminary Ship Design for Intact and Damage Stability in Operation', Polish Maritime Research, Vol. 1, No. 2, Gdansk, December 1994.

9. Formal Safety Assessment. IMO document: MSC 62/24/3, London, 2nd March 1993.

10. Formal Safety Assessment. IMO document: MSC 66/14, London, 1st March 1996.

11. A Methodology for Formal Safety Assessment of Shipping. IMO document: MSC 66/INF.8, London, 1st March 1996.

12. MODARRES M: 'What every engineer should know about: Reliability and Risk Assessment'. Center for Reliability Engineering, University of Maryland, Marcel Dekker, Inc., New York, Hong Kong 1993.

13. GERIGK M: 'Main algorithm for the parametric method for ship safety estimation', Report of the Faculty of Ocean Engineering and Ship Technology Technical University of Gdañsk, No. 24/96, Gdañsk 1996.

14. GERIGK M: 'Theoretical model for the parametric method for ship safety estimation',.Report of the Faculty of Ocean Engineering and Ship Technology Technical University of Gdañsk, No. 15/97, Gdañsk 1997.

15. GERIGK M: 'A Computer System for Preliminary Ship Design of Operational Stability'. International Maritime Conference: `The Impact of New Technology on the Marine Industries', Southampton Institute, Warsash Campus, Southampton 13-15 September 1993.

16. BELENKY V, GERIGK M: 'Motions and Seakeeping for the System Approach', Internal Report of the Technical University of Gdañsk, No. 35/94, Gdañsk 1994.

17. FRACKOWIAK M, STASIAK J, GERIGK M: 'Manoeuvrability Analysis of Jan Heweliusz Ferry' (in Polish). Internal Report of the Technical University of Gdañsk, No. 28/95, Gdañsk 1995.

18. CAZZULO R P: 'Maritime safety and risk acceptance criteria'. 22nd WEGEMT Graduate School on `Accidental Loadings on Marine Structures: Risk and Response' Technical University of Denmark, 24th-29th April 1995.

19. Lloyd's Register of Shipping, 1994: 'Lloyd's List Annual Casualty Return'.

20. ALDWINCKLE D S: 'Ship Casualties and Some Loss Control Indicators for Safety Management', Conference on `Safety at Sea and in the Air - Taking Stock Together ', Lloyd's Register of Shipping, 13-15 November 1990.

21. FALTINSEN O M: 'Sea Loads on Ships and Offshore Structures', Cambridge University Press 1990.

22. IMO - Consolidated text of the International Convention for the Safety of Life at Sea, 1974, and its Protocol of 1978. London 1992.

23. SEN P, GERIGK M: 'Some Aspects of a Knowledge-Based Expert System for Preliminary Ship Subdivision Design for Safety', 5th International Symposium PRADS'92, Newcastle 1992.

24. FRACKOWIAK M, STASIAK J, GERIGK M: 'Stability Loss of Jan Heweliusz Ferry', (in Polish). Internal Report of the Technical University of Gdañsk, No. 21/95, Gdañsk 1995.

25. DUDZIAK J: 'Theory of Ships' (in Polish). Wydawnictwo Morskie, Gdañsk 1988.

26. ABRAMOWICZ-GERIGK T: 'Numerical Analysis of the Hull-Propeller-Rudder System Using an Open Data Base'. P.hD. thesis, Technical University of Gdansk, Gdansk 1977.

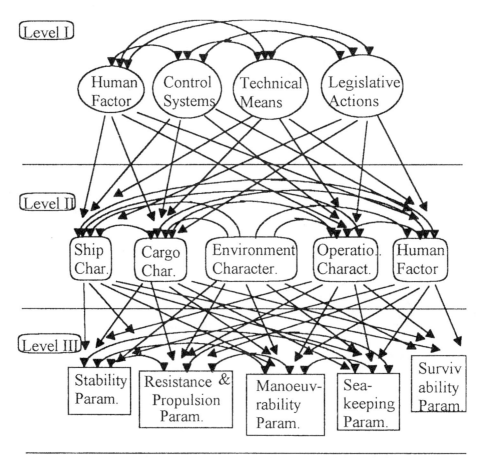

Remark: Environment can not be affected by any factor.

Fig. 1 Levels of factors affecting a ship's safety

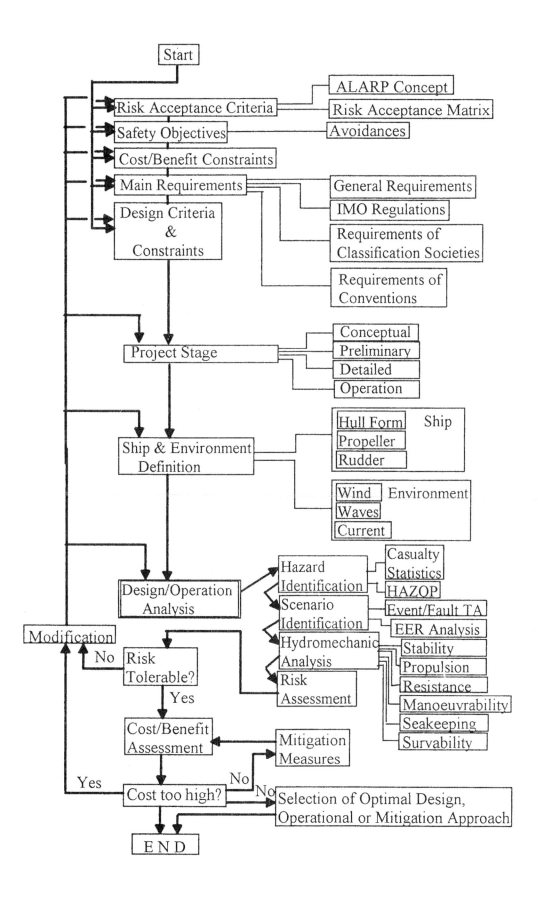

Fig. 2 Logical structure of the ISSEM design system

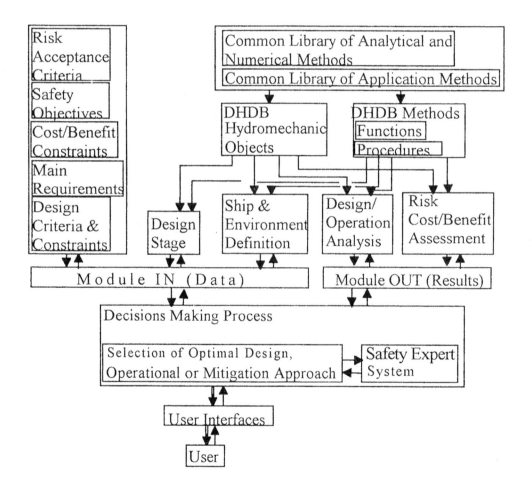

Fig. 3 Structure of the DHDB data base

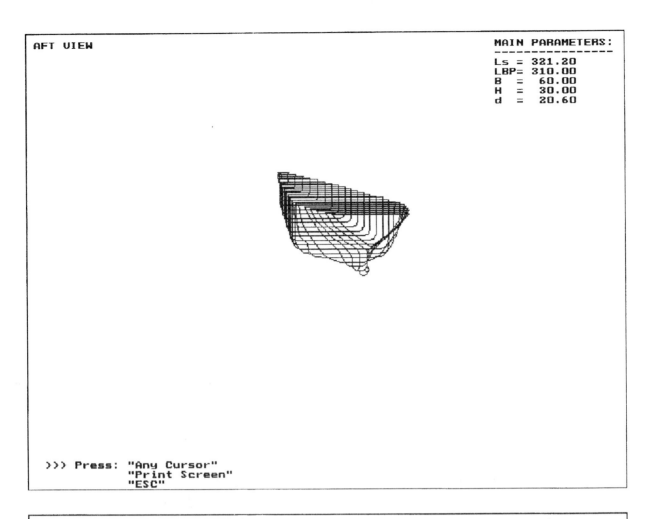

MAIN PARAMETERS:

Ls = 321.20
LBP= 310.00
B   = 60.00
H   = 30.00
d   = 20.60

>>> Press: "Any Cursor"
           "Print Screen"
           "ESC"

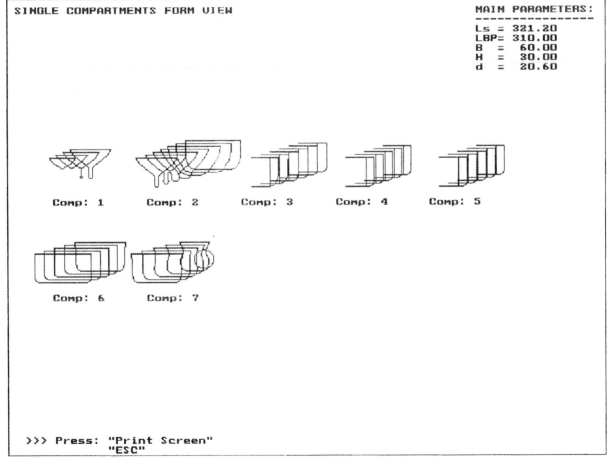

SINGLE COMPARTMENTS FORM VIEW

MAIN PARAMETERS:

Ls = 321.20
LBP= 310.00
B   = 60.00
H   = 30.00
d   = 20.60

Comp: 1   Comp: 2   Comp: 3   Comp: 4   Comp: 5

Comp: 6   Comp: 7

>>> Press: "Print Screen"
           "ESC"

Fig. 4 Examples of a ship's definition

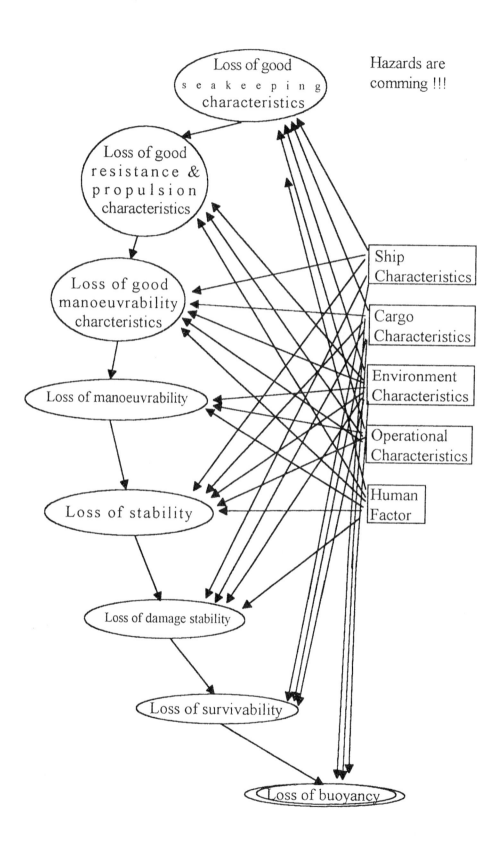

Fig. 5 A simple ISSEM event tree

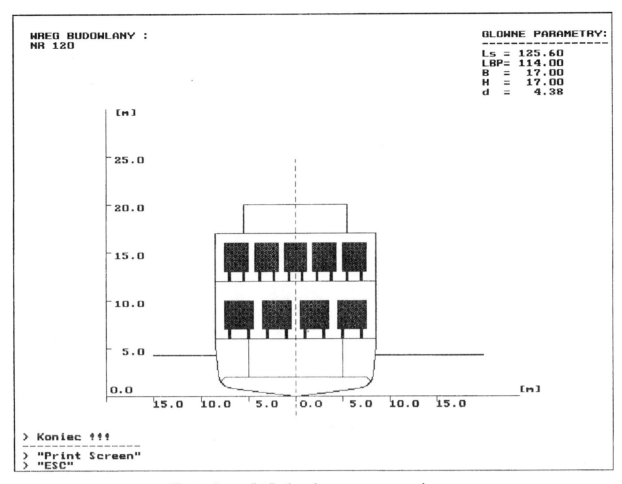

Fig. 6 Cargo distribution of a cargo-passenger ferry

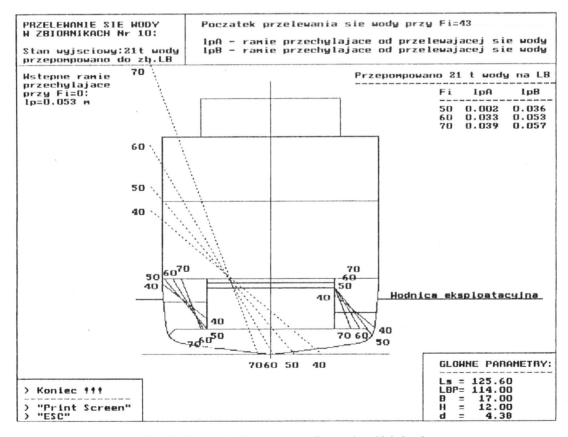

Fig. 7 Ballast distribution according to the ship's heel

13

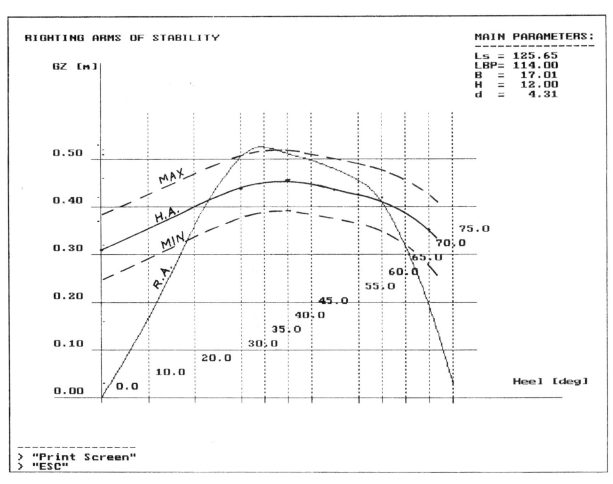

Fig. 8 Righting and heeling arms

TABLE 2

Stage of the Project	Intolerable Risk Values concerning:	Risk Reduction Decisions
conceptual	metacentric height to small, poor stability	changing main ship dimensions; changing position of centre of gravity
preliminary	metacentric height to small, poor stability	changing hull form representation including body lines; changing arrangement of internal spaces; changing cargo and ballast distribution or position of centre of gravity
detailed/operation	metacentric height to small, poor stability	only possibility is changing cargo and/or ballast distribution

TABLE 3

Safety level	1	2	3	4
Effect on crew, passengers, ship	normal, nuisance	operating limitations	significant reduction in safety margins, injuries	very serious injuries, deaths, loss of ship
Frequency	?	?	?	?
Frequency category	frequent	reasonably probable	remote	improbable
Category of effect	minor	minor	major, hazardous	catastrophic

PAPER NO.15.

ON THE USE OF FORMAL SAFETY ASSESSMENT WHEN ANALYSING THE RISK FOR CARGO SHIFT IN ROUGH SEAS

by Anna Ericson, J Persson, O Rutgersson, Division of Naval Architecture, and
T Thedéen, Centre for Safety Research, KTH, Stockholm, Sweden

Paper presented at the

International Conference

**DESIGN AND OPERATION FOR
ABNORMAL CONDITIONS**

21 22 OCTOBER 1997 GLASGOW

VI. THE USE OF FORMAL SAFETY ASSESSMENT TECHNIQUES TO ASSESS THE RISK FOR
LARGE SHIPS IN ROUGH SEAS

ON THE USE OF FORMAL SAFETY ASSESSMENT WHEN ANALYSING THE RISK FOR CARGO SHIFT IN ROUGH SEAS

Anna Ericson, Johan Persson, Olle Rutgersson, Division of Naval Architecture, and
Torbjörn Thedéen, Centre for Safety Research
KTH, Stockholm

SUMMARY

This paper reports on work done on a research project, Ship Safety in Rough Seas, just started at KTH. In the paper the reasons for integrating Formal Safety Assessment methods and computational studies of the risk of cargo shifting in rough seas are presented and discussed. Examples of the chain of events considered in a risk analysis of the cargo shift process are given. A simplified static model for computation of the risk for cargo shifting of a cargo unit with four lashings is presented together with numerical results. In the concluding remarks it is proposed that the outlined methods will offer results useful in the design process of future cargo ships, when some further development of non-linear calculations of ship motions in extreme waves can be combined with dynamic models for lashing systems.

AUTHORS' BIOGRAPHIES

Miss Anna Ericson is a Swedish Naval Architect who is doing postgraduate research to gain her doctorate. She has had experience as a trainee naval architect.

Mr Johan Persson holds a Masters degree in Engineering and is also working towards his doctorate. He has practical marine experience.

Professor Torbjörn Thedéen is the Head of the Centre for Safety Research at KTH, Stockholm. He has conducted projects related to risks in technical systems in collaboration with technical specialists, for example in the nuclear sector and the fields of dam safety, structural mechanics and transportation.

Dr Olle Rutgersson has been a Professor of Naval Architecture at KTH, Stockholm, since 1992. From 1970 to 1992 he was with SSPA in Gothenburg, where he was involved in the testing and development of naval architectural methods and ship design. He worked on the development of the propulsion and design of high speed craft for naval and civilian operation.

1 INTRODUCTION

A research project, Ship Safety in Rough Seas, with the aim to develop risk based models for the safety of cargo ships operating in rough seas, has been started at KTH. The idea is to combine modern risk analysis methods with non-linear models for ship dynamics in rough weather. The risk for cargo shift will be used as a limiting criterion for acceptable ship motions.

The objectives of the project will be obtained through a close integration of development of Oceanographic and Naval Architectural research with risk analytic methods, now in use in many technical sectors. In the present paper the different problem areas are defined and discussed together with some numerical examples. Further integration and results from the research work will be presented in future reports.

1.1 CARGO SHIFT AND SHIP SAFETY

In the World Casualty Statistics, yearly published by Lloyds Register of Shipping [1], casualty incidents are categorised as follows, with the yearly (1994) loss rate per 1000 ships within brackets, viz:

- Foundered (1.2)
- Fire/Explosion (0.4)
- Collision/Contact (0.7)
- Wrecked/Stranded
- Others

The category "foundered" includes ships which sank as a result of heavy weather, springing of leaks, breaking in two, etc., but not as a consequence of the other categories listed above. Many of the foundered ships capsized before they sank.

A further study of the statistics shows that the risk of foundering is largest for general cargo ships, refrigerated cargo vessels and Ro-Ro cargo ships. In many cases water ingress and list due to cargo shift were reported. Cargo shifting in heavy weather is believed to be a major cause in a considerable number of casualties for cargo ships.

Coastal ships and fishing vessels experience the risk of "instant" capsizing in heavy weather especially when operated in following seas where the risk of broaching is of major concern. For larger ships capsizing is always preceded by a series of "unlucky events" deteriorating the ships capability to withstand the heavy weather. The shifting of cargo is obviously one of these "unlucky events" which increase the risk of capsizing. More over, the problem of cargo shift contains a series of events which could be initiated by the action of isolated extreme waves deteriorating the lashing quality. The frequency and severity of extreme waves on a certain route is therefore probably more significant from the cargo securing point of view than the average significant wave heights.

Cargo shifting in heavy weather causes considerable damages and costs for insurance companies and cargo owners, also when capsize does not occur. An increased risk for cargo shift is therefore chosen as a limiting criterion for acceptable motions of cargo ships in rough seas.

1.2   SHIP DESIGN FOR LIMITED OPERATION

Cargo ships and the systems onboard should be designed for safe operation in all environmental conditions expected in the waters intended for the design. Ships operated on the big oceans and in areas where typhoons may hit without warning therefore probably should be designed to withstand abnormal waves as described by Faulkner *et al* [2].

For ships designed for operation in the vicinity of more sheltered waters ,where weather forecasts are expected to warn for extreme weather conditions, it would however be possible to use a different strategy where operational limitations are required to avoid the most dangerous situations.

"Good seamanship" is used as the definition of safe handling and operation of most ships today. "Good seamanship" is however seldom defined in terms of limiting operable weather conditions or safe speeds or headings in rough weather. These decisions are left to the ship master and his experience. In the design it is therefore not possible to use a more precise limiting condition for the optimisation of a ships structure and it's motions in waves. With the advent of more refined tools for the evaluation of new designs and the consequences of different handling of them it will be possible to optimise new ship designs against certain operational limits. The new high speed code [3] is a step in that direction.

The objective of the KTH project "Ship Safety in Rough Seas", outlined in Fig. 1, is to develop tools which could be used in the process of analysing new ship designs for certain routes and balancing the ships ability to manage waves of large magnitude against limitations put on operation of the ship in certain extreme weather conditions. As a result it might be possible to offer safer and more cost efficient solutions to future ship operators.

1.3   FORMAL SAFETY ASSESSMENT

Formal safety analysis is often used as an overall term for the process where risk based methods are used for estimation of the level of safety of a product and measures to minimise the risks involved in its use. Formal Safety Assessment (FSA) in connection with design and operation of ships is very much connected to IMOs work on guidelines for the use of FSA in their rule-making process [4]. In the present work FSA is used as a framework of logical connections between hazards, faults, events and consequences where

calculation methods for ship motions and lashing forces can be used to support the derivation and comparison of risks from different sources.

The strength of the FSA methodology in this process is very much the ability to support qualitative discussions in a very early design phase as well as serving as an organiser of quantitative calculations in a more detailed analysis as is proposed in [5].

2   THE PROJECT: SHIP SAFETY IN ROUGH SEAS

The tragic accidents with the Ro-Ro-ferries HERALD OF FREE ENTERPRISE and ESTONIA have drawn much of the attention of ship safety towards problems related to damaged stability of cargo ships. The present work is however focused on problems concerning the stability of an intact cargo ship in rough seas which also is believed to be a major safety problem which recent accidents, with ships like VINCA GORTHON and JAN HEWELIUZS, confirm.

As shown in the project outline in Fig. 1 the main efforts in the development of the methods apart from the risk analysis, will be models for ship dynamics in large waves, data and models for extreme waves and modelling of cargo dynamics.

2.1   DATA AND MODELS FOR EXTREME WAVES

In the treatment of ships behaviour in a random sea, a longcrested, stationary Gaussian process with a Rayleigh distribution of wave heights is usually presumed. Using a spectrum representation of the wave heights and a summation model of the random sea according to [6] we end up with a very convenient methodology as long as linear motions are applicable. Wave statistics and representation of wave data also uses the linear representation with significant wave height and modal period as parameters [7].

For studies of ships safety, phenomena like slamming, water on deck and rolling are of utmost importance. For these phenomena extreme waves with a non-linear appearance is important and can generate significantly different results compared to the linear representation [8]. In order to generate a basis for safer forecasts of waves in the Baltic Sea with influences of shallow waters and shore lines it is therefore discussed to start a co-operative work with the Swedish Meteorological and Hydrological Institute.

Measurement of actual wave profiles and wave amplitudes in critical locations in the Baltic Sea would form the basis for modelling of extreme waves as well as improved interaction with existing meteorological models. Safer routing of ships and better representation of extreme waves in the Baltic Sea would be parts of the outcome of such a project.

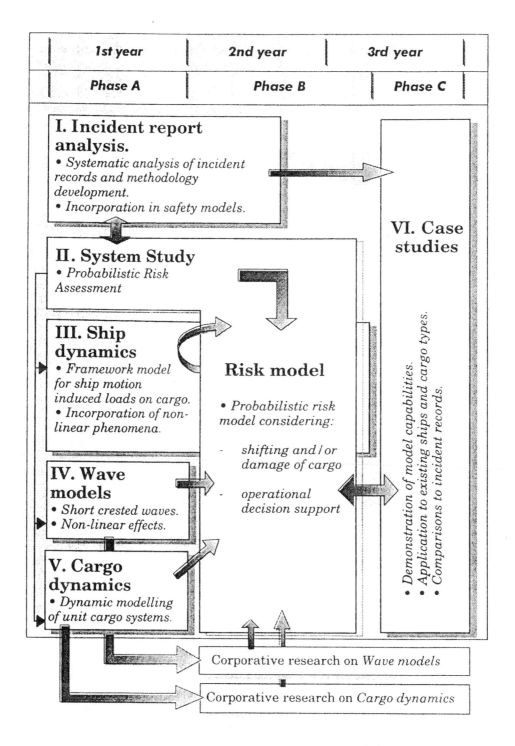

Fig. 1 Project Outline - Ship Safety in Rough Seas

2.2 CARGO ARRANGEMENTS AND LASHING TECHNIQUES

In the development of modern cargo ships the roll-on/roll-off of some kind of unit-load has a predominant role. Obviously a minimum time in harbour is a key-factor for cost efficient shipping. In order to create a good balance between rapid handling of the cargo and safety without too much lashing a number of different cargo handling concepts are used on modern ships. Accurate treatment of these concepts therefore also includes accurate modelling of the securing system used in each case, which could be a major task if dynamic models are needed. The studies of securing systems so far are usually based on static analysis of the lashings needed to fulfil the requirements of the authorities [9].

3 RISK ANALYSIS AND FSA METHODS

This work is concerned with the safety of a cargo ship in rough seas. The main hazard is that the cargo, being a large number of unit loads lashed on the ship, may shift which might eventually lead to a total capsize. In order to analyse the effects of safety measures, risk analytic methods should be used. Lack of relevant data at system level will make for the use of probability methods, such as Fault Tree Analysis (FTA) and Event Tree Analysis (ETA) according to [10,11 and 12]. These methods have been used with success in the aviation and nuclear field and have lately been introduced by IMO under the name of Formal Safety Assessment (FSA). In the present work it has been decided that in the analysis the proposed IMO FSA-methodology [4] should be used, with the following main objectives:

- To look into the IMO FSA-potential.

  The main purpose of the IMO developing FSA, is to provide a tool for IMO and other authorities, suitable for evaluating rules and regulations. The IMO FSA - methodology offers tools that, applied on an entire ship, its systems and subsystems, would require a substantial amount of work. However, by adapting relevant parts of the methodology on selected ship systems, proposed methods may be feasible also to other actors within shipping such as ship owners, classification societies, etc., with a reasonable work load.

- To study the cargo shift mechanism in order to develop a thorough understanding of the pheno-menon and how shifting of cargo could be avoided, controlled or mitigated.

- To derive the frame work of the cargo shifting process and point out specific problems that may be addressed by computational methods. Further, when this framework has been identified, to implement results of the quantitative calculations, thereby obtaining a more complete model of the process.

The following work plan was anticipated, with focal point at the event "initial cargo shift", initial hazards are derived and analysed by applying the fault tree tech-nique. From the fault trees, event trees are built to study the propagation of the chain of events eventually leading to the ships capsize. Remedial, restoring and mitigating actions are considered in various phases of the cargo shifting process.

3.1 THE CARGO SHIFT PROCESS AND HAZARD IDENTIFICATION

Shifting of cargo on a ship with lashed cargo units, can be described as a chain of events arising as a result of the interaction between wave loads, ship dynamics, lashings and cargo dynamics. When the limits for cargo shifting are exceeded initial cargo shift will occur. The rate at which the shifting process will then proceed is related to the amount of shifted cargo, since cargo units that are free to move influence both ship dynamics and cargo units that are still lashed. An increasing amount of cargo shift might finally, by affecting ship stability, cause the ship to capsize according to the process indicated in Fig. 2.

A model of the process should incorporate the cargo, the lashings that prevent the cargo motion, and the ship as the cargo platform, inducing the cargo movement.

3.1.1 Definitions

Risk is a combination of the terms probability of occur-rence of the event and the consequences of the event.

In the analysis, the term **hazard** is used in the meaning of a state in a system or in a chain of events with potential of leading to an undesired event for the ship and crew safety. The event may not in itself have the potential to significantly affect the safety, but may be a link in a chain of events leading to another hazard that will end up doing this.

In the Hazard Identification part of the FSA, the hazards have been categorised in the areas:

- Functional hazards
- Operational hazards
- Outer hazards

The **functional** hazard is characterised by that it may be related to the reliability of a system of technical nature.

An **operational** hazard is a hazard caused by personnel operating a technical system and includes thereby what is referred to as the "human factor", but also organisa-tional errors and errors in routines, etc.

An **outer** hazard is characterised by that this cannot be influenced by ship and ship personnel. A typical outer hazards is weather conditions, the behaviour of other ships, etc. However, the gravity of such hazard is related to how the ship responds to it, thus to operational and functional hazards. Previous experience has shown that it is most often the combination of multiple hazards that cause an accident.

A certain correlation between the three kinds of hazards exists. A hazard can be said to be both operational and functional; *e.g.* an operational hazard like "applying too high tension in lashings" will end up in the functional hazard "excessive wear to lashings". Nevertheless, such categorisation of hazards contains information about the hazard propagation and failure modes, thereby also about the nature of the remedial actions.

3.2 THE IMO FSA METHODOLOGY APPLIED TO CARGO SHIFTING

The proposed methodology for Formal Safety Assessment consists of the following main steps:

1. Hazard identification
2. Risk Assessment
3. Risk control options
4. Cost benefit assessment
5. Decision.

The objective of the study is to analyse cargo shifting in rough weather with FSA-methods rather than to perform a complete FSA. Therefore focus will be on step one to step three.

3.2.1 Hazard Identification

In this process potential hazards have been identified by interviews with experienced personnel, ship crew and officers and by the brainstorming technique. According to the different origins in the cargo shifting process discussed above, the hazards are referred to as:

- Lashing related hazards
- Cargo related hazards
- Ship related hazards

These hazards are regarded as events or situations with the potential of propagating to a situation with an initial cargo shift.

3.2.2 Risk Assessment

3.2.2.1 *Fault tree analysis*

A fault tree is a diagrammatic risk analysis tool representing the potential components / events that may lead to failure in a specific element in a "top-down" structure. When building a fault tree, identifying the top event (in our analysis the top event is initial cargo shifting), is the first step.

When following the tree down to events that may lead to this state, at each new event identified allowing for further branching, one finally reaches basic events, i.e. events at a level where no further branching is meaningful. In the present analysis ship related, cargo related or lashing related hazards are used as basic events as shown in Fig. 3.

In order to reach the top event, initial cargo shifting, by definition the cargo units have to be set free from constraining forces from the lashings. This may happen by that either fully functional lashings are overloaded by forces on cargo, or that a defect in cargo and lashings allows for cargo setting free at a lower level of forces, which is described in the tree.

The events in the fault tree levels of probability, are obtained by a quantitative study. The probability of ship operation exceeding limits are obtained by computations, discussed in the next section.

The main objectives for building a fault tree is to monitor the potential events that may lead to a failure, but also to calculate the probability for the top event by assigning failure rates and probability levels to the base events.

3.2.2.2 *Event tree analysis*

The event tree procedure is also used to represent the possible sequences of events which could result from a given initiating event. In our case, from the initiating event initial cargo shift, event trees are used to trace the propagation of a failure. Opposite to the fault tree, the event tree is constructed according to a "bottom-up" structure, i.e. starting from the initiating event and branching up the various events that may occur.

3.2.3 Risk Control

In each state of the cargo shifting process there are ways, more or less practicable, to take actions both to prevent the cargo shifting from further propagation, and to restore the cargo shifting process to a lower level of severity. The remedial/mitigating actions that can be taken are related to the level of cargo shifting the ship is subject to, and also to the specific ship and cargo configuration. In Fig. 5 an attempt is made to list restoring actions suitable in the different phases of the cargo shift process. At a later stage the intention is to study the transitions between states by a Markovian model.

To what extent the actions proposed are practicable, are related to the ability at the ship to respond to a cargo shift in a proper way, thus to the abilities of the crew, the cargo and lashing configuration, the weather and the status of other ship systems, etc.

However the first step in responding to cargo shifting is to monitor that a cargo shift is about to occur. Obviously, the more shifting that has occurred, the easier this is to monitor. On the other hand, the more shifting that occurs, the less likely this is to be restorable.

4 NUMERICAL METHODS TO ANALYSE CARGO SHIFTING

4.1 SHIP DYNAMICS IN ROUGH SEAS

When performing calculations on the risk of cargo shifting, the methods to estimate the ship motions are of

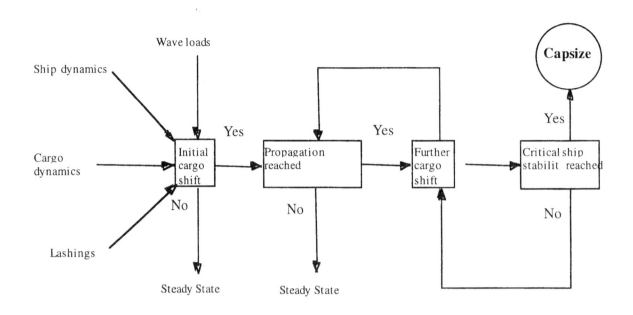

Fig. 2 The mechanism of cargo shifting

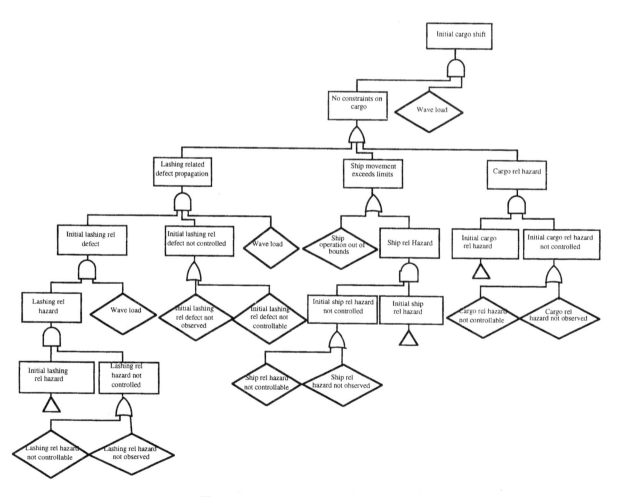

Fig. 3 Fault tree - initial cargo shift

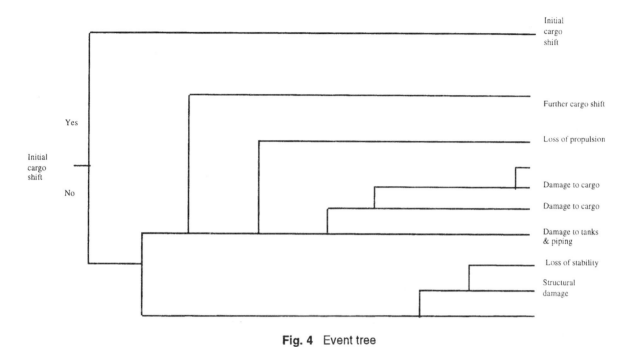

Cargo shift controlled	Damage to tanks & piping	Additional free surfaces	Disruption in fuel distribution	Oil/water in cargo space	Reduced friction	Structural damage	Water ingress	Further cargo shift

Initial cargo shift

Yes

Initial cargo shift

No

Initial cargo shift

Further cargo shift

Loss of propulsion

Damage to cargo

Damage to cargo

Damage to tanks & piping

Loss of stability

Structural damage

Fig. 4 Event tree

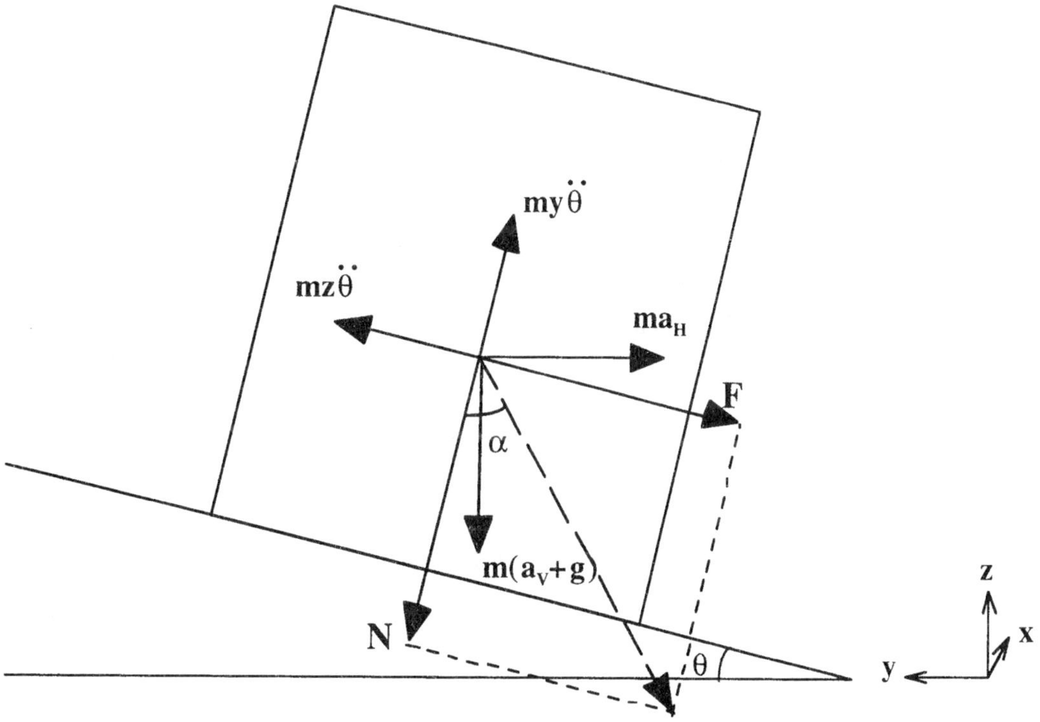

Fig. 6 Definition of equivalent roll angle α

7

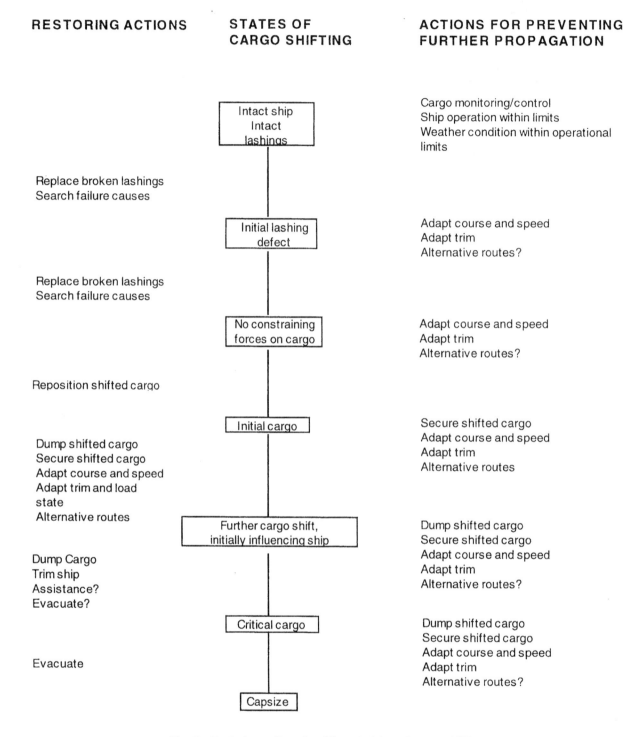

RESTORING ACTIONS	STATES OF CARGO SHIFTING	ACTIONS FOR PREVENTING FURTHER PROPAGATION
	Intact ship Intact lashings	Cargo monitoring/control Ship operation within limits Weather condition within operational limits
Replace broken lashings Search failure causes	Initial lashing defect	Adapt course and speed Adapt trim Alternative routes?
Replace broken lashings Search failure causes	No constraining forces on cargo	Adapt course and speed Adapt trim Alternative routes?
Reposition shifted cargo	Initial cargo	Secure shifted cargo Adapt course and speed Adapt trim Alternative routes
Dump shifted cargo Secure shifted cargo Adapt course and speed Adapt trim and load state Alternative routes	Further cargo shift, initially influencing ship	Dump shifted cargo Secure shifted cargo Adapt course and speed Adapt trim Alternative routes?
Dump Cargo Trim ship Assistance? Evacuate?	Critical cargo	Dump shifted cargo Secure shifted cargo Adapt course and speed Adapt trim Alternative routes?
Evacuate	Capsize	

Fig. 5 Restoring actions for different states of cargo shifting

8

the utmost importance. At present ship motions under normal conditions can be easily and accurately calculated using STRIP theory, [15]. However under severe conditions ship motions are no longer linearly dependent of wave motions. As shown in this paper cargo shifting is strongly dependant of the sea state, i.e. wave height and length. To assess the problems of cargo shifting, it is therefore of great importance to improve the representation of non-linear phenomena in ship motions.

Not only do ship motions become non-linear in rough weather. Extreme waves are strongly non-linear, and the methods used for describing irregular waves as combinations of regular components, no longer applies. So non-linear waves are another area of concern when analysing cargo shifting, as stated above.

4.2   NUMERICAL STUDIES USING A SIMPLIFIED MODEL

For the present study the risk of cargo shifting has been calculated for a Ro-Ro ship, BALTIC BRIGHT. A simple model of a container and its lashings has been used. Cargo shifting is assumed to occur when the cargo either slides or tips. This is a somewhat simplified model of the true criteria for cargo shifting, but should still give a good idea of the relative risk of cargo shifting.

4.2.1   The ship

The ship used in this study, is a small Ro-Ro vessel in traffic between Sweden and the UK, i.e. in the Baltic Sea and North Sea. It has the following main characteristics:

L_{PP}	120.8 m
B	20.0 m
D	5.7 m
∇	9933.5 m³
LCB fw $L_{PP}/2$	-6.432 m
trim, positive aft	0.66 m
KG	8.85 m

4.2.2   Forces acting on the cargo unit

The concept of equivalent roll angle, defined by Hua [13], is used to examine cargo shifting. Equivalent roll angle is a way of translating the different motions of a ship into two forces acting vertically and transversally in the ships co-ordinate system. In other words a certain combination of roll angle, vertical, transversal and roll acceleration is transformed into a pure heel problem, see Fig. 6. The forces F and N have the same effect on the cargo, as if the cargo was placed on a plane with the heel of the equivalent roll angle, α.

F, N and α are defined as:

$$F = m(-a_V \sin\theta + a_H \cos\theta - z\ddot{\theta} - g\sin\theta) \qquad (1)$$

$$N = m(a_V \cos\theta + a_H \sin\theta - y\ddot{\theta} + g\cos\theta) \qquad (2)$$

$$\tan\alpha = \frac{F}{N} \qquad (3)$$

where
	a_V	vertical acceleration
	a_H	transversal acceleration
	θ	roll angle
	$\ddot{\theta}$	roll acceleration
	m	mass of cargo unit

The vertical, transversal and roll acceleration and the roll angle are almost linearly dependent of the wave height and can be calculated with good accuracy using STRIP theory and spectrum theory. That is knowing the irregular wave spectra the response spectra can be calculated. However the forces F and N are not linearly dependent of the wave height and therefore their spectra cannot be calculated in this way. Instead time simulation has been used to calculate F(t) and N(t). Based on these time series the probability density of the required pre-tension has been estimated. These results have been used to calculate the risks of cargo shifting as described below.

4.2.3   The simplified cargo model

The cargo model is a simple container model as shown in Fig. 7. The problem is regarded as a two dimensional problem, i.e. β and γ are small and can be neglected, see Fig. 8. Longitudinal forces are not possible to calculate using STRIP theory [15], which means that would have to be estimated. One way of taking account for the longitudinal forces, in a more complex model, could be to estimate their spectra.

4.2.4   Criteria for cargo shifting

The lashings are supposed to have a pre-tension, Fp. Cargo shifting is assumed to occur when the cargo either slides or tips. The forces in the lashings are assumed to be equal to the pre-tension until the cargo shifts. This means that the criterion for sliding or tipping can be expressed as a function of the pre-tension, or rather the required pre-tension can be expressed as a function of the outer forces. In reality the cargo will not necessarily shift because it starts sliding or tipping, since the lashings will be able to withstand more load than the pre-tension value. However if the cargo starts sliding or tipping it is most probable that the cargo will shift. The risk of cargo shifting will be somewhat over-estimated using this simplified model. For comparative risk studies, to establish the influence of different parameters on the risk of cargo shifting or comparing different ships, it should be sufficiently accurate.

In Fig. 9 the forces acting on the cargo are shown. The lashings will prevent the cargo from sliding if the friction force, Ff, is larger than the applied horizontal force, F. Tipping will be prevented if the moment around the corner A is negative. The following criteria for the pre-tension, Fp, can be obtained:

Before sliding or tipping the forces F_1 and F_2 are equal to the pre-tensions *i.e.* F_p.

No sliding if $F < F_f = \mu(N + 4F_p \cos \varphi)$ (4)

$\Rightarrow$ if $F_{PS} > \dfrac{F/\mu - N}{4 \cos \varphi}$ no sliding will occur   (5)

No tipping if $M_A = FG - NB/2 - 2BF_p \cos \varphi < 0$

(6)

$\Rightarrow$ if $F_{PT} > \dfrac{2FG - NB}{4B \cos \varphi}$ no tipping will occur   (7)

By using the calculated forces $F(t)$ and $N(t)$ the required pre-tension to avoid sliding and tipping have been calculated, i.e. $F_{PS}(t)$ and $F_{PT}(t)$, see Fig. 9. Note that the required pre-tension is calculated as the equality in equations (5) and (7). The peak values have been used to estimate the probability density of F_{PS} and F_{PT}. These have been compared to the probability density of the true pre-tension F_{PA}, that is the pre-tension actually applied to the lashings, see below.

If at some time the required pre-tension, F_{PS} or F_{PT}, is higher than the actual pre-tension, F_{PA}, the cargo will shift. The risk of cargo shifting is calculated by comparing the probability densities of F_{PS} and F_{PT} with F_{PA}, see below.

The actual pre-tension, F_{PA}, has been calculated based on the above criteria, equations (5) and (7), using the Swedish National Maritime Administration's rules. The rules state that the lashings shall withstand the forces $F=0.5mg$ and $N=1mg$, F and N as above. Since the lashings are elastic, a considerable relaxation takes place, and thus the actual pre-tension is lower than expected. To account for this a distribution of F_{PA}, according to P Andersson [14], has been used when estimating the risks. It is worth noting that the actual pre-tension can also be higher than expected.

As stated above the method used in this study to model cargo shifting, is a simplified model of a complex phenomena. It is also important to note that many of the parameters regarded as constants, are in reality seldom fixed, i.e. the friction coefficient, μ, the mass of the cargo, the location of the centre of gravity etc. In an enhanced model these are important parameters to take into account.

The method used to calculate the required pre-tensions, results in negative pre-tensions in the lashings, see Fig. 10, which of course is not physically possible. A pre-tension is always positive, and a negative required pre-tension should be interpreted as 'no pre-tension needed'.

4.2.5   Ship motion and pre-tension calculations

The ship motions have been calculated in MacSkepps, a computer program for calculation of ship motions using STRIP theory [15]. The transfer functions of the motions have been used in time simulations of the forces F and N, defined above. From these time series the probability densities of the required pre-tensions have been calculated as described above.

Indirect time-domain simulations, [13], used in this study, are based on simulations of irregular sea states using JONSWAP spectra. In each simulation the wave phase is randomised, and the calculations correspond to 120s, real time. 120 simulations have been performed for each heading, wave height and wave period, corresponding to a real time of four hours.

The ship motions have been calculated at the centre of the main deck, i.e. as close to the centre of rotation as possible.

Data, apart from main characteristics, used in STRIP calculations:

Speed	15 knots
Radius of gyration for pitch and heave motion	$0.25{*}L_{PP}$
Radius of gyration for roll motion	$0.35{*}L_{PP}$
Roll damping coefficient	0.10
Average thickness of plating	0.015m

Cargo parameters used for calculations of pre-tension:

B	2.44 m
C	3 m
H	2.6 m
L	6 m
G	1 m
C	3 m
m	20000 kg
μ	0.4

4.2.6   Risk calculations

The risk, i.e. probability, of the required pre-tension, F_P, with the probability density $f_P(x)$, exceeding the actual pre-tension, F_{PA}, with $f_{PA}(x)$, is:

$$P(F_P > F_{PA}) = \int_{y_0}^{\infty} f_{PA}(y)\left(\int_{y}^{\infty} f_P(x)dx\right)dy \quad (8)$$

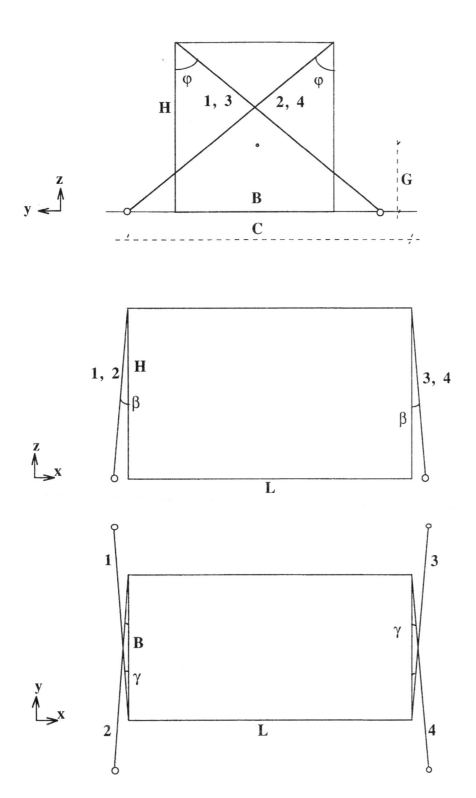

Fig. 7 The cargo in the ship's co-ordinate system

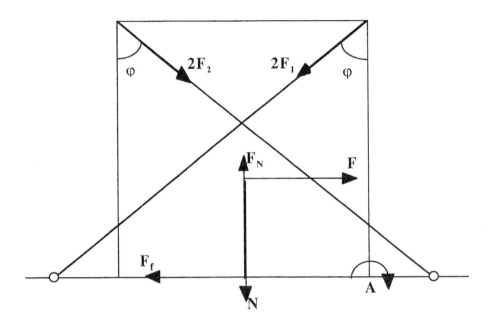

Fig. 8 The forces acting on the cargo model

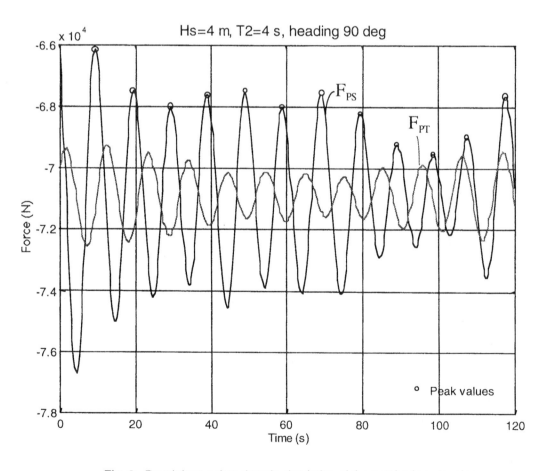

Fig. 9 Result from a time domain simulation of the required pre-tensions

12

The risk of cargo shifting has been calculated for different headings and sea states. Note that the speed has been kept constant at 15 knots. The heading has been varied from 0° to 330° with 30° increment. For each of these headings the required pre-tension has been calculated for different sea states. The sea states are defined by a JONSWAP spectrum, with a significant wave height, H_S, a modal wave period, T_m and a peak factor, γ The modal period is the period of the peak and equals $T_2/0.71$, where T_2 is the mean zero-crossing period. The sea states have been varied according to:

H_S 1 to 6 m, with 1 m increment
T_2 3 to 9 s, with 1 s increment
γ 3.3

i.e. 42 different sea states, chosen from wave statistics.

As stated above the risk of cargo shifting has been calculated for a cargo unit placed at the centre of the main deck. The ship motion and thus the risk of cargo shifting varies with the position on board. This variation has not been examined in the present study.

No long term distributions have been calculated, but it can be done by summarising the risk for all headings, wave heights and periods. Each parameter must then be weighted by its probability to occur during for example a year. This is a delicate task, requiring both good weather statistics and knowledge of the operation of the ship.

4.2.7   Results

In Fig. 11 the calculated risk is presented as a function of wave height and wave period. It is clear that these are important parameters with respect to the risk of cargo shifting. Another interesting result is that the largest risk of cargo shifting is from sliding, see Figs. 9 and 10.

The risk of cargo shifting increases strongly at significant wave heights over 3 to 4 metres, that is relatively small wave heights. Low wave periods give higher risks. This means that high short waves increase the risk of cargo shifting, which can be expected since ship motions are increased with the wave height and accelerations are high in short waves. It should be noted that very short wave periods do not occur for very high wave heights, so in wave height of 6 m periods below 4s do not exist, [7].

5   CONCLUDING REMARKS

After some very early work of developing tools and methodology to study the Safety of Cargo Ships in Rough Seas, presented in the present paper, some concluding remarks can be made:

* Using the formal structure of risk analysis offered by the FSA methodology some positive features can be obtained:

– Early design qualitative estimation of risks involved in new cargo lashing systems, can be obtained as well as focus on weak spots in suggested arrangements.

– Improvements in the safety, introduced as limitations in the operational practise, can be compared with the effects of modifications in the design.

– FSA offers a frame work for introducing results of numerical calculations in the risk analysis and thus making quantitative predictions based on a qualitative base model.

*A study of the risk for cargo shift have been carried out, using a static simplified cargo model demonstrating some of the difficulties involved in computational cargo shift predictions. For further work improvements are needed regarding:

– Data and models for extreme waves in rough weather.

– Non linear methods for ship motion calculations in large waves.

– Dynamic models for different lashing systems used on cargo ships.

– More data on the performance and treatment of used lashing systems.

*After introducing some of the proposed development, it is anticipated that a methodology along the ideas outlined in the present paper, may improve the future safety of ships carrying lashed cargo. It will also make it possible to compare the influence of new design features and operative limitations.

6   REFERENCES

1. World Casualty Statistics 1994. Lloyds Register of Shipping, London.

2. FAULKNER, D and WILLIAMS, R A: 'Design for Abnormal Ocean Waves'. RINA Spring meeting London, 1996.

3. IMO High Speed Code.

4. IMO-MSC 67/13: Formal Safety Assessment. Draft Guidelines for FSA application to the IMO rule-making process. July 1996.

5. SEN, P, BIRMINGHAM, R, CRIPPS, R M and CAIN, C: 'A Methodology for the Integration of Formal Safety Analysis into the Design of Lifeboats', Sixth International Marine Design Conference. Newcastle upon Tyne, 1997.

6. ST. DENIS, M and PIERSON, W J: 'On the Motions of Ships in Confused Seas.' SNAME Transactions, Vol.61, 1953.

7. HOGBEN, N and LUMB, F E: 'Ocean Wave Statistics', Her Majesty's Stationary Office, London, 1967.

8. HUA, J: 'Wave Load Mechanism to Avoid Bow Visor Damage', The Naval Architect, January 1996.

9. LARSSON, M: 'Design Loads on Securing Systems for Paper Reels.', KTH Msc Report TRITA-FKT/SKP/EX-97/16-SE. Stockholm 1997.

10. BARLOW, E and PROSCHAN, D: 'Reliability and Fault Tree Analysis - Theoretical and Applied Aspects of System Reliability and Safety Assessment.', 1975.

11. MELCHERS, R E and STEWART, M G: 'Probabilistic Risk Assessment', Rotterdam, 1993.

12. HOYLAND, A and RAUSAND, M: 'System Reliability Theory, Models and Statistical Methods.', Wiley, New York, 1994.

13. HUA, J: 'A Probabilistic study of the Simultaneous Effect of Ship Motions on the Cargo Shifting Onboard'; Marine Technology no1 Jan. 1996.

14. ANDERSSON, P: 'Optimum Safety Factors for Securing of Cargo on Board Ships'; Research report; MariTerm AB; 1986.

15. SALVESEN, N, TUCK, E O, FALTINSEN, O: 'Ship Motions and Sea Loads'; Trans.SNAME Vol.78 1970.

16. TURNBULL, S R, and DAWSON, D: 'The Securing of Vehicles on Roll-on/Roll-off Ships'; RINA Transactions 1995.

17. DALLINGA, R P: 'Safe Securing of Trailers and Deck Cargo'; Ro-Ro-94 Session 8.

18. ANDERSSON, P: 'Safe Stowage and Securing of Cargo on Board Ships'; MariTerm AB 1982.

19. BRENNEN, E G, PEACHEY, J H.: 'Recent Research into Formal Safety Assessment Safety Assessment for Shipping'; Lloyd's Register Technical Association, Paper No. 7. Session 1995-96.

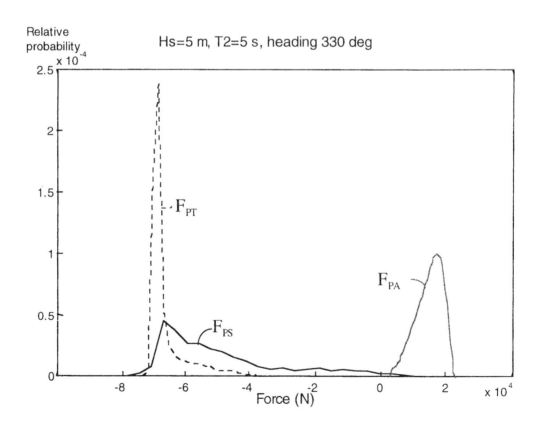

Fig. 10 Probabililty density of the required and actual pre-tensions

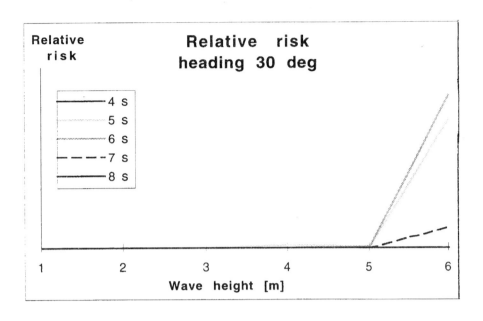

Fig. 11 The relative risk as a function of the significant wave height and mean zero crossing period

ELASTIC/VISCOPLASTIC DYNAMIC RESPONSE OF HULL PLATING SUBJECTED TO ABNORMAL LOADS

by P A Caridis MRINA, Assistant Professor, Department of Naval Architecture and Marine Engineering, National Technical University of Athens, Greece

Paper presented at the

International Conference

DESIGN AND OPERATION FOR ABNORMAL CONDITIONS

21 22 OCTOBER 1997 GLASGOW

ELASTIC/VISCOPLASTIC DYNAMIC RESPONSE OF HULL PLATING SUBJECTED TO ABNORMAL LOADS

P.A. Caridis MRINA
Assistant Professor
Department of Naval Architecture and Marine Engineering
National Technical University of Athens, Greece

SUMMARY

A numerical simulation of the response of a flat plate subjected to a line load impact is presented. The formulation is based on a time domain solution of the large deflection plate equations using a finite difference mesh. The material behaviour is elastic/viscoplastic, following the classical Perzyna model and the procedure is validated against a series of model collision experiments. The correlation results were found to be good and the procedure was subsequently used to predict the response of plating subjected to wave impact loads.

AUTHOR'S BIOGRAPHY

Dr. Piero Caridis is Assistant Professor at the Department of Naval Architecture and Marine Engineering, National Technical University of Athens. His previous experience is as follows: 1988-1994 Lecturer at the National Technical University of Athens; 1987-1988 Research Assistant at the Department of Naval Architecture and Ocean Engineering, Glasgow University; 1982-1987 Research Assistant at the University of Glasgow (Ph.D. awarded 1987); 1980-1982 Marine Superintendent; Nereus Shipping S.A., Piraeus, Greece. He is currently active in ship structural analysis research in several fields including dynamic response of ship hull components; design and analysis of ship stiffened panels using numerical procedures; ultimate strength of hull girders using analytical approaches; marine casualty analysis, repair and maintenance of ship hulls. He is a member of ISSC Committee III.I (Ultimate Strength) (1991-) and the EU Concerted Action on Casualty Analysis (national co-representative)

1. ABNORMAL LOADS ON SHIP PLATING

The purpose of this paper is not to address the important question as to what ought to be considered to be "abnormal loads" on ship hulls, but rather to aim efforts in the understanding of the response to certain "undesirable" loads that act on parts of the hull structure. It is hoped that the results of the present work may contribute to an improved understanding and formulation of the definition of abnormal loads, since improved tools of analysis can reveal the effects of loading. Qualitative load descriptions should not therefore be based solely on probabilistic considerations but ought to also involve consideration of the effects that these have on the structure.

In conventional quasi-static analyses the vessel is considered as either perched on the crest of a wave amidships or as suspended between two crests at the fore and aft ends. This simplistic approach can lead to results which are excessively conservative. In any case, the loads that act on the external surfaces of ship hulls include quasi-static as well as dynamic ones. Furthermore, the effect of the loading can be either immediate (ductile or brittle collapse) or long-term (fatigue). The loads listed in the following table are considered in Royal Navy design procedures as described in [1].

In Table 1 static loads are understood to be those loads that remain constant so that they can be allowed for in design procedures using static methods of analysis. Time-varying loads are those that change with time but which do not precipitate a dynamic response of the loaded structure. Examples are the longitudinal bending and the horizontal bending of the hull girder due to wave action. Dynamic loads are on the other hand those time-varying loads that cause the structure to respond dynamically (e.g. slamming, wave impact, collisions, explosions). In the case of time-varying loads it is usual to obtain equivalent static loads and design the structure using static methods. However the analysis of the response of the structure subjected to dynamic loads has to be performed using methods that can adequately allow for both material and geometrical nonlinearities in the dynamic range.

The last column in Table 1 is included in order to indicate whether a particular type of load can be allowed for at the design stage. In the case of warships in which the structural design stage is deep and takes place over a long period, a large proportion of the loads listed above are allowed for. In the case of merchant ships, the process of structural design is not so extensive. However the table includes a number of loads that are not included in design procedures since they result from undesirable (accidental) conditions. These include groundings, collisions and excessive (abnormally high) wave bending and wave impact loads.

It is the purpose of this paper to address two of these types of loads, viz. collisions and hydrodynamic wave impacts and to demonstrate that it is possible to obtain accurate predictions for the effects that these have on the response of the structure.

Table 1 Classification of loads acting on ship structures

No	Load	Type of Load	Included in design methodologies
1	Longitudinal still water bending	static	yes
2	Longitudinal wave bending	time-varying	in part
3	Wave shear forces on hull girder	time-varying	in part
4	Slamming	dynamic	in part
5	Green sea loading	dynamic	in part
6	Transverse loads	time-varying	yes
7	Horizontal bending	time-varying	usually ignored
8	Torsional loads	time-varying	when required
9	Wind Loads	dynamic	usually ignored
10	Inertial Loads	dynamic	when required
11	Thermal Loads	static	yes
12	Ice Loads	static-dynamic	when required
13	Propulsion Train	time-varying	when required
14	Wheel Loads	static-dynamic	when required
15	Internal Deck Loads	static	yes
16	Dock and Slipping Loads	static	yes
17	Berthing Loads	static	when required
18	Launching Loads	static	yes
19	Grounding Loads	dynamic	no
20	Collisions	dynamic	no
21	Towing Loads	static	when required
22	Weapon Launching Loads	dynamic	when required
23	Underwater Explosion Loads	dynamic	when required

In the next part of the paper is described the basis of the numerical procedure with particular reference to the question of numerical stability. The method is assessed in relation to other iterative numerical approaches.

The part that follows is devoted to a description of the mathematical description of elastic/viscoplastic materials as proposed by Perzyna. The incorporation of this model of material behaviour in the numerical procedure is described by means of a table and a flow chart (Fig. 4).

In the sections that follow two applications of the procedure are described. These include a correlation with a series of small-scale (low energy) collision tests and also a study on the effect of severe hydrodynamic wave impact near the bow of a large vessel.

2. NUMERICAL SOLUTION

In its most general form the equation of motion of a deformable body includes inertial, viscous and stiffness terms. These are the components of the equation of motion of a body treated as a generalized single-degree-of-freedom system. In the case of undamped motion the viscous term is not included and therefore the external disturbance is opposed only by the inertial force and the internal spring stiffness. Work done on the body thus gives rise to rigid body motion and an internal stress field. The equation of motion then is:

$$\rho \ddot{x} = P(t) \qquad (1)$$

where ρ is the mass density of the struck body and $P(t)$ is the forcing function.

Dynamics problems are characterised by their time-dependence and are thus propagation problems, although the occurrence of buckling means that in many cases eigenvalue solutions are sought. They are thus initial boundary value problems, since it is necessary to specify initial conditions in the time domain as well as the behaviour along the boundaries of the physical domain over which the differential (field) equations are integrated. In this particular case these are the boundary conditions along the edges of the struck plate.

Numerical solutions to equation (1) are extensively described in the literature and are generally classed as explicit, implicit or mixed (implicit-explicit). The distinction between these lies in the nature of the matrix operator L_i which is included in the following:

$$L_i x_{n+1} = L_o(x_n, x_{n-1}, \ldots) + f \qquad (2)$$

where x_{n+1} is the value of the dependent variable at time t_{n+1}, which is seen to be a function of values at previous intervals and the operators L_i and L_o whereas f is a vector used to specify initial conditions. Equation (2) is the general form of a numerical integration procedure written as a direct integration operator [2]. The operator is explicit if the matrix L_i can be expressed in upper or lower triangular form; otherwise it is implicit. Consequently it is of the former type if x_{n+1} is obtained from x_n, x_{n-1}, etc. without solving the simultaneous equations, while for the latter it is necessary to solve a set of simultaneous equations [3]. In other words, the key difference between the two classes of methods is that in explicit methods there is no need to solve a linearized problem in each non-linear iteration as is required in implicit methods [4].

In linear problems implicit operators are the most suitable because, since they are in most cases unconditionally stable, no restriction is imposed on the upper limit of the time increment used. Consequently, this is chosen solely on the basis of accuracy of the solution. In the case of explicit algorithms the solution is conditionally stable and thus an upper limit to the time interval exists. However, when a non-linear problem is considered, as in the present study, the advantage of a larger time step is overshadowed by the necessity to solve a large set of non-linear algebraic equations at each time interval [5].

Dynamic relaxation, the algorithm implemented in this study was used to solve the equations of motion in conjunction with a finite difference representation of the structure. However, as has been pointed out [6], [7], this algorithm can equally well be used to solve the problem using a finite element representation. This has been done in the past [8], [9], [10], and can be viewed either as a second order Richardson process [11], or as a second order (accelerated) Jacobi method [12]. It is classed as a two-parameter, three-stage recursive method.

Most finite element solvers use some form of direct method to solve the equations of equilibrium in matrix form. However there is increasing interest in iterative methods which are suitable for three-dimensional (large scale) problems or for use in conjunction with adaptive refinement. The need to solve problems of ever-increasing size will not cease and iterative methods are consequently expected to play a more important role in finite element analysis in future.

The numerical performance of the more advanced iterative methods is broadly similar to that of each other, with a superior performance to the simpler methods such as the Jacobi iteration. These include the dynamic relaxation method, the method of steepest descent and the conjugate-gradient method, of which the second and third have been used in optimisation theory. Crisfield [6] has demonstrated that in general, pre-conditioning (scaling) improves the rate of convergence of these methods. Another advantage of iterative methods is that they have significantly lower storage requirements than direct solution techniques, particularly in the case of large models, and furthermore they can be more easily implemented using vector and parallel programming [7]. This is supported by the results of another comparative study, in which it was shown that iterative methods are superior to direct equation solvers and also that their efficiency can be improved by preconditioning [7]. One other quality that these methods have is their robustness in the solution of non-linear problems. In

comparisons conducted between the advanced iterative methods, Crisfield [6] concluded that the preconditioned conjugate gradient method has the fastest convergence rate. Papadrakakis [7] on the other hand has reported results of comparisons between a non-linear form of the conjugate gradient method and the dynamic relaxation method and found that the latter showed superior characteristics. In this instance, the modifications to the conjugate gradient method related to the way in which the step length is calculated, which in the non-linear method is computed iteratively using a line search approach rather than in closed form.

The selection of a suitable method in non-linear structural mechanics is not easy because it is difficult to develop a general methodology which is universally valid and which can be used to handle the diversity of non-linear structural behaviour. The choice is thus highly dependent on the particular characteristics of the problem being studied and it is advisable to carry out comparative studies for each class of problem.

In dynamic relaxation, as in other explicit schemes, a heuristic approach to ensuring numerical stability would be to select a time increment which does not lead to violations of physical reality. The speed of propagation of a stress wave through a medium has a definite value and if a time interval which requires higher speeds of propagation is chosen the numerical scheme becomes unstable. Since $C = \Delta x / \Delta t$, where, if Δx, the spatial interval and C, the speed of propagation of the stress wave are known, a value for the time increment which will deliver a stable solution can be found. This approach was used in early finite difference studies of structural sections [12], [13].

Incidentally, it is seen that as the mesh is successively refined, the time increment reduces and therefore computation time increases not linearly but at a higher rate, since the number of increments required to describe the response over a given period also increases.

Owen and Hinton [14] use another criterion, which is related to the period of vibration of the complete structural assembly in it's fundamental mode and hence to the eigenvalues of vibration of the structure. The relationship $2/\omega_{max} \geq \Delta t$ is given, where Δt is the upper limit to the time increment and ω_{max} is the highest circular frequency of the finite element mesh. It is then argued that it is not necessary to solve the eigenvalue problem for the complete structural assembly because the highest eigenvalue will be bounded by the highest eigenvalue of the individual elements, as stated in a theorem proposed by Irons and discussed in [15].

In this study use is made of Gerschgörin's theorem, [6], which relates the maximum and minimum eigenvalues of the (unassembled) stiffness matrix to the magnitudes of the individual terms. It is thus seen that Irons' theorem is implicitly applied in the present approach. It should be made clear that in iterative methods it is not

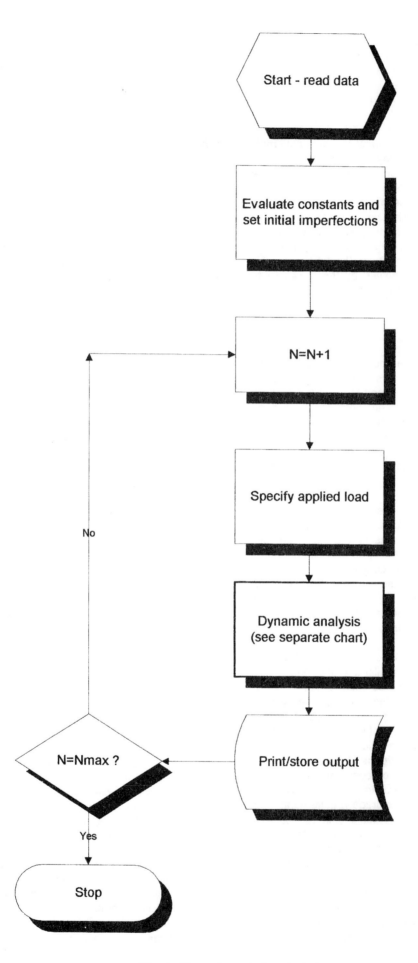

Fig. 1 - Dynamic analysis calculations

necessary to form the stiffness matrix as is done in direct methods, in which the solver carries out a matrix inversion. For dynamic relaxation, it has been shown that the optimum values of the two parameters (Δt, ρ) which characterise the algorithm are given by the following equation [4]:

$$\frac{\Delta t^2}{\rho} = \frac{4}{\lambda_{min} + \lambda_{max}} \qquad (3)$$

where ρ is the mass density and λ_{min}, λ_{max} are the minimum and maximum eigenvalues, evaluated at all nodes of the finite difference mesh. Since $\lambda_{max} \gg \lambda_{min}$, the minimum eigenvalue can be ignored and thus, by substituting for the maximum eigenvalue using Gerschgörin's theorem and rearranging, the following expression is obtained for the critical time increment:

$$\Delta t = \sqrt{\frac{4\rho}{b_G}} \qquad (4)$$

b_G is the Gerschgörin bound of the equation of motion. Numerical stability is ensured in the non-linear range through the (automatic) introduction of corresponding terms in the calculation of each bound. Thus, since the magnitude of the bound increases, the time increment will decrease. In practice, the decrease in Δt is not found to exceed 10 per cent, when all non-linearities are included.

The program used in this study, PANEL-2D can be implemented to study the response of flat and stiffened plates under both static and dynamic loading. Details are given in [16] and the description that follows relates to the constitutive relations. A general flow chart is included in Fig. 1 whereas the sequence of calculations that relate to material behaviour (stress-strain relations) is outlined in Fig. 4.

When dynamic relaxation is used to carry out a dynamic analysis the method should not be classed as iterative, since it functions as an explicit time integration method. In dynamic analyses, the calculations carried out at each time increment generate results which form part of the final solution. There are therefore no redundant calculations and the term "dynamic relaxation" becomes misleading. For this reason the term "real-time dynamic relaxation" was introduced in [17], to differentiate from dynamic relaxation as used in statics problems. In statics solutions convergence to a result which differs by an acceptable margin from a corresponding exact one is required. In this case the intermediate calculations are redundant and do not form part of the solution. For this reason it is possible to optimize the performance of the algorithm by choosing the most appropriate values of mass density and a pseudo-time increment, without necessarily adhering to physical reality.

3. CONSTITUTIVE EQUATIONS FOR DYNAMIC LOADING

It has been established that, in the case of certain metallic materials, it is necessary to allow for the effect of strain rate on the static yield stress of the impacted structure. Laboratory measurements of uniaxial strain rate have been carried out under certain conditions but in general there is a lack of sufficient data for the behaviour of materials under the widely differing conditions and configurations encountered in practice. The effect of strain rate on the static yield stress is also affected by temperature. Thus if the temperature is lowered, the dynamic yield stress increases. The effect is more accentuated when the strain rate increases [18]. In the case of ship structures, however, this effect can be ignored since the temperatures changes that are experienced are small (a change in 100°C about 0°C produces a corresponding change of 17 N/mm² in the yield stress of mild steel for a strain rate of 10 s⁻¹).

Hardening causes increases in material strength in the plastic range. The degree to which this may occur is affected by pre-treatment and affects different materials to different extents [19].

The material constants used in this study are generally available in the literature and have been obtained from beam impact tests, [20], whereas the problem studied concerns thin plate behaviour. A second difference relates to the nature of the external disturbance. The published test data relate to localized impacts caused by a solid striker whereas the present problem has been formulated as a spatially uniform, time-varying disturbance caused by impacting water. A further difficulty relates to the effect of scale. Minorsky, in a discussion to [21] raised this point, given that the data gained from small-scale laboratory measurements has to be extrapolated to full-scale, for ship structures. It was pointed out that since for the same elastic modulus and mass density the velocities of the striker and struck ship are the same and since the penetrations and deformations are in scale ratio, it follows that the strain rates cannot be the same for the ship and model.

It becomes apparent that a number of questions need to be answered before a clear picture of the behaviour of the material emerges.

From the theoretical viewpoint, several models have been proposed in order to describe the effect of strain rate, a number of which have been gaining recognition in recent years. In a review paper Krempl [19] considered several approaches which were classed as of the overstress type and as those which do not use the overstress concept. By overstress is meant the extent to which the value of the equivalent stress exceeds the static yield stress. In earlier studies the phenomena of creep and plasticity were considered as distinct, whereas more recently a unified approach has been followed, on the basis of the following equation:

$$\dot{\varepsilon}_{ij} = \dot{\varepsilon}_{ij}^e + \dot{\varepsilon}_{ij}^p \qquad (5)$$

5

It is implicit in equation (5) that viscous properties become manifest only after passage to the plastic state and that these properties are not essential in the elastic region. The total strain rate can therefore be resolved into an elastic and an inelastic part, where the inelastic part includes plastic and viscous effects. The formulations considered in [19] were all except one based on this approach. Perzyna's model, which was selected in this study has been used in numerical procedures [22] and has gained acceptance due to it's generality. It was chosen because it enables a description of the effect of the complete strain rate tensor on the yield stress, in contrast to the one-dimensional Cowper-Symonds model [20].

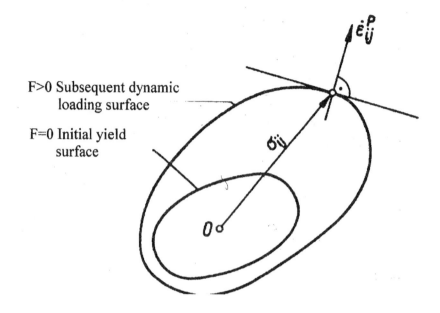

Fig. 2 Dynamic loading surface and inelastic strain-rate vector [24]

Perzyna's model [23], [24] is a extension of the equations originally proposed by Hohenemser and Prager. For general states of stress, these are:

$$2\eta \, \dot{\varepsilon}_{ij}^{P} = 2k < F > \frac{\partial F}{\partial \sigma_{ij}} \qquad (6)$$

where $\dot{\varepsilon}_{ij}^{P}$ is the inelastic strain rate tensor, s_{ij} is the stress tensor and η is a coefficient of viscosity. The function F is given by:

$$F = \frac{f(J_2)}{c} = \frac{\sqrt{J_2}}{k} - 1 \qquad (7)$$

where J_2 is the second invariant of the stress deviation tensor and k is the static yield stress in pure shear. The magnitude of F is thus seen to depend on the excess of the equivalent dynamic stress (overstress) above the static yield stress. The symbol <F> is defined as follows:

$$<F> = \begin{cases} 0 & \text{for } F \leq 0 \qquad (8a) \\ F & \text{for } F > 0 \qquad (8b) \end{cases}$$

It is seen that the inelastic strain rate tensor is related to the function F, which is a measure of the excess load above the static yield condition of the material. For a non-workhardening material, the constitutive relations are:

$$\dot{e}_{ij} = \frac{1}{2\mu} \dot{s}_{ij} + \gamma^{\circ} \Phi(F) \frac{\partial F}{\partial \sigma_{ij}} \qquad \text{for } F>0 \qquad (9a)$$

$$\dot{e}_{ij} = \frac{1}{2\mu} \dot{s}_{ij} \qquad \text{for } F \leq 0 \qquad (9b)$$

$$\dot{\varepsilon}_{ii} = \frac{1}{3K} \dot{\sigma}_{ii} \qquad (9c)$$

where μ, K are the shear and bulk moduli of the material respectively and $\Phi(F)$ may be chosen to represent results of tests on the behaviour of metals under dynamic loading. By definition, $s_{ij} = \sigma_{ij} - p\delta_{ij}$ and $J_2 = (1/2)s_{ij}s_{ij}$.

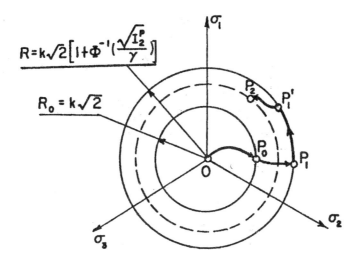

Fig. 3 - The Mises yield locus for elastic/viscoplastic materials [24]

Therefore, $s_{ij} = \partial J_2 / \partial \sigma_{ij}$. Substituting in equation (9a) from $\gamma = \gamma^o/2k$ we obtain:

$$\gamma^o \frac{\partial F}{\partial \sigma_{ij}} = 2k\gamma \frac{\partial F}{\partial J_2} \frac{\partial J_2}{\partial \sigma_{ij}} = \gamma \frac{s_{ij}}{\sqrt{J_2}}$$

Hence,

$$\dot{e}_{ij} = \frac{1}{2\mu} \dot{s}_{ij} + \gamma \, \Phi(F) \frac{s_{ij}}{\sqrt{J_2}} \qquad \text{for } \sqrt{J_2} > 0 \qquad (10a)$$

$$\dot{e}_{ij} = \frac{1}{2\mu} \dot{s}_{ij} \qquad \text{for } \sqrt{J_2} \leq 0 \qquad (10b)$$

$$\dot{\varepsilon}_{ii} = \frac{1}{3K} \dot{\sigma}_{ii} \qquad (10c)$$

It is seen that the inelastic strain rate tensor is in the direction of the stress deviator tensor, s_{ij}, but otherwise it is a function of the (scalar) overstress. It is therefore not a true overstress theory [19]. Since the elastic component is independent of the strain rate, the choice of a suitable yield criterion is facilitated, since initial yielding will occur under the same conditions as those for inviscid materials under static conditions. Equation (6) can be generalized to include work-hardening materials, by letting $K=\kappa$, a work-hardening parameter. The static yield surface is assumed regular and convex,

and for a work-hardening, rate-sensitive elastic-plastic material the constitutive relations become:

$$\dot{e}_{ij} = \frac{1}{2\mu} \dot{s}_{ij} + \frac{1-2v}{E} \dot{s} \delta_{ij} + \gamma \langle \Phi(F) \rangle \frac{\partial f}{\partial \sigma_{ij}} \qquad (11)$$

or,

$$\dot{e}_{ij} = \frac{1}{2\mu} \dot{s}_{ij} + \frac{1-2v}{E} \dot{s} \delta_{ij} + \frac{\gamma^o}{\kappa} \langle \Phi(F) \rangle \frac{\partial f}{\partial \sigma_{ij}} \qquad (12)$$

In order to obtain the dynamic yield condition for elastic/viscoplastic work-hardening materials, it is necessary to consider the inelastic component of the total strain rate tensor:

$$\dot{\varepsilon}_{ij}^P = \gamma \Phi(F) \frac{\partial f}{\partial \sigma_{ij}} \qquad (13)$$

Squaring both sides of equation (12) and denoting by $\sqrt{I_2^P} = (1/2) \dot{e}_{ij}^P \dot{e}_{ij}^P$, the invariant of the inelastic strain rate tensor, this becomes:

$$\sqrt{I_2^P} = \gamma \Phi(F) \left(\frac{1}{2} \frac{\partial f}{\partial \sigma_{kl}} \frac{\partial f}{\partial \sigma_{kl}} \right)^{1/2} \qquad (14)$$

A relation for the dynamic yield condition for elastic/viscoplastic, work-hardening materials can thus be obtained:

$$f(\sigma_{ij}, e_{kl}^P) = \kappa(W_p) \left\{ 1 + \Phi^{-1} \left[\frac{\sqrt{I_2^P}}{\gamma} \left(\frac{1}{2} \frac{\partial f}{\partial \sigma_{pq}} \frac{\partial f}{\partial \sigma_{pq}} \right)^{-1/2} \right] \right\} \qquad (15)$$

7

where $k(W_p)$ is a workhardening parameter, defined as a function of the plastic work dissipated. The inelastic strain rate tensor considered as a vector in the nine-dimensional stress space is seen to be always directed along the normal to the subsequent loading surface (see Fig. 2). For a non-workhardening Mises material, equation (11) becomes:

$$\dot{e}_{ij} = \frac{1}{2\mu}\dot{s}_{ij} + \gamma\Phi\left(\frac{\sqrt{J_2}}{\kappa} - 1\right)\frac{s_{ij}}{\sqrt{J_2}} \qquad (16a)$$

and

$$\dot{\varepsilon}_{ii} = \frac{1}{3K}\dot{\sigma}_{ii} \qquad (16b)$$

The dynamic yield criterion is then:

$$\sqrt{J_2} = k\left[1 + \Phi^{-1}\left(\frac{\sqrt{I_2^p}}{\gamma}\right)\right] \qquad (17)$$

In the inviscid theory of plasticity for work-hardening materials, there exist three possibilities, according to whether the rate of change of J_2 is greater than zero (loading), equal to zero (neutral loading), or less than zero (unloading). Since in viscoplasticity J_2 is a function of the strain rate, plastic flow occurs if $J_2 > k^2$, regardless of the sign of the time rate of change of J_2. Therefore, the material will be elastic along the path OP_o, but along the path $P_oP_1P_1'P_2$ it will be elastic/viscoplastic (Fig. 3).

It is possible to ignore the elastic components of the total strain when the kinetic energy imparted to the impacted body is significantly larger than the elastic strain energy absorbed by it. In this case, a rigid-plastic analysis can give satisfactory results. If we assume that the function $\Phi(\mathbf{F})$ has the form F^δ then, for rigid-plastic materials the constitutive relations become:

$$\dot{e}_{ij} = \dot{\varepsilon}_{ij}^p = \gamma\Phi\left(\frac{\sqrt{J_2}}{k} - 1\right)^\delta \frac{s_{ij}}{\sqrt{J_2}} \qquad (18)$$

In the case of one-dimensional states of stress this reduces to the Cowper-Symonds law. The values of γ and δ can be chosen to fit experimental data for particular materials.

4.   IMPLEMENTATION OF ELASTIC/VISCOPLASTIC MODEL IN NUMERICAL PROCEDURE

The sequence of calculations required to evaluate stresses and strains using Perzyna's constitutive relations is given below:

Step 1:	$\varepsilon_{ij}^e = \varepsilon_{ij} - \varepsilon_{ij}^p$	elastic strain tensor
Step 2:	$\sigma_{ij} = \mathbf{D}\varepsilon_{ij}^e$	total stress tensor
Step 3:	$J_2 = f(\sigma_{ij})$	second invariant of stress tensor
Step 4:	$F = \dfrac{\sqrt{J_2}}{k} - 1$	yield function
Step 5:	If F<0 go to step 12	
Step 6:	$\Phi(F) = F^\delta$	
Step 7:	$\dot{\varepsilon}_{ij}^p = \gamma\Phi(F)\dfrac{\partial f}{\partial\sigma_{ij}}$	viscoplastic strain rate tensor
Step 8:	$\varepsilon_{ij}^p = \varepsilon_{ij}^p + \dot{\varepsilon}_{ij}^p \Delta t$	total viscoplastic strain tensor

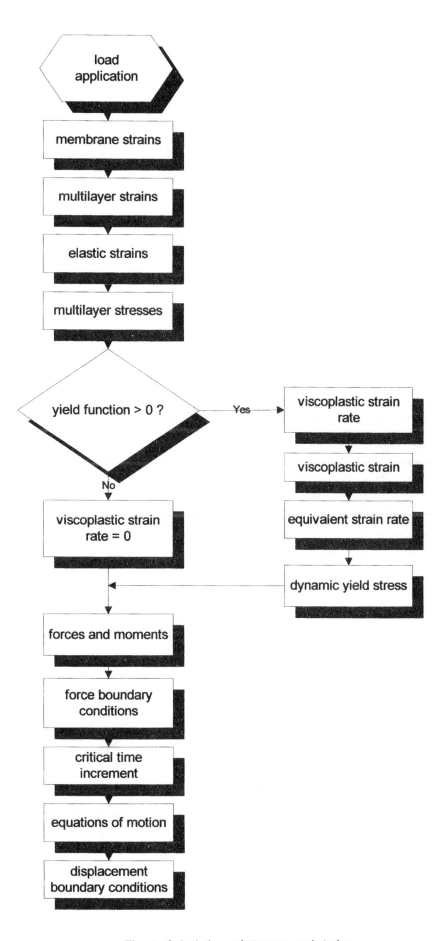

Fig. 4 Calculations of stresses and strains

(cont.....)

Step 9:	$\sqrt{I_2^p} = \gamma\Phi(F)\left(\dfrac{1}{2}\dfrac{\partial f}{\partial\sigma_{kl}}\dfrac{\partial f}{\partial\sigma_{kl}}\right)^{1/2}$	2nd invariant of plastic strain rate tensor
Step 10:	$\sqrt{J_2} = k\left[1 + \Phi^{-1}\left(\dfrac{\sqrt{I_2^p}}{\gamma}\right)\right]$	dynamic yield surface
Step 11:	go to 13	
Step 12:	$\dot{\varepsilon}_{ij}^p = 0$	viscoplastic strain rate tensor is set to zero
Step 13:	continue	

The flow chart given overleaf indicates the layout of the calculations required to describe material behaviour.

5.   HULL PLATING SUBJECTED TO LOW-ENERGY COLLISIONS - MODEL EXPERIMENTS

In this section a description of the results of a comparison between numerical and experimental results is given. The correlation study relates to data obtained during a series of small-scale ship model collision tests which are described in [17]. The test setup consisted of a model of a wall-sided vessel which was struck by a rigid wedge in several locations. The wedge was positioned on an inclined carriageway which was arranged so as to enable it to come into contact with the vessel along a vertical line of length 145 mm. The velocity of the striker when contact was made with the plating was adjusted by varying the height of travel.

A series of tests were carried out for a variety of configurations. Two groups of tests were carried out.

Firstly dry tests, during which the struck model was suitably supported at its boundaries in air. The second series of tests was conducted with the model floating on water and kept in position by small magnets, until the point of impact. For each group of tests a series of results with strikers of differing masses and velocities at contact was obtained.

Furthermore, in certain cases water was introduced into the impacted tank. The idealized configuration considered in the numerical study is shown in Fig. 5. It is seen that the struck model is treated as an isolated clamped plate along whose boundaries no deflections or rotations are permitted.

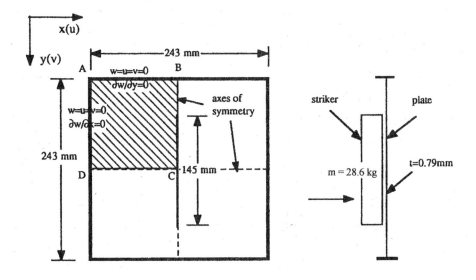

Fig. 5   Idealization of side plating of 1:60 scale model of tanker

10

The results from these tests are shown in Fig. 6 which also includes predictions based on earlier theoretical formulations. In this diagram the total energy absorbed by the struck plate is plotted against the predicted permanent deflection at the plate centre. The upper bound to the total energy absorbed by the struck plate is equal to the kinetic energy loss of the striker, which is given by:

$$\Delta E = \frac{1}{2} m_s (v_f^2 - v_i^2) \qquad (19)$$

where v_i, v_f are the initial and final velocities of the striker and m_s is it's mass. The permanent deflection is assumed to be the deflection measured at the plate centre at the instant at which separation occurs. Following separation, the plate performs damped oscillations about this position until it finally comes to rest.

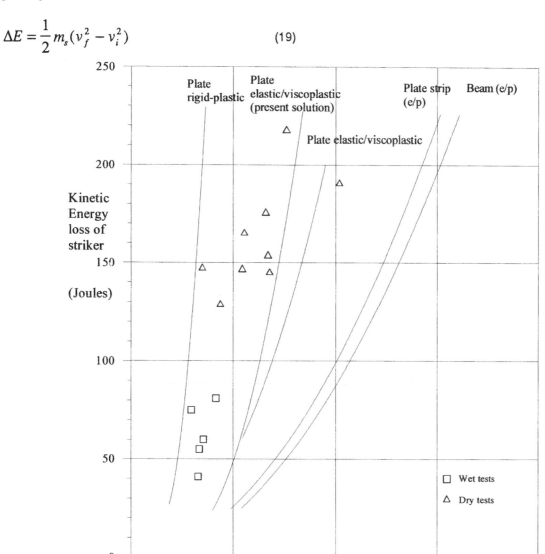

Fig. 6 Comparison between scale model collision test data and theoretical predictions

A study of Fig. 6 shows that there is very good agreement between the predicted results and the experimental data, particularly so in the case of the dry tests. The predicted permanent deflections exceed the measured values because in the numerical model the rotational energy absorbed by the struck plate is ignored. The discrepancy is larger in the case of the wet tests but this is to be expected for several reasons. Firstly, differences will arise as a result of the movement of the struck model in the water. In this case a not insignificant proportion of the absorbed energy contributes to the motion of the model and the surrounding fluid. The predicted permanent deflections will therefore exceed the measured ones, as noted in Fig. 5. Furthermore, in a number of tests the model was struck in a position which did not coincide with the vertical axis of symmetry of the plate but was offset by a specified amount. This also contributes to a reduction of the observed deflection.

In the diagrams that follow results from an individual impact will be used to illustrate in more detail aspects relating to a) further details relating to the motion of the struck plate b) material behaviour and c) variation in energy and plastic work dissipated. Material behaviour of the struck plate is described in Figs 8-9.

Table 2 Correlation study with ship small-scale collision model test results

Test no.	Striker mass (kg)	Initial velocity (m/s)	Kinetic energy loss (J)	Final deflection (mm)	Rebound velocity (m/s)	Kinetic energy loss (J)	Final deflection (mm)
			Experimental results			Numerical results	
D1	28.6	3.30	147	10.9	-1.676	115	12.92
D2	28.6	3.40	154	13.4	-1.687	124	13.48
D3	39.9	3.40	218	15.2	-1.450	189	15.91
D4	39.9	3.10	176	13.2	-1.430	151	14.69
W1	55.4	1.18	41	6.58	-0.973	12	6.24
W2	55.4	2.33	55	6.71	-1.171	112	13.42
W3e	55.4	2.25	60	7.11	-1.166	103	12.61
W4e	55.4	2.17	75	5.92	-1.154	94	12.39
W5e	55.4	2.63	81	8.37	-1.200	151	14.71

Figure 7 contains time-domain variations of the deflection at four positions of the plate, described in the accompanying table.

Curve No.	Plate position
1	Centre of whole plate
2	Quarter-span position along line of impact
3	Midway between line of impact and plate side
4	Centre of quarter section

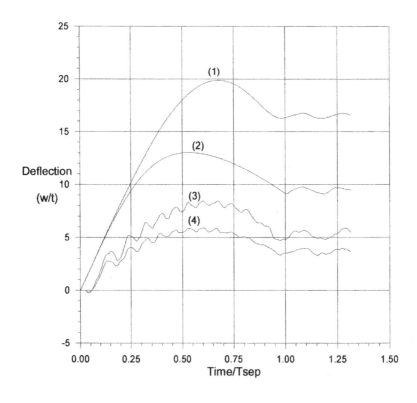

Fig. 7 Time-domain variation of deflection at various positions of the plate

A plot of the variation of the deflection is included in Fig. 7. The deflection has been non-dimensionalised with respect to the plate thickness. The maximum deflection occurs at the plate centre as expected, since the line of impact traverses this point. Curve 2 corresponds to a location beyond the line of impact, along the axis of symmetry of the plate. The deflection is seen to closely follow the value measured at the centre (curve 1) until inelastic behaviour commences ($t/t_{sep}=0.25$). From that point onward the magnitude of the deflection becomes much smaller than the maximum value. Curves 3 and 4 indicate the presence of high-frequency vibrations.

In the figures that follow the horizontal axis has been non-dimensionalised with respect to the time at which separation occurred. This has been determined as the instant at which the contact force reduces to zero.

In order to determine the contact force it is necessary to consider the dynamic equilibrium of the striker and the struck plate. Since for the striker it is assumed that no internal energy dissipation takes place, the inertial force acting on the striker will equal the external applied force. For the striker therefore,

Applied Force = Inertial Force (20a)

For the struck plate, however, internal stresses do arise and the external applied force on it produces deformations as well as accelerations. The equation of dynamic equilibrium is in this case

Applied Force = Contact Force + Inertial Force (20b)

For dynamic equilibrium of the plate-striker system,

$$P_s(t) + P_p(t) = 0 \qquad (21)$$

i.e.

$$P_s(t) = - P_p(t) \qquad (22)$$

Since

$$P_s(t) = m_s \frac{d\dot{w}_s}{dt} \qquad (23a)$$

and

$$P_p(t) = m_p \frac{d\dot{w}_p}{dt} + P_{con}(t) \qquad (23b)$$

The contact force is given by:

$$P_{con}(t) = - m_s \frac{d\dot{w}_s}{dt} - m_p \frac{d\dot{w}_p}{dt} \qquad (24)$$

The first term in equation (24) represents the inertial force acting on the striker. In the present analysis this is found by summing the inertial forces acting at the impacted nodes. At any time t the nodal velocities are known and if it is assumed that the acceleration during the preceding cycle of duration Δt is constant, then the acceleration of the i-th impacted node at time t can be found from:

$$\left(\frac{d\dot{w}_s^i}{dt}\right)_{t=t} = \left[\left(\frac{dw_s^i}{dt}\right)_{t=t} - \left(\frac{dw_s^i}{dt}\right)_{t=t-\Delta t}\right]\frac{1}{\Delta t} \qquad (25)$$

The corresponding inertial force acting on the striker at time t is then $m_s^i \left(\dfrac{d\dot{w}_s}{dt}\right)^i_{t=t}$ where m_s^i is the striker mass that is in contact with the i-th node of the plate. The total inertial force acting on the striker at time t is then:

$$\sum_{i=1}^{N} m_s^i \left(\frac{d\dot{w}_s^i}{dt}\right)_{t=t} = m_s \sum_{i=1}^{N}\left(\frac{d\dot{w}_s^i}{dt}\right)_{t=t} \qquad (26)$$

where N is the number of struck nodes. The inertial force acting on the plate is found from

$$m_p\left(\frac{d\dot{w}_p}{dt}\right)_{t=t} = m_p \sum_{i,j=1}^{i=i_{max} \atop j=j_{max}}\left(\frac{dw_p^{i,j}}{dt}\right)_{t=t} \qquad (27)$$

where i, j are the node numbers in the cartesian finite difference plate grid.

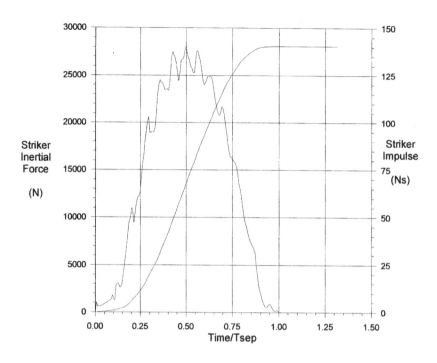

Fig. 8 Inertial force and impulse on striker

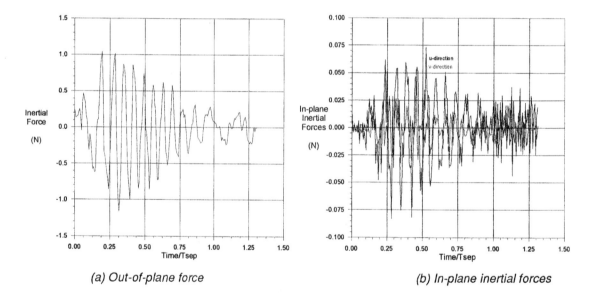

(a) Out-of-plane force

(b) In-plane inertial forces

Fig. 9 Inertial forces acting on the struck plate

Figure 8 shows the variation in the inertial force and impulse of the striker whereas Fig. 9 shows the inertial forces acting on the struck plate in the out-of-plane direction (Fig. 9a) and the in-plane directions (Fig. 9b). It is seen that the inertial forces acting on the plate are negligible in comparison to those acting on the striker. This is due to the large striker mass to plate mass ratio ($\cong 75$) and thus the contact force, which produces the deformations of the plate can be obtained from:

$$P_{con}(t) = -m_s \frac{d\dot{w}_s}{dt} \qquad (28)$$

Separation is determined at individual nodes and is consequently defined as the instant at which all nodes cease to be in contact with the striker. The impulse on the striker, shown in Fig. 8, is determined as the time integral of the contact force. In the present analysis this is determined from:

$$(I_s)_{t=t} = \int_{t=0}^{t=t} m_s \left(\frac{d\dot{w}_s}{dt}\right) dt = (I_s)_{t=t-\Delta t} + m_s \left(\frac{d\dot{w}_s}{dt}\right)_{t=t} \qquad (29)$$

14

This is seen to agree with the rate of change of momentum of the striker for the total period in contact with the plate, calculated from:

$$\left(I_s\right)_{t=t_{sep}} = m_s\left[\left(\frac{dw_s}{dt}\right)_{t=0} - \left(\frac{dw_s}{dt}\right)_{t=t_{sep}}\right] =$$

= 28.6(3.3-(-1.676)) =142.31 Ns

The time at which separation occurs is t_{sep}= 9.907 msec.

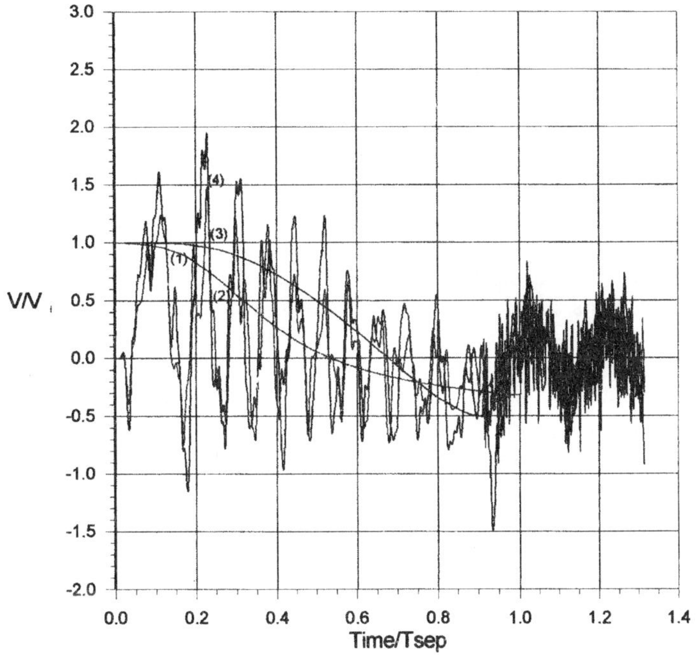

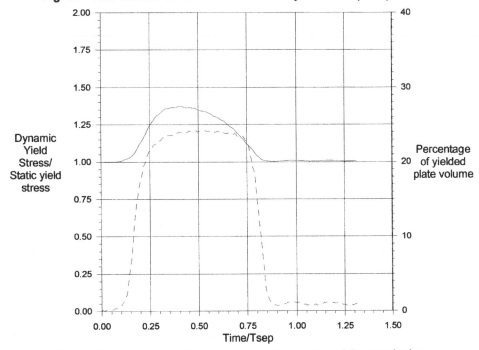

Fig. 10 Time-domain variation of lateral velocity at various plate positions

Fig. 11 Time-domain variation in material properties of the struck plate

Figure 10 depicts the variation in lateral velocity of the plate at the points described in Fig. 7. The velocity at the impacted points (1) and (2) reduces gradually from the initial value until a peak negative value is reached. Following separation the velocity fluctuates as the plate executes damped (elastic/viscoplastic) vibrations. At the other two locations large accelerations that accompany the high frequency vibrations are observed.

Figure 11 contains a plot of the spatial average of the dynamic yield stress in the time-domain (continuous line). Also included in this figure is the variation in the percentage of the viscoplastic material at each time interval (dotted line). It is evident that there is an

15

increase in the dynamic yield stress following impact which reaches a peak value at approx. $0.4t/t_{sep}$. Following that the yield stress decreases until it reaches the static value, which is the value at separation. The peak value of the average dynamic yield stress is $1.35\sigma_o$, which corresponds to a spatial average strain rate of 0.25 s^{-1}. This is not a high value which could lead to the impression that this problem can be treated as a quasi-static one; it should however be noted that the local strain rates, observed in way of the impacted nodes, are substantially higher than the average value. This is corroborated by the second curve included in this diagram which is a measure of the distribution of the viscoplastic material. Thus, for highly localised yielding the actual strain rates will be substantially higher than those observed in the cases of more uniform loading. In this problem it is seen that the volume of viscoplastic material increases rapidly at approximately $0.25t/t_{sep}$ and then remains approximately constant during the interval $0.25 < t/t_{sep} < 0.75$, during which a maximum of 24% is observed. It subsequently decreases and fluctuates about a value of approximately 1% following separation. The distribution and extent of viscoplastic material is directly related to the distribution and magnitude of the applied load and therefore for other types of dynamic loads these distributions will differ significantly.

6.   EFFECT OF LARGE WAVE IMPACTS

In this section results obtained in a study of the response of rectangular plating under large wave impacts are given [25]. Wave impacts can, under particular circumstances, cause severe damage to hull side shell plating, particularly near the bow of the vessel. Under normal conditions the loading does not lead to ductile failure but weakens the structure through the process of fatigue. It can therefore be said that it is necessary to consider the effects of wave impact throughout the load range in order to gain a complete understanding of it's effects. In the following, consideration will be given to what can be considered to be unusually high loads. The magnitude of the loads considered is considered "abnormal" in the sense that such loads are not usually encountered; nevertheless the values considered have ben measured during full-scale measurements at sea (Kawakami).

A related problem that has surfaced in recent years involves the loss of large sections of the side shell plating of large bulk carriers [26]. Although the damage caused in these cases is primarily due to loss of stiffness due to severe corrosion of the transverse frames which cease to provide any lateral support to the shell plating, the external action that leads to rupture is wave impact. This is particularly so in cases where the damage occurs near the bow of the vessel, since further aft the stresses in the plating may also include longitudinal bending components. A weakened structure therefore becomes particularly susceptible to wave impact loading, and serious local damage may result.

The analysis of a thin rectangular steel plate that is supported by longitudinal stiffeners and frames is performed. The geometry and loading particulars follow an analytical treatment of this problem (Wierzbicki). This question has been treated in some detail in [25] and the most important results are given here.

Details are included in the following table.

Table 3 Particulars of rectangular plate under wave impact loading

Aspect ratio	a/b		6.15
Slenderness	b/t		50
Initial geometrical distortion	w_o/t		0
Young's Modulus	E	GPa	207
Yield Stress	σ_0	MPa	245
Boundary Conditions		C-C-C-C	
Peak Load	p_o	MPa	2.27
Pulse Duration	τ	msec	50

The form of the load variation with time is given in Fig. 12 and is described by equation (30).

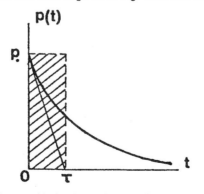

Fig. 12 Hydrodynamic wave impact load

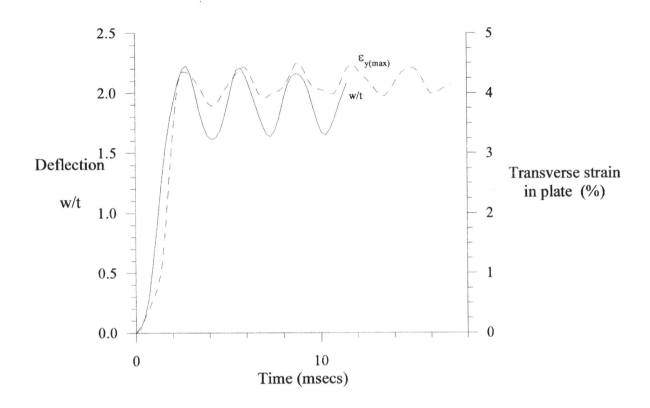

Fig. 13 Time variation of deflection and strain of plate subjected to a single impact

$$p(t) = p_o e^{-t/\tau} \qquad (30)$$

The response of the plate is considered under a single, two and multiple wave impacts and failure is assessed in relation to rupture. In order to determine whether the plate retains it's integrity the maximum strain that develops at any point within the plate is compared with the rupture strain. This is determined on the basis of semi-empirical data available for this type of material and geometry. In this particular case the rupture strain is considered to be 5%, and the results given for the various types of loading indicate the cases in which rupture may be expected to occur.

In the case of a single impact, a spatially constant, time varying load is applied to the plate whose particulars are given in Table 2. Selected results are given in Fig. 13. The stiffness and strength of the plate are described by the deflection ratio and by the maximum strain respectively. Failure is defined as the exceedance of the critical rupture strain.

In the diagrams that follow, results are given for multiple wave impacts for two peak pressures. The plate considered is the same, as is the form of loading. In this

case, however, the number of cycles is extended from two to twelve. Figure 14 includes results for p_o/p_{sc} = 1.5, whereas Fig. 15 gives results for p_o/p_{sc} = 4.25. (Please note p_o = peak pressure, p_{sc} = pressure for static collapse.

Figure 14 shows that the transverse strain lies below the critical rupture strain and as N is increased, it converges to a constant value. The variation in deflections shows a large increase after the fourth wave impact with a levelling off of the peak value as the number of impacts increases. The deflections in this case are in the range $0.17 < w/t < 0.28$, which corresponds to the small deflection range in static analysis. It may be concluded that in this case the cyclic loading leads to shakedown and thus the structure reaches a stable condition. Further loads of equal magnitude will not cause failure, which may occur due to either alternating plastic strains or to incremental plastic collapse.

Figure 15 shows that the critical rupture strain is exceeded after a small number of cycles (N_{cr}=4 for p_o/p_{sc} = 4.25). However, even in the absence of rupture the continuing increase in residual plastic strains will lead to incremental plastic collapse.

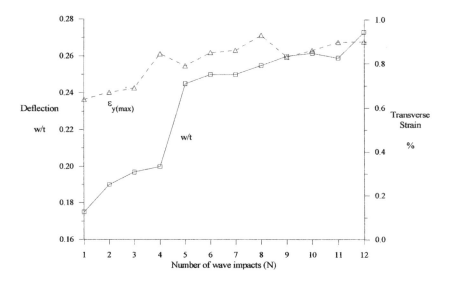

Fig. 14 Effect of multiple wave impacts on the stiffness and strength of the plate (p_o/p_{sc} = 1.5)

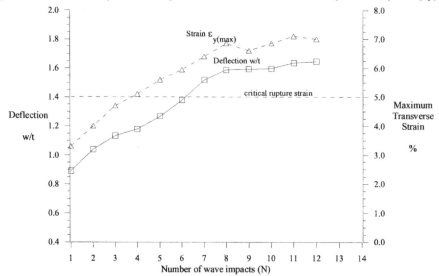

Fig. 15 Effect of multiple wave impacts on the plate stiffness and strength (p_o/p_{sc} = 4.25)

From these results it is clear that multiple wave impacts produce larger strains and deflections in the plate than those predicted by single impact analyses. It is shown that in order to ensure structural integrity under such loading conditions it is necessary to establish the safe operating range for the selected external loads. The aim of the designer ought to be to aim for shakedown so that failure by either incremental plastic collapse (high cycle fatigue) or alternating plastic strains (low cycle fatigue) is avoided.

7. CONCLUDING REMARKS

This paper describes the application of a new approach to problems that are related to ship's plating when subjected to abnormally high loads. Two cases are considered viz. low-energy collisions and hydrodynamic wave impact. Both of these types of problems have been the object of extensive research over many years. The present work aims at providing a tool which may lead to an improved understanding and which can thus

lead to improved design applications. Substantial further work in both directions is required.

The method described is based on a finite-difference model of the structure. The governing equations of motion are solved using the real-time dynamic relaxation method (RT-DR) which has been successfully used in the past in the solution of problems involving geometrical and material non-linearities. In this approach material nonlinearity is modelled using Perzyna's approach. Details of the numerical code are given in the paper. The sequence of calculations is described using a series of flow charts and further details are given in other publications. A series of correlation studies with low-energy collision tests are described and it was concluded that the approach is capable of accurately modelling the response of plating loaded dynamically. The collision tests are described in some details and the time-domain variation of several other parameters is considered. The method can be used not only to predict permanent deflections but also the variations in energy content and material properties of the struck plate.

In the last section of the paper a study of the effect of multiple wave impacts is described. This study showed that it is necessary to consider the effect of multiple wave impacts since the observed strains and deflections can increase, leading to incremental plastic collapse, when impact loads exceed a threshold value. When this threshold value is not exceeded, the strains approach constant values so that further wave impacts do not cause further permanent set. It is therefore important to determine the safe operating limit for each case in order to ensure a damage-free operating life of the structure.

REFERENCES

1. CHALMERS D.W.: 'Design of Ships Structures', Ministry of Defence, HMSO, London 1993.

2. NICKELL R.E.: 'Direct integration methods in structural dynamics'. Trans. ASCE, Jnl Engng Mechanics, Vol. 99, No EM2, (1973); 303-317.

3. SHAO W.J., FRIEZE P.A.: 'Geometrically Non-linear Elastic Dynamic Analysis of Doubly Curved Shells Using Dynamic Relaxation'. Dept. of Naval Architecture and Ocean Engineering Report No. NAOE-83-36, University of Glasgow, June 1986.

4. PAPADRAKAKIS M.: 'A Method for the Automatic Evaluation of the Dynamic Relaxation Parameters'. Computer Methods in Applied Mechanics and Engineering, 1981, 25; 35-48.

5. NOOR A.K., KNIGHT Jr N.F.: 'Non-linear dynamic analysis of curved beams'. Computer Methods in Applied Mechanics and Engineering, Vol. 23, (1980); 225-251.

6. CRISFIELD M.A.: 'Finite Elements and Solution Procedures for Structural Analysis'. Vol. 1: Linear Structural Analysis. Pineridge Press, Swansea, U.K., 1986.

7. PAPADRAKAKIS M.: 'Solving Large Scale Problems in Mechanics. The Development and Application of Computational Solution Methods'. John Wiley & Sons, Chichester, 1993.

8. KEY S.W., STONE C.M., and KRIEG R.D.: 'A solution strategy for the quasi-static large deformation inelastic response of axisymmetric solids'. In: Nonlinear Finite Element Analysis in Structural Mechanics. Wunderlich W. et al (Ed.), Springer Verlag Berlin, 581-620, 1981.

9. LYNCH R.D., KELSEY S., SAXE H.C.: 'The application of DR to the finite element method of structural analysis'. Technical Report No. THEMIS-UND-68-1, University of Notre Dame, 1968.

10. PICA A., HINTON E.: 'Transient and pseudo-transient analysis of Mindlin plates'. International Journal of Numerical Methods in Engineering, Vol. 15, 189-208, 1980.

11. FRANKEL S.P.: 'Convergence rates of iterative treatments for partial differential equations'. Math Tables Aid Comp., Vol. 4, 65-75, 1950.

12. MORINO L., LEECH J.W., WITMER E.A.: 'An Improved Numerical Calculation Technique for Large Elasto-Plastic Transient Deformations of Thin Shells', Part 1-Background and Theoretical Formulation. Trans. ASME, Journal of Applied Mechanics; June 1971, 38; 423-428.

13. MORINO L., LEECH J.W., WITMER E.A.: 'An Improved Numerical Calculation Technique for Large Elasto-Plastic Transient Deformations of Thin Shells', Part 2-Evaluation and Applications'. Trans. ASME, Journal of Applied Mechanics, June 1971, 38; 429-436.

14. OWEN D.R.J., HINTON E.: 'Finite Elements in Plasticity: Theory and Practice'. Pineridge Press, Swansea, U.K., 1980.

15. IRONS B.M., AHMAD S.: 'Finite Element Techniques'. Ellis Horwood, Chichester, U.K., 1980.

16. CARIDIS P.A: 'PANEL-2D: A Program for the Static and Dynamic Full-Range Analysis of Unstiffened and Stiffened Plates'. Structural Engineering Review, Vol. 8, No. 4, pp 337-344, 1996.

17. SAMUELIDES E., FRIEZE P.A.: 'Rigid Bow Impacts on Ship-Hull Models'. In: Ship Collisions with Bridges and Offshore Structures, Copenhagen, 1983; 264-269.

18. MACAULAY M.A.: 'Introduction to Impact Engineering'. Chapman and Hall, London, 1992.

19. KREMPL E.: 'Models of Viscoplasticity. Some Comments on Equilibrium (Back) Stress and Drag Stress'. Acta Mechanica, 69, 25-42 (1987).

20. COWPER G.R., SYMONDS P.S.: 'Strain-hardening and Strain-Rate Effects in the Impact Loading of Cantilever Beams', Technical Rept No. 28, Brown University, Rhode Island, 1957.

21. JONES N.: 'Plastic Behaviour of Ship Structures', Trans SNAME, 1976, Vol. 84, 115-145.

22. OWEN D.R.J., HINTON E.: 'Finite Elements in Plasticity. Theory and Practice'. Pineridge Press, Swansea, U.K., 1980.

23.   PERZYNA P.: 'Fundamental problems in viscoplasticity'. In: Advances in Applied Mechanics, Vol. 9, 1966, Academic Press, New York; 243-377.

24.   PERZYNA P.: 'The constitutive equations for rate sensitive materials'. Quart. Applied Mathematics, (1963), Vol. XX, No. 4; 321-332.

25.   CARIDIS P.A., STEFANOU M.: 'Dynamic elastic/viscoplastic response of hull plating subjected to hydrodynamic wave impact'. Journal of Ship Research, Vol. 41, No. 2, June 1997, pp 120-136.

26.   Lloyd's Register of Shipping. Bulk Carriers - an update. London, January 1996.

PAPER NO.17.

ENHANCEMENT OF WAVE INDUCED LOAD EFFECTS FOR SHIPS IN ABNORMAL CONDITIONS

by H Rathje and T E Schellin
Germanischer Lloyd, Germany

Paper presented at the

International Conference

**DESIGN AND OPERATION FOR
ABNORMAL CONDITIONS**

21 22 OCTOBER 1997 GLASGOW

ENHANCEMENT OF WAVE INDUCED LOAD EFFECTS FOR SHIPS IN ABNORMAL CONDITIONS

H Rathje and T E Schellin
Germanischer Lloyd

SUMMARY

A method was developed to enhance wave induced load effects for ships in severe seaways. The method comprised extrapolating dynamic pressures at the still-water level obtained from accurate linear computations to the surface wave elevation at the ship's hull. The method accounts for the three-dimensional shape of the hull and the effects of the non-vertical sides that may deform the wave itself, causing it to break as it ascends the sides of the ship. The method was applied to analyse wave induced vertical hull girder loads of a large containership design in equivalent design waves corresponding to abnormally severe seaway conditions. The waves were selected with periods that resulted in maximum rule values of vertical midship bending moment. Head wave and following wave conditions were analysed. Bending moments at three stations and shear forces at two stations along the length of the ship were investigated and compared with linear results obtained under the same wave conditions. Significant differences occurred.

AUTHORS' BIOGRAPHIES

From 1986 to 1990 Mr H Rathje worked for Maersk Shipping Line as a freight coordinator in Hamburg, Germany. In 1994 he graduated as a Dipl.-Ing. from the University of Hamburg. Since then he has been a member of the Basic Research Department of Germanischer Lloyd, working as a naval architect specialising in the areas of ship hydrodynamics and vibration analysis.

Dr. T E Schellin graduated from the Massachusetts Institute of Technology, Cambridge, USA, in 1964 with an MS in Naval Architecture and from Rice University, Houston, USA, in 1971 with a Ph.D. in Mechanical Engineering. He has worked for Shell Development Co. in Houston and at the GKSS Research Institute in Geesthacht, Germany, before coming to work for Germanischer Lloyd, Hamburg, in 1976. Presently a member of the Basic Research Department, he is project leader responsible for the development of hydrodynamic analysis methods for ships.

1. INTRODUCTION

The enhancement of wave induced load effects for ships in severe seas needs to be specially considered in the design stage. Generally, the practical prediction of wave loads and their effects cannot be accomplished by standard analysis codes based on linear theory alone, especially for ships with large flare at the ends. Nonlinear effects directly influence the hull girder load behaviour. Past full-scale measurement programs [1] proved that ratios of sagging to hogging bending moments are not equal to unity, which should be the case for linearsignals. These sag/hog ratios tend to be larger for slender ships such as modern containerships than for fuller ships such as tankers and bulkers. Non-linear effects mainly result from the non-vertical sides of the ship. Recent experimental measurements with models of a Wigley hull [2] showed that the presence of bow flare causes a significant increase in vertical bend-

ing moments and that maximum bending moments in the flared bow region reached the same magnitude as midship bending moments.

Ship motions in severe wave conditions can be calculated with reasonable accuracy using linear theory [3]. Vertical hull girder loads, however, can be nonlinear even though the motions are linear. For practical applications, therefore, codes based on linear theory may suffice to provide motion predictions even for ships in severe seas. These linear results can then serve as a basis for a suitable extension to nonlinear wave loading. The purpose of the present investigation was to develop a method capable of extending linear results to nonlinear wave loading. To enable the analysis of ships in severe seas, the method accounts for the three-dimensional shape of the hull and the effects of the non-vertical sides that may deform the wave itself, causing it to break as it ascends the sides of the ship.

Using a panel code [4,5] that has been verified by practical application, the method developed here starts with obtaining accurate three-dimensional linear pressure predictions up to the still-water level of the ship advancing at constant speed in regular waves. The next step consists of deriving formulas for the surface wave elevation and the dynamic pressure in the still-water region up to the wave contour for a finite amplitude regular wave of given period, heading and phase. The final step comprises applying these pressures to nodal points of the idealized hull surface and adding them to the linearly computed pressures to obtain total pressures acting at the ship's hull. Integrating total pressures yields hull girder loads. The stepwise change of vessel position and wave phase simulates the motion behaviour of the ship in the regular wave train.

The formulas derived to calculate surface wave elevation and dynamic pressure in the still-water region were based on previous developments [6] that extend linear strip theory results to nonlinear wave loading [7].

Procedures based on these developments were used to compare the long-term distribution of nonlinear wave induced vertical bending moments with rule values for a containership [8] and for three tankers [9]. An alternative procedure [10] starting with linear results obtained from the same panel code was developed earlier to investigate local pressures on bow doors of ro-ro ships.

The past decade has seen extraordinary progress in the practice of ship structural design. Dimensioning based on rational stress analysis that accounts for variable loads during the ship's expected service life in a most realistic way augments and, in many cases, replaces the conventional selection of scantlings according to the rules of classification societies. For practical application, the rational stress analysis usually relies on defining wave induced loads for the global finite element analysis of the ship structure. These loads combine the advantages of the common statistical load assessment and the comprehensive deterministic analysis of the ship's structural response. By superimposing these wave loads to selected cargo loading conditions, procedures such as the Advanced Design Wave Concept [11] and the Dynamic Load Approach [12] demonstrated the application of this rational analysis to recent designs of containerships and tankers.

Positioning a typical containership in the design wave subjects the finite element model to pressures extrapolated up to the wave contour. Nonlinear effects due to the ship's shape at its ends generally cause a decrease of the wave hogging moment and an increase of the wave sagging moment. These moments, used together with the design bending moments given in the rules of classification societies, define design load cases for hogging and sagging. The stress ranges produced by the rule wave bending moments - meanwhile unified within the International Association of Classification Societies (IACS) - compare favorably with those obtained from long-term measurements [13], specially for the low-frequency region, implying that design waves derived from the rules are a realistic basis for structural hull design.

To demonstrate the application of the developed method, wave induced vertical hull girder loads of a large containership with dramatically increased container capacity were analysed in equivalent design waves corresponding to abnormally severe seaway conditions. Three design waves were selected with periods that resulted in maximum rule values of vertical midship bending moment. Head wave and following wave conditions were analysed. Bending moments at three stations and shear forces at two stations along the length of the ship were investigated and compared with linear results obtained under the same wave conditions. Significant differences occurred.

2. THEORY AND NUMERICAL METHOD

The wave induced pressure acting on a section of the ship's hull comprised an hydrostatic part and an hydrodynamic part. The hydrostatic part was determined from the hydrostatic head up to the momentary still-water level of the ship, which was a function of the ship's momentary position. The hydrodynamic part consisted of the linearly computed hydrodynamic pressures up to the still-water level and a nonlinear extension to account for pressures due to wave loading in the region between still-water level and wave contour. Fig. 1 shows a schematic diagram of the pressure distribution on a typical cross section of the ship's hull due to the passage of a wave crest. The nonlinear wave load extension yielded pressures that were extrapolated from three-dimensional linearly computed hydrodynamic pressures acting on the hull at the still-water level as well as surface wave elevations specifying the wave contour along the side of the hull. The extrapolated pressures depended on the momentary phase of the wave relative to the ship's position, the wave frequency of encounter, and the flare of the ship section.

In this method, a time harmonic velocity potential with amplitude ϕ and frequency ω equal to the wave encounter frequency is defined describing the two-dimensional flow in the vicinity of the still-water level at the side of the ship. Applying Bernoulli's equation to express pressure p_s in the plane r,s tangent to the ship's side yields

$$\frac{p_s}{\rho} + \frac{\partial \phi}{\partial t} + \frac{1}{2}\left[\left(\frac{\partial \phi}{\partial r}\right)^2 + \left(\frac{\partial \phi}{\partial s}\right)^2\right] + g\,s\cos\alpha = const.$$

(1)

where ρ is the density of water, g is the acceleration of gravity, and t is time. Coordinate r proceeds along a tangent at the ship's still-water level, and coordinate s, orthogonal to r, extends from the still-water level positive upward along the side of the ship. The origin of the r,s coordinate system is located at the intersection of the still-water level and the considered ship section. Angle α, measured between the vertical and the ship's side, designates the flare of the ship section.

Assuming ship motions are small, velocity components normal to the hull are set equal to zero. The potential function ϕ is thus a function of r and s and can be expressed in terms of its velocity components as follows:

$$\phi(r,s) = (\varphi_r - v_o)r + \varphi_s s \qquad (2)$$

where

$$v_r = \partial\phi/\partial r = (\varphi_r - v_0) \quad \text{and} \quad v_s = \partial\phi/\partial s = \varphi_s$$

(3)

and where v_0 is the steady forward speed of the ship. Since v_r and v_s are constant quantities, component v_s describes the velocity of the surface wave elevation in the s-direction. For a harmonic wave with an amplitude ζ_a and encounter frequency ω, the surface wave elevation ζ is written as

$$\zeta = \zeta_a\, e^{i\omega t} \tag{4}$$

where $i = \sqrt{-1}$. On the wave contour the velocity in the s-direction is thus

$$v_s = \dot{\zeta} = i\omega\zeta_a\, e^{i\omega t} = i\omega\zeta = \varphi_s \tag{5}$$

Substituting (5) into (2) results in the relation

$$\phi(r,s) = (\varphi_r - v_0)r + i\omega\zeta s \tag{6}$$

Partial derivatives of $\phi(r,s)$ with respect to t, r and s are, respectively,

$$\partial\phi/\partial t = (\partial\varphi_r/\partial t)r - (\partial v_0/\partial t)r + (\partial\varphi_s/\partial t)s,$$
$$\partial\phi/\partial r = \varphi_r - v_0 \quad \text{and} \quad \partial\phi/\partial s = i\omega\zeta \tag{7}$$

and partial derivatives of φ_s and v_0 with respect to t are, respectively,

$$\partial\varphi_s/\partial t = -\omega^2\zeta \quad \text{and} \quad \partial v_0/\partial t = 0 \tag{8}$$

Substituting (8) into (7) leads to the expression

$$\partial\phi/\partial t = (\partial\varphi_r/\partial t)r - \omega\zeta^2 s \tag{9}$$

Substituting these partial derivatives into equation (1) yields

$$\frac{p_s}{\rho} - \omega^2\zeta s + \frac{\partial\varphi_r}{\partial t}r + \frac{1}{2}\left[(\varphi_r - v_0)^2 + (i\omega\zeta)^2\right]$$
$$+ g s\cos\alpha = const. \tag{10}$$

Applying this equation at a point on the still-water level (where $r = s = 0$ and p_{WL} = dynamic pressure at still-water level) results in the expression

$$\frac{p_{WL}}{\rho} - \frac{1}{2}\omega^2\zeta + \frac{1}{2}(\varphi_r - v_0)^2 = const. \tag{11}$$

Equating (10) and (11) and setting $r = 0$ results in the following relationship for the pressure p_s along the side of the ship:

$$p_s = p_{WL} - \rho(g\cos\alpha - \omega^2\zeta)s \tag{12}$$

The influence of the so-called Smith effect [14] is shown by the gradient of this pressure, determined by differentiating p_s with respect to s:

$$dp_s/ds = -\rho(g\cos\alpha - \omega^2\zeta) \tag{13}$$

At the wave crest ($\zeta > 0$) the pressure gradient is reduced, leading to an increase of surface wave elevation. At the wave trough ($\zeta < 0$) the pressure gradient is increased, causing a decrease of surface wave elevation.

Solving the quadratic equation (12) for ζ while setting $s = \zeta$ and $p_s = 0$, which are the boundary conditions for the wave contour, yields the surface wave elevation. Only the smaller of the two solutions is physically meaningful, resulting in the following expression:

$$\zeta = \frac{g\cos\alpha}{2\omega^2} - \sqrt{\left(\frac{g\cos\alpha}{2\omega^2}\right)^2 - \frac{p_{WL}}{\rho\omega^2}} \tag{14}$$

A real solution can be attained only if

$$|p_{WL}| \leq \rho\left(\frac{g\cos\alpha}{2\omega}\right)^2 \tag{15}$$

Pressure p_{WL} denotes the amplitude of the pressure variation at the still-water level. If the pressure at still-water level under a wave crest exceeds this value, the maximum wave elevation reaches its limit and the wave breaks. In this case the dynamic pressures is given by

$$p_s = p_{WL} - \frac{1}{2}\rho g s\cos\alpha \tag{16}$$

The maximum surface wave elevation occurs at the crest when $p_{WL} = \rho(g\cos\alpha/2\omega)^2$ and, half a wave period later, the minimum levation l is at the trough when $p_{WL} = -\rho(g\cos\alpha/2\omega)^2$. Substituting these pressures into (14) results in the following expressions for wave amplitude:

$$\zeta_{max} = \frac{g\cos\alpha}{2\omega^2} \quad \text{at the crest and}$$

$$\zeta_{min} = -(\sqrt{2} - 1) \frac{g \cos \alpha}{2\omega^2} \quad \text{at the trough} \qquad (17)$$

The maximum wave height is thus

$$H_{max} = \zeta_{max} - \zeta_{min} = \frac{g \cos \alpha}{\sqrt{2}\omega^2} \qquad (18)$$

Practical results achieved are within realistic bounds. For instance, a deep water wave not disturbed by the presence of the ship ($\omega^2 = 2\pi \, g/\lambda$, where λ denotes wave length) breaking at a vertical ship section (no flare, thus $\alpha = 0$) has a height to length ratio of approximately one to nine, a value somewhat less than the theoretical limit of one to seven.

To summarize, dynamic pressures are obtained from (12) or, if the wave breaks, from (16) with the surface wave elevation ζ determined according to (14). Dynamic pressures below the still-water level become unrealistic when their absolute values exceed the hydrostatic pressures. In that case they are set equal to the negative value of the hydrostatic pressure, causing the total pressure to vanish.

The theory of the panel code that solved the linear three-dimensional problem assumes high encounter frequency and approximates the velocity potentials by their zero-speed values. Diffracted and radiated potentials are expressed by superimposing potentials of pulsating sources located on panels distributed over the ship's wetted surface. On the ship's hull, the boundary condition is linearised under slender ship assumptions; on the free surface, the boundary condition is linearised without accounting for the ship's forward speed.

This panel code constitutes a first order panel method because it takes flat planar panels and assumes the strength of the singularities to be constant over the surface of each panel. Therefore, the singularity distribution varies as a step function from panel to panel, and the accuracy is directly a function of panel size. High accuracy was obtained through the use of a large number of low order panels. The numerical treatment of this problem required the development of efficient computational procedures based on optimized parallel mathematical subroutine libraries. An SGI Power Challenge L with four R-8000 processors and 512 Mbytes of main memory was used. The complete motion analysis for 20 wave frequencies of a ship discretised into 2650 surface panels required about 50 min of CPU time.

To apply this method in connection with a three-dimensional panel code, it was first necessary to define a ship section through the centroid of each surface panel. Along this section the surface wave elevation was then computed to decide if this particular panel is located above or below the wave contour. This required

the identification of the surface panel passing through the still-water level which was located vertically either above or below this panel. In case the panel was located above the still-water level, the surface wave elevation was computed and the amount of submersion of the panel was determined. This necessitated calculating the angle between the vertical and the inclination of the panel. To also facilitate the practical handling of panels characterized by extreme flare, which are generally situated at the ends of ships, the flare angle was based on a line extending from the intersection point at the still-water level to the centroid of the panel located two panels above this panel.

The four corner points of quadrilateral panels normally did not lie in one plane. To determine their centroid, quadrilateral panels were subdivided into two triangles. The line connecting the centroids of the two triangles was established, and the point where this line intersected the ship section defined the centroid of the quadrilateral panel. To avoid asymmetric wave induced loading of the ship, it was important to discretise both sides of the hull into symmetrically similar surface panels together with an appropriate numbering of nodes for the corners of the panels. The numerical procedure required the ship's hull to be discretised into panels also above the still-water level to a height somewhat greater than the wave contour. Accurate results were obtained when the height of panels located near the still-water level was relatively small, specifically, when the ratio of wave height to panel height was larger than ten.

3. RESULTS

Sample computations for the advanced design concept of an 8000 TEU post-Panamax containership of Howaldtswerke-Deutsche Werft AG were performed to analyse wave induced vertical hull girder loads in severe seas. The ship was considered homogeneously loaded with containers weighing 14 t per TEU while carrying 100 percent provisions. It was assumed floating at the design draft of 14 m while traveling at a constant service speed of 25.3 knots. Principal particulars of the ship are listed in Table 1. Its longitudinal weight distribution, extending from the aft perpendicular (AP) to the forward perpendicular (FP), is shown in Fig. 2. To provide increased deck area, the lines of the ship were designed with extreme flare at the bow and the stern. This feature can be deduced from the surface panel idealization of its hull shape shown in Fig. 3.

Linear computations were performed by the panel method of Germanischer Lloyd. These computations, yielding vessel motions and hull girder sectional loads caused by regular deep water waves of unit amplitude, were based on discretising the ship's hull into 5062 surface panels, with 2986 of these panels located below the design load waterline. The resulting heave and pitch motions as well as the midship vertical bending moment for the ship in head waves and following waves are given as transfer functions in Fig. 4.

The extended nonlinear computations were performed for three regular waves having periods of 12.8, 13.5 and 14.2 s and corresponding wave length to ship length ratios of 0.79, 0.87 and 0.96, respectively. They were selected because, in the neighbourhood of these wave periods, the linearly computed midship vertical bending moments attained their maximum values (Fig. 4). Consequently, to demonstrate the application of the present method for the analysis of wave induced loads in abnormal, i.e., severe conditions, these periods were selected for the equivalent regular design waves. Amplitudes for these design waves were chosen to result in the rule value for the midship vertical wave bending moment for seagoing steel ships as internationally agreed upon by classification societies, see for example Section 5B.2.1, Chapter 1, of [15]. The maximum bending moment of the subject containership is in the hogging condition. Therefore, the rule value for hogging of 6477 MNm was decisive here, leading to the design wave amplitudes of around 6.4 m for head wave conditions and 8.6 m for following wave conditions.

Wave induced vertical hull girder loads were investigated at three stations along the length of the ship, namely, at the midship section located a distance of 158.40 m from the AP, at a forward section located halfway between the midship section and the FP, and at an aft section located halfway between the midship section and the AP. At the midship section, only the vertical bending moment was of interest; at the fore and aft sections, the vertical bending moment as well as the vertical shear force were examined.

For each design wave, computations were performed at two wave positions, corresponding to the hogging and the sagging condition. For the hogging condition in head waves, the wave crest was located a small distance of around 1.7 m ahead of the midship section. With the wave crest at this position, the vertical wave bending moment for the hogging condition reached its maximum value. For the sagging condition in head waves, the wave trough was located at this position. For the hogging condition in following waves, the wave crest was located a small distance of around 2.4 m behind the midship section. For the sagging condition in following waves, the wave trough was positioned here.

Hull girder loads were computed not only for the hogging and sagging conditions, but also for the still water condition. This enabled the determination of amplitudes and mean values. Taking half the sum of the absolute values for hogging and sagging yielded the amplitude; subtracting this amplitude from the sum of the values for hogging and for the still water condition gave the mean value. The resulting amplitudes and mean values in head waves are summarized in Table 2; the corresponding values in following waves, in Table 3. Listed are vertical bending moments at the fore, aft, and midship sections and vertical shear forces at the fore and aft sections of the ship. The design wave amplitude and the wave crest position from amidships for the hogging condition are listed in as well.

For comparison, these same vertical hull girder loads were determined also from linear calculations, taking as a basis the design wave amplitudes used for the nonlinear computations. For linear cases, of course, amplitudes of hull girder loads in the hogging condition are equal to those in the sagging condition, and mean values are equal to hull girder loads in the still water condition. A schematic representation of how amplitudes and mean values of nonlinear and linear hull girder loads were obtained is shown in Fig. 5. The percentage deviations of the nonlinearly computed values from their respective linear values are listed in Table 4 for head wave conditions and in Table 5 for following wave conditions. Positive deviations denote an increase over linear results; negative deviations, a decrease from linear results.

4. DISCUSSION

The wave contour at the ship's side as well as the fluid pressures, integrated over the wetted surface to obtain hull girder loads, were significantly affected by the wave breaking criterion and the sectional flare at the ship's ends. These effects were more pronounced for the ship advancing in head waves than in following waves as seen in Fig. 6. In head waves the resulting design wave contours show that the crests are more severely flattened in the vicinity of the ship's midship region under hogging conditions (Fig. 6a) and at the ship's ends under sagging conditions (Fig. 6b). The corresponding pressure distributions on the ship's hull are given in Fig. 7. The darker panels on the wetted surface designate high pressure zones; the lighter panels, low pressure zones. As expected, the hogging condition (Fig. 7a) shows higher pressures (on the ship's bottom) and larger wave elevations (at the ship's side) in the midship region, whereas the sagging condition (Fig. 7b) depicts higher pressures and larger wave elevations at the ship's ends.

Tables 4 and 5 indicate that nonlinearly computed amplitudes were generally larger and nonlinearly computed mean values smaller than comparable linear results. The only exceptions were the aft bending moments in head seas for the two longer (larger period) design waves. Furthermore, deviations from linearly obtained hull girder loads were larger under head wave conditions than under following wave conditions. In head waves, deviations of amplitudes as well as mean values increased with the design wave length. In following waves, only deviations of the amplitudes were larger for the longer design waves.

Increases of midship bending moment amplitudes over corresponding linear results were larger in head waves than in following waves, namely, 15 and 6 percent, respectively, for the longest design wave considered. Decreases of mean values from corresponding linear results were greater for longer design waves, but only under head wave conditions (43 percent for the longest wave considered). In following waves, decreases of mean values were greater in shorter design waves (25 percent for the shortest wave considered).

Increases of forward bending moment amplitudes over corresponding linear results were significantly larger in head waves than in following waves, namely, 66 and 18 percent, respectively, for the longest design wave considered. Decreases of mean values from corresponding linear results were greater in head waves than in following waves, namely, 49 and 18 percent, respectively, for the longest design wave considered.

Deviations of aft bending moment amplitudes from corresponding linear results were relatively small for all design waves considered, namely, less than 8 percent. However, decreases of mean values from corresponding linear results were significant, varying between 22 and 29 percent.

Significant increases of forward shear force amplitudes over corresponding linear results occurred only in head waves, specifically, up to 14 percent for the longest design wave considered. However, decreases of mean values from corresponding linear results were relatively large, particularly under head wave conditions (79 percent for the longest design wave considered).

Similar to the forward shear forces, significant increases of aft shear forces over corresponding linear results were only found under head wave conditions, specifically, up to 13 percent for the longest design wave considered. Mean values decreased up to 25 percent under head wave conditions for the longest design wave considered.

5. CONCLUSIONS

The method developed to analyse wave induced loads for ships in severe seas was applied on an advanced containership design. The analysis was performed in equivalent regular design waves under head and following wave conditions that cause maximum vertical midship bending moments. Vertical bending moments and shear forces in hogging and sagging, computed at three stations along the length of the ship, show that significant differences occurred compared with corresponding linear results. Nonlinearly computed amplitudes were generally larger and mean values smaller than linear values, more so in head waves than in following waves.

Although heights of design waves investigated here are extreme (13 m in head seas, 18 m in following seas), the occurrence of greater wave heights in even more abnormal conditions can not be excluded. A recent investigation [16] showed that classification society rules implicitly assure that ship structures possess reserve strength against ultimate failure under such conditions.

6. ACKNOWLEDGMENTS

Past developments of the panel code used to obtain linear results started with the analysis of wave loading on fixed and floating offshore structures [17,18,19]. References [4] and [5] are later improvements including modifications to enable the analysis of wave loads on slender ships with forward speed.

Permission to publish results of hydrodynamic wave induced load calculations was kindly given by Howaldtswerke-Deutsche Werft AG, Kiel. Financial support for this work was partially provided by the German Federal Ministry of Education, Science, Research and Technology (BMBF) under research contract MTK 0574.

The authors are indebted to A. Köhlmoos for his assistance with the numerical calculations.

REFERENCES

1. SMITH, C S: 'Measurement of Service Stresses in Warships', Proc. Int. Conf. Stresses in Service, Inst. of Civil Engrs., London, 1966, pp. 1-8.

2. ADEGEEST, L: 'Third-Order Volterra Modelling of Ship Responses Based on Regular Wave Results', Preprts. 21st Symp. on Naval Hydrodynamics, Trondheim, National Academy Press, Washington, D.C., 1996, pp. 141-155.

3. LIN, W M, MEINHOLD, M J, SALVESEN, N and YUE, K P: 'Large-Amplitude Motions and Wave Loads for Ship Design', Proc. 20th Symp. on Naval Hydrodynamics, Santa Barbara, National Academy Press, Washigton, D.C., 1995, pp. 205-226.

4. PAPANIKOLAOU, A D and SCHELLIN, T E: 'A Three-Dimensional Panel Method for Motions and Loads of Ships with Forward Speed', Ship Tech. Res. 39(4), 1992, pp. 147-156.

5. ÖSTERGAARD; C and SCHELLIN, T E: 'Development of an Hydrodynamic Panel Method for Practical Analysis of Ships in a Seaway', Trans. STG, Vol. 89, 1995, pp. 561-576 (in German).

6. HACHMANN, D: 'Determination of Wave Elevation at Ship Sections Based on Pressure Variations at Design Waterline under the Influence of the Smith Effect', Report MTK 325 II, Germanischer Lloyd, Hamburg, 1986 (in German).

7. HACHMANN, D: 'Calculation of Pressures on a Ship's Hull in Waves', Ship Tech. Res. Vol. 38, 1991, pp. 111-132.

8. GUEDES SOARES, C and SCHELLIN, T E: 'Long-Term Distribution of Nonlinear Wave Induced Vertical Bending Moments on a Containership', Marine Structures, Vol. 9, 1996, pp. 333-352

9. GUEDES SOARES, C and SCHELLIN, T E: 'Nonlinear Effects on Long-Term Distributions of Wave Induced Loads for Tankers', Proc. 15th Int.

Conf. on Offshore Mechanics and Arctic Engineering (OMAE'96), ASME, New York, Vol. II, 1996, pp. 79-85.

10. ÖSTERGAARD, C, RATHJE, H, and SAMES, P C: 'RoRo Ship Bow Door Design: First Principle Analysis of Wave Loads and Stresses', Proc. 13th Int. Conf. & Exhibition on Marine Transport using Roll-on/Roll-off and Horizontal Handling Methods (RORO96), Lübeck, Vol. 2, BML Business Meetings Ltd., Herts, 1996.

11. PAYER, H G and FRICKE, W: 'Rational Dimensioning and Analysis of Complex Ship Structures', Trans. SNAME, Vol. 102, 1994, pp. 395-417.

12. LIU, D, SPENCER, J, ITOH, T, KAWACHI, S, and SHIGEMATSU, K: 'Dynamic Load Approach in Tanker Design', Trans. SNAME, Vol. 100, 1992, pp. 143-172.

13. HANSEN, H.J: 'Results of Long-Term Measurements on Ships at Sea', Trans. STG, Vol. 87, 1993, pp. 351-360.

14. SMITH, W E: 'Hogging and Sagging Strains in a Seaway as Influenced by Wave Structure', Trans. INA, Vol. 24, 1883.

15. Germanischer Lloyd: 'Rules for the Classification and Construction, Part 1: Seagoing Ships, Chapter 1: Hull Structures,' Hamburg, 1997.

16. ÖSTERGAARD, C, OTTO, S, TEIXEIRA, A, and GUEDES SOARES, C: 'A Reliability Based Proposal for Modern Structural Design Rules of the Ultimate Vertical Bending Moment of Containerships,' Trans. STG, Vol. 90, 1996.

17. ÖSTERGAARD, C, SCHELLIN, T E, and SÜKAN, M: 'Hydrodynamic Analysis of Compact Structures', Schiff und Hafen, Vol. 1, 1979. pp. 71-79 (in German).

18. SÜKAN, M: 'Computation of Wave Action on Compact Arbitrary Offshore Structures', Schiffstechnik, Vol. 29., 1982, pp. 135-175 (in German).

19. PAPANIKOLAOU, A D: 'On the Evaluation of Motions And Loads of Arbitrary Bodies in Waves,' Proc. Symp. Ocean Space Utilization '85, Tokyo, Springer, 1985.

TABLE 1: Principal particulars of subject containership

Length on design load waterline	326.67 m
Length between perpendiculars	325.00 m
Beam	46.00 m
Draft	14.00 m
Deadweight	89270 t
Service speed	25.3 kn
Metacentric height	3.28 m
Location of center of gravity from AP	156.73 m

TABLE 2: Vertical hull girder loads (head waves)

Design wave period [s]	Design wave amplitude [m]	Wave crest position for hogging [m]	Amplitude or mean value	Forward bending moment [10^6 kN m]	Midship bending moment [10^6 kN m]	Aft bending moment [10^6 kN m]	Forward shear force [10^4 kN]	Aft shear force [10^4 kN]
12.8	6.43	1.65	Amplitude	2.68	7.87	3.52	8.52	8.07
			Mean	2.92	4.26	3.10	1.40	6.64
13.5	6.49	1.70	Amplitude	3.57	8.54	3.58	9.89	8.98
			Mean	2.41	3.63	2.83	0.79	6.13
14.2	6.35	1.75	Amplitude	4.37	8.97	3.43	10.29	9.69
			Mean	1.90	3.24	2.76	0.63	5.75

TABLE 3: Vertical hull girder loads (following waves)

Design wave period [s]	Design wave amplitude [m]	Wave crest position for hogging [m]	Amplitude or mean value	Forward bending moment [10^6 kN m]	Midship bending moment [10^6 kN m]	Aft bending moment [10^6 kN m]	Forward shear force [10^4 kN]	Aft shear force [10^4 kN]
12.8	9.08	-2.10	Amplitude	2.41	7.92	3.95	7.89	8.71
			Mean	3.09	4.24	2.82	1.58	6.69
13.5	8.44	-2.42	Amplitude	2.63	7.80	4.01	7.80	8.42
			Mean	3.05	4.32	2.91	1.72	6.77
14.2	8.26	-2.73	Amplitude	2.79	7.78	4.07	7.78	8.30
			Mean	3.04	4.41	2.99	1.85	6.84

TABLE 4: Percentage deviation of vertical hull girder loads from linear values (head waves)

Design wave period [s]	Amplitude or mean value	Forward bending moment	Midship bending moment	Aft bending moment	Forward shear force	Aft shear force
12.8	Amplitude	24.1	6.2	0.6	6.2	5.2
	Mean	-21.5	-25.0	-21.5	-53.2	-13.8
13.5	Amplitude	42.2	9.2	-7.0	9.6	8.7
	Mean	-35.2	-36.1	-28.4	-73.6	-20.4
14.2	Amplitude	66.2	15.4	-7.8	14.1	13.3
	Mean	-48.9	-43.0	-30.1	-78.9	-25.3

TABLE 5: Percentage deviation of vertical hull girder loads from linear values (following waves)

Design wave period [s]	Amplitude or mean value	Forward bending moment	Midship bending moment	Aft bending moment	Forward shear force	Aft shear force
12.8	Amplitude	5.2	0.6	0.8	-0.1	-0.7
	Mean	-16.9	-25.4	-28.6	-47.2	-13.1
13.5	Amplitude	12.9	3.9	3.6	2.5	1.8
	Mean	-18.0	-23.9	-26.3	-42.5	-12.1
14.2	Amplitude	18.2	6.4	6.3	4.6	3.8
	Mean	18.3	-22.4	-24.3	-38.1	-11.2

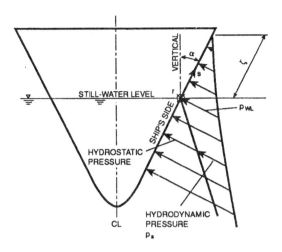

Fig. 1 Schematic of pressure distribution on a ship cross section

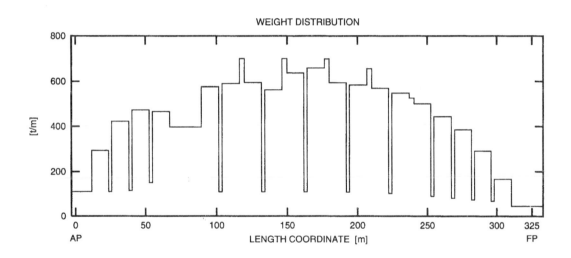

Fig. 2 Weight distribution of subject containership

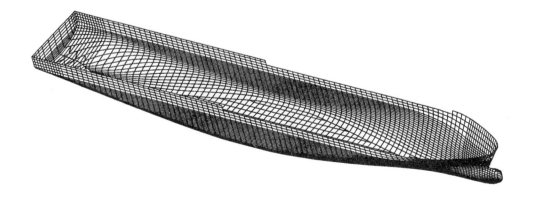

Fig. 3 Discretization of ship's hull into surface elements

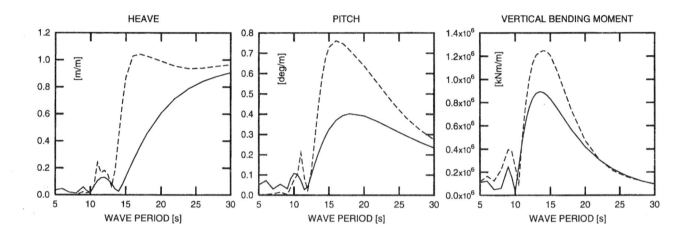

Fig. 4 Transfer functions of heave, pitch, and vertical midship bending moment of subject containership in head waves (dashed line) and following waves (solid line)

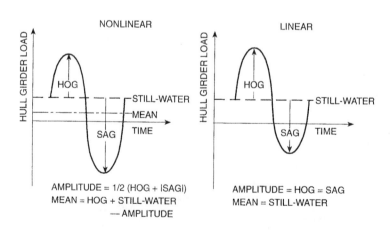

Fig. 5 Schematic representation of nonlinearly and linearly computed amplitudes and mean values of vertical hull girder loads

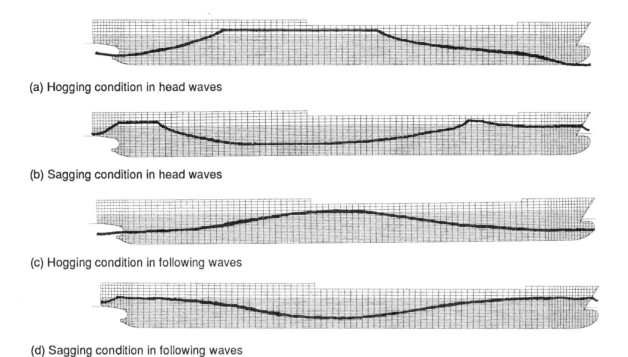

(a) Hogging condition in head waves

(b) Sagging condition in head waves

(c) Hogging condition in following waves

(d) Sagging condition in following waves

Fig. 6 Wave contour at side of subject containership for the 13.5 s period design wave

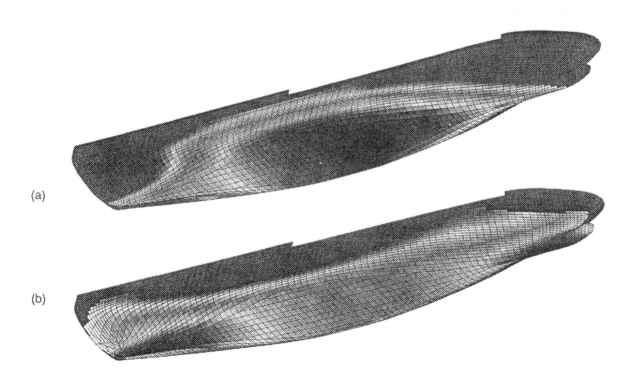

(a)

(b)

Fig. 7 .Pressure distribution on hull of subject containership in the hogging condition (a) and the sagging condition (b) for the 13.5 s period design wave

PAPER NO.18.

SUMMARY REPORT OF DISCUSSIONS

by E C Tupper, RINA

International Conference

DESIGN AND OPERATION FOR
ABNORMAL CONDITIONS

21 22 OCTOBER 1997 GLASGOW

SUMMARY REPORT OF DISCUSSIONS

by E C Tupper, CEng, FRINA, RCNC

SESSION 1 - ABNORMAL CONDITIONS

In the Chair: **Professor D Faulkner,**
Emeritus Professor, UK

The Chairman opened by welcoming everyone to this latest RINA conference. He then introduced Sir Robert Easton, President, IESIS.

OPENING ADDRESS

by Sir Robert Easton, President, IESIS

Sir Robert welcomed delegates on behalf of the RINA and added a warm welcome to Scotland from the Institution of Engineers and Shipbuilders in Scotland. In Gaelic - "Ceud mille failte" - a hundred thousand welcomes.

On abnormal conditions he said that the Port of Glasgow was on a man made river. Once the river could be forded five miles west of the city centre. The city merchants decided that ships must be brought into the heart of the city. They hired the best engineering brains and the solution was to dig a river and the River Clyde became capable of taking the world's largest ships. There is a saying that "Glasgow made the Clyde, but the Clyde made Glasgow". It was the container revolution that spelled the end of the Clyde's supremacy as it did for so many other great seaports.

Sir Robert was pleased to see so much talent present to discuss a topic that has challenged naval architects for a long time. The forces of nature remain capable of producing the most unexpected and terrifying power with no warning. Power that could break up ships and smash steel structures.

How does a designer cope? Should design be based on what is thought realistic, or on the unexpected. If the latter what power of the unexpected is envisaged and how are the cost consequences to be dealt with? What might be considered abnormal for one marine design may be normal for another! What is certain is that ships should have a degree of survival margin to cope with the abnormal.

The offshore operator has seen the results of the worst that the sea can do, not least in the areas around the Shetlands. The sea has no friends and takes no prisoners! The offshore designer must now consider wave heights of around 40 metres.

This conference must activate the thoughts of all designers, whether ship or rig orientated, and those associated with the international rules, in an endeavour to reach a consensus on a reasonable answer to this problem. Use of new materials, improved construction techniques, the latest technology and, by no means least, practical experience of the real problem, are vital, covering hull design, traffic, route, loading and environment.

He wished everyone an informative and worthwhile two days.

PAPER 1

WHAT IS ABNORMAL? - DEFINING THE UNDEFINABLE

Presented by A W Gilfillan, Yard Ltd, UK

Mr E C Tupper (RINA) agreed that hindsight, or experience, was a wonderful thing. He asked if the author felt there had been enough feedback from the sea on the conditions ships had to meet and how they reacted? There had been some feedback and several interesting case histories had been given in the presentation. Had there been enough? Mr Tupper reminded the meeting of RINA's initiative in encouraging, and enabling young naval architects to get more time at sea. The author remarked that experience and a good database were the naval architect's strongest tools, but they never did get enough feedback, particularly in the commercial area. In the naval area there was a more structured way of getting feedback. For HMS SCOTT the safety case approach was of great help to both the designer and operator. It showed what underlay the design. Some changes were made when it was learnt how the operators planned to use the ship based on their seagoing experience.

Mr J Sadden (Yarrows) said the paper made the case for the safety case approach but did the profession have enough data to use it sensibly? For example, how had the designer learnt about the katabatic winds which were so important to the design of the THETIS? How did he decide that 150 knots was the right figure to use and not 170, say? The author agreed the lack of data but the situation was improving. The katabatic wind speed used was a design figure provided by the Danish Navy. This was only one of several features peculiar to operating in these high latitudes; for example, ice accretion. The Chairman referred to recent experiences in a survey ship in the Pacific. The ship had experienced steady winds of 135 knots, gusting to 165.

1

Mr S Smith (Amerada Hess) said that the offshore industry used the safety case approach. Although data might be limited it caused one to look at the quality of data and enabled the designer to ask, "what if?". For example, what would be the consequence of a stronger wind?

Mr H Osborn (Westminster Dredging) commented that katabatic winds could arise in other areas due to local topography. For example, in Loch Striven they were significant to fish farms.

The Chairman felt naval architects had been too absorbed by the standard wave calculation for strength, closing their minds to the possibility of higher waves.

PAPER 2

RAPID FAILURE, RAPID SINKING

Presented by D Brown, Independent Consultant, UK

Mr E Haig (YARD), referring to instances of the interaction between structure and survivability being addressed in a safety case analysis, said one example was an MoD floating dock. The MoD were concerned about possible structural failure following collision with the dock. This was explored and small structural improvements made. Fortunately the basic design of the dock led to a reserve of strength after such damage. This would not be the usual case for ships and he would like to see investigations made of structural strength following collision and extensive flooding. An analysis of some 1800 cases of damage and loss in warships in WWII showed very few cases where structural failure occurred as a result of the flooding although the initial damage did in some cases. He had been impressed by the ability of ships to withstand structural damage.

Mr A Gutierrez (Bilbao Plaza Maritima) supported training for personnel. New vessels had to carry too many manuals. Information had to be in a much more readily assimilated form. This might avoid many accidents. For example, on one occasion a captain had been unaware there was a carbon dioxide fire fighting system on board his brand new ship.

Mr E Vossnack (Ret.NA) expressed concern at the banning of some good protective coatings because of pollution. When he was at Lloyds he found ships had too little time for maintenance, and coatings peeled off. The author agreed the importance of coating systems, particularly where corrosive cargoes (for example fertilisers) were carried. Often the surface subject to attack was also part of the ship's watertight boundary.

Mr W Buckley (Consultant), referring to large holes in the bow, was concerned at the very high pressure heads that would be developed in steep seas. Did current design standards deal with this? The author said he thought they did not. He had many similar illustrations, in passenger and cargo ships. The master should be made aware of what was happening forward. This could be achieved by using strain and pressure gauges. They were available. The Chairman confirmed that large bulk carriers could plunge in 3 or 4 minutes once the two forward holds, say, were flooded.

Mr J Aston (Salvage Association) said that besides waves as a cause of structural failure, corrosion could be a major factor. Could the author comment on the relative importance of the sea conditions met versus the ship condition? Could he expand upon the cases of operators switching off their stress monitoring systems? The author agreed on corrosion. One view was that once a bulk carrier had made one voyage she was an old bulk carrier. The problem could be aggravated by the use of high strength steels to increase the amount of cargo that could be carried. Inspection was vital as was adequate maintenance. He had knowledge of ships which had turned off their sensors. The watchkeeper was not required to use the system. More feedback from trials of stress monitoring was needed.

SESSION II - THE ABNORMAL WAVE

In the Chair: Professor D Faulkner

PAPER 3

LONG TERM TRENDS IN ALTIMETER MEASURED SIGNIFICANT WAVE HEIGHT, AND THE IMPLICATIONS FOR EXPECTED EXTREME VALUES

Presented by Dr P D Cotton, Southampton Oceanography Centre, University of Southampton, UK

The Southampton Oceanography Centre (SOC) achieved a retrieval accuracy of +/-0.5s, in comparison with buoy data, in extracting wave period from satellite altimeter data. SOC were working on a paper on this topic which will be published in the refereed literature.

Mr W Buckley (Consultant, US) noted that the ratio of significant wave heights off Ireland for winter maximum and summer minimum was given as 2:1. His analysis for the American east coast gave the same ratio.

Mr E C Tupper (RINA) referred to Dr Hogben's suggestion to the RINA two years ago that the increase in mean wave heights in the north Atlantic might be due to the increased frequency of storms. Waves did not die down fully in the interval so that new storms had a rough initial surface to aid the transfer of wind energy into the waves. Did the author support this theory? Was there evidence of a global increase in wave energy or were we seeing a redistribution of energy? For example, the paper mentioned less energy in the north Pacific when the Atlantic waves were severe.

The author showed a graph supporting the increase in frequency of winter storms in the north Atlantic. This increase might be due to different recording systems over the years. Until there was more data available he did not feel able to comment on total energy content globally. He would not expect it to increase even with global warming. He was unaware of any research into the effect of global warming on global wave climate. A group, WASA (WAves and Storms in the North Atlantic), was studying the effect of doubling the atmospheric CO_2 on the wave climate in the north Atlantic. It was led by Professor Hans Von Storch of the Max Planck Institut fur Meteorologie, Hamburg, Ref. 15.

The author explained why there were difficulties in determining extreme wave height by satellites. To generate extreme value predictions (of wind speed or significant wave height) from altimeter data their practice had been to assume some particular form of probability distribution function, fit the available data to this form, and then extrapolate to find the required value. It was clear that if these values were to be reliable, then algorithms had to be applicable, and calibrations accurate right into the tails of the distribution functions. In order to generate true occurrence statistics, it was also important that the altimeter sampled all ranges of wind speed or wave height with an equal reliability.

Because of the transient nature of intense weather systems, high quality data of any kind was difficult to come by. Satellite data were no different in this regard. Unfortunately, on the rare occasions when a satellite altimeter track did pass close to the centre of an intense weather system, the radar signal often suffered heavy attenuation due to the high water content of the atmosphere and so became degraded, leading to unreliable data. Thus not only did they have an undersampled range of wind and wave data (for the purposes of their statistics) but they suffered from a lack of reliable co-located altimeter and in-situ data with which to test algorithms and generate calibrations.

To extend the results from the tested region, it was currently simply assumed that they could linearly interpolate from the lower values. However, if these untested calibrations were inaccurate at high values then this could well have a significant affect on climatological means and predicted extreme values.

A design of ship intended to extract energy from waves was mentioned and there was a discussion of the reasons for steep waves off the south east coast of Africa. These were a combination of winds, currents and topography. Some results of studies had been published. It was important to manoeuvre the ship appropriately in these conditions. Refs. 16, 17, and 18 related to abnormal seas off South East Africa.

Mr P Caridis (Athens) queried the differences between the wave heights in the north Atlantic and Pacific since climatic differences were not that great. The author could not explain this but research was underway. He confirmed that there was no evidence of a global increase in significant wave height. Increases in one area were compensated by reductions in others. He confirmed that altimeters could not provide profiles of individual waves as measurements were averaged over the 7 to 10 kilometre footprint.

REFERENCES

15. The WASA Project: 'Changing Storm and Wave Climate in the North East Atlantic and Adjacent Seas?', WASA Group, 1995, Proceedings of the Fourth International Workshop on Wave Hindcasting, Banff, Canada, October 16-20, 1995, 31-44

16. GRUNDLINGH, M L, 1994: 'Evidence of surface wave enhancement in the southwest Indian Ocean from satellite altimetry'. Journal of Geophysical Research, 99(C4), 7917-1927.

17. SHILLINGTON, F A and SCHUMANN, E H 1993: 'High waves in the Agulhas Current'. Mariners Weather Log, 37(4), 24-28.

18. TORRANCE, J D 1995: 'Some aspects of the South African coastal low and its rogue waves'. Weather, 50(5), 163-170, 1995.

PAPER 4

WAVE PROFILES ASSOCIATED WITH EXTREME LOADING IN RANDOM WAVES

Presented by Dr K Drake, University College London, UK

The Chairman felt that differences in horizontal asymmetry were less important for green seas loading than those in vertical asymmetry. The author agreed with this view. The Chairman also drew attention to the work of Klaus of Berlin on irregular waves and that of Buckley in defining the wave profiles in Hurricane Camille.

Mr W Buckley asked, in relation to the 14m significant wave height, what was the modal period and the JONSWAP shape enhancement factor? The author said in a written reply that the JONSWAP spectrum was computed using a peak-shape parameter of 3.3 (ie The mean JONSWAP spectrum). The period corresponding to the peak of the spectral density function was 13.5 seconds. Referring to earlier work, Mr Buckley said that whilst showing flattening of the trough and enhancement of peaks a second order mathematical approach gave unrealistically steep wave fronts. How would the author allow for breaking waves? The steep waves shown would break over the forecastle causing large whipping stresses. It would be unwise to ignore these. The author accepted that the second order approach was not the end of the story.

Mr J Millar (HSE) said that he had responsibility for assessing safety cases. What did the author mean by "using the latest guidance on green seas loading"? The author said he was not referring to the regulatory framework (eg HSE guidelines) but to the latest published papers. The Chairman suggested it was too early to draw up firm proposals. Mr Millar pointed out that there was a Joint Industry Project working on this topic.

Mr T Haug (DNV) said that the shape of waves was very important in establishing wave loading at the fore end. This was a very non-linear phenomenon without a practical means of evaluation. There was some feedback from sea. DNV had issued preliminary rules. More work was needed in this area.

Mr H Rathje (Germanischer Lloyd) said that the geometry of the hull forward was very important in assessing wave loading. Paper 17 dealt with bow flare. The author said he had not attempted to get ship loading, only the appropriate wave form to use in ship design.

PAPER 5

DEMAND AGAINST CAPABILITY - BREAKING WAVES AGAINST SHIP DESIGN AND OPERATION

Presented by E Dahle, Det Norske Veritas, Norway

The Chairman welcomed the excellent Norwegian contribution to ship safety.

Dr K Spyrou (UCL) queried the use of a breaking wave for defining the demand since ships could capsize in other than breaking waves. Why was the theory based on a stationary ship? How could we match demand and capability? On the last point the author emphasised that we had to accept some risks and not alter designs in response to every accident unless that alteration was justified. He did not find the ALARP concept meaningful. He agreed that breaking waves were not needed to cause capsize but he had used such a wave to test models, associated with the probability of meeting such a wave.

Mr A Bain (MoD) said that the MoD was developing design guidance for warships on conditions in which the ship was safe to operate rather than simply laying down arbitrary rules. Had the author a view on the reduction in accident rates if his proposed method were used? The author said fishing vessels did not operate in conditions in which they could not use their fishing gear. They needed to establish the conditions under which such waves were likely to be met so that the ship could run to port. Buoys which were needed as satellites could not provide the data on steepness.

SESSION III - SHIP DYNAMICS AND DESIGN

In the Chair: A W Gilfillan,
                  YARD Ltd.

PAPER 6

CRITICAL SURVIVAL CONDITIONS FOR SHIP DESIGN

Presented by Professor D Faulkner, UK

Mr D. Hulse (Met Office) said that the Met Office made a lot of data available commercially to the offshore industry but very few approaches were received from ship designers. He suspected that cost was a factor.

Mr D Cotton (SOC) queried the reliability of data for the southern hemisphere in deriving the climatic operability criteria.

Mr Buckley was confident of the envelope in diagram (5). It agreed well with Dr Hogben's data and the Pierson-Moskowitz spectra. Data had only become available in the last 10 years. Dr Hogben gave data for the area between southern Australia and the Cape of Good Hope.

Mr P Cotton (SOC) said we lacked long term series data in the southern hemisphere.

The Chairman referred to para 4.2 of the paper. What could the designer do now without additional research? The author said his aim had only been to guide discussion. Personally he would like to see a more refined time domain analysis for longitudinal strength, than that used for DERBYSHIRE. Paper 4 of this conference should help. Water impact studies were very important.

Written Contribution

Mr R V Turner (FRINA, FIESIS): This paper (and some others) in the proceedings of the Conference contains the implication that ship designers should take into account with large ships the possibility that waves of up to 100 ft in height may be experienced along weather decks under abnormally severe conditions (see Fig. 2). Examples of the damage done to the wheelhouse of the QUEEN ELIZABETH and the bridge front of the MICHAELANGELO in the North Atlantic are certainly grim reminders of the types of structural failure which can result from the action of the sea. However to suppose that entire waves could reach those sites without the ship being totally overwhelmed seems to be unrealistic and another more logical mechanism for the damages must be sought.

It is well known in breakwater design that very large amounts of seawater can be thrown high into the air by breaking waves impacting on the fixed structures. The damage caused by these masses of seawater descending from 70m or so is also well documented. If at sea a ship is so large that it can act for a time virtually as a solid object there would appear to be every reason to expect that similar excursions upwards will occur but with the added complications arising from the forward motion of the ship and the possible acceleration in the horizontal plane of the flying water by the pressure of the wind. Very high relative speeds can be expected especially at a great height above the mean waterline and it is in the writer's opinion that the damages referred to were caused by the impact of such flying masses of water, not solid waves.

If this hypothesis is correct then while ship designers must take note of the pressures resulting from such a phenomenon they should not normally be expected to postulate that their ships will meet walls of water at the wheelhouse level having all the characteristics of solid waves. Obviously with large ships of low freeboard and without fo'c's'les there is every possibility that solid waves will sweep over the bows and extend aft with a great depth of water on deck but that is not the same as saying that such waves can reach virtually intact the heights indicated in Fig. 2. The damage to the crow's nest of the ATHENE was almost certainly caused by a flying mass of water, not a solid wave which would have taken the foremast overboard, not just smashed the windows in.

This is not to say that in settling the main scantlings of large ships, designers should be encouraged to ignore the existence of exceptionally high waves which, among other evidence presented at this Conference, have been reliably measured from platforms, but their acceptance that such waves will occur is likely to be more readily obtained if exaggerated examples are avoided.

PAPER 7

BEHAVIOUR OF SHIPS IN SEVERE ASTERN SEAS

Presented by M Tsangaris, University of Strathclyde

Mr Van Wijnen (Confederation of European Shipmasters Association) said that we must avoid capsize. We needed good, well behaved, ships with good masters and crew, particularly for abnormal conditions. Recently crew standards had gone down steeply and the Dutch were trying to set realistic standards. Ship's staff and naval architects had to co-operate to avoid disasters.

Mr T Dahle (DNV) noted that the video showed waves accelerating the ship. He asked if we could avoid broaching and capsize by reducing initial speed? The author said the master sometimes had limited ability to control speed and heading.

Dr K Spyrou (UCL) suggested that reducing speed below a Froude Number of 0.3 could help avoid broaching but could bring other problems.

Professor D Faulkner (UK) pointed out that most talk of capsize was in stern seas. Was there evidence for capsize in other conditions? It was difficult to visualise in head seas but beam seas which were non-linear would appear possible candidates. The author agreed that beam seas were important for capsize. He said that he had also seen cases quoted of capsize in head seas.

Mr Van Wijnen (CESA) said that changing speed or heading could help and a master might decide to take way off and wait for conditions to moderate. The Chairman reminded the delegates of the GAUL. It was last seen running with the wind and the waves and possibly was lost when turning or in stern seas.

Mr E Haig mentioned the use of a heavy hawser trailed aft by sailing ships to reduce the risk of broaching. Had this been investigated? The answer was "No".

Mr H Osborn (WDC), as a dinghy sailor, said it helped to have a grip on the water provided by a centre board.

Mr W Buckley (USA) said drogues were available commercially.

Dr E A Dahle (DNV) said a rope was good advice for sailing ships but it might foul the propellers. GAUL had a large superstructure which could ice up and some of its openings had been open. Norway had special requirements for fishing vessels which were intended to operate in these very severe conditions.

PAPER 8

ON THE NONLINEAR DYNAMICS OF BROACHING-TO

Presented by Dr K J Spyrou, University College, London, UK

In clarifying points for **Professor D Faulkner** (UK), the author said the test fisheries tank used was near Tokyo, and the standards were for both designer and operator. The paper showed many instances of broaching at speeds lower than Froude Number 0.3, which was generally accepted as safe. The author said that the waves in these cases were much higher than those usually assumed.

Dr K Drake (UCL) asked what was the influence of random waves on the results. The author said the type of randomness would need to be specified and could be incorporated into the analysis, but he could not say what the result would be.

Mr T Dahle (DNV) asked if the water particle motions around the rudder were allowed for and could the characteristics of the autopilot used be varied? Was automatic steering best to avoid broaching? The author said that the wave particle motions, although significant in practice in quantitative analyses, were not important for this paper's qualitative analysis and he could afford to neglect them. The ship could be in manual or auto control. The latter was used in analysis to eliminate the human factor. In his experience a ship would usually be in manual control for severe conditions.

The author said that putting guidance to operators in simple terms was his next challenge.

PAPER 9

CRITICAL CAPSIZING CONDITIONS IN SURVIVABILITY SEAWAYS

Presented by W Buckley, Consultant, USA.

Dr K Spyrou (UCL) drew attention to extensive experiments in Japan over the last 10 years. Also, he said, much research had been done at the fundamental level on broaching and capsize. He asked how this knowledge could be built into the author's work? It was said masters should select an optimal heading to minimise risk of capsize. How could he do this? The author said that it was vital to be able to control heading but he was unaware of any international requirement for

ships to have directional control in extreme seas. We needed to look at steep waves in model testing. The main factors in capsize were: how far was the ship from dead down seas, and, if it was caught off part way, how much directional control was there to get the ship back on course? If the ship was caught beam on in steep waves with crest amidships, capsize was possible.

Mr T Haug (DNV) asked if model test results had been compared with analytical data? Viscous damping was very non-linear and he wondered if there would be a significant change in the vessel's behaviour if damping was different? The author was unaware of data he could use to make comparisons. A challenge for the software was to be able to account for the actual stability of the ship at any instant with the crest amidships in a very steep wave.

Written Discussion

Mr R V Turner, (FRINA, FIESIS): In the first paragraph on Page 3 of the paper there is an implication from the SL-7 experiments that twin rudders located in the propeller races would have been preferable to a centreline rudder in controlling broaching-to. However there is evidence from destroyer experience with twin rudders that when a ship is heeled over, the rudder on the high side loses lift due to air-drawing or emergence, and that the consequent reduction in restoring force leads to excessive yaw, inducing an inflow angle to the submerged rudder angle beyond the stall point, with almost complete loss of directional control.

It would thus seem to be important in any future research programme to explore the possibility that twin rudders may be ineffective in those extreme conditions where the main engine controls may have to be set to reduce power so as to avoid `surfing'. Under such conditions, far from aiding the action of the rudders, the propellers may be blocking the flow into the rudders and destroying their lift in a manner known to occur in single-screw ships with single rudders, particularly with controllable pitch propellers where a zero power order may send the blades to zero pitch. With so many ferries and cruise liners having large superstructures carried well aft, and of necessity due to the restricted draught having twin rudders, it would seem important that studies into this combination should be given high priority for any services where very severe conditions may be experienced.

The lack of directional stability reported from the SL-7 experiments is in marked contrast to the writer's experience with numerous large liners having similar types of semi-balanced single rudder, many of which had a high reputation world-wide for good manoeuvrability and directional stability under all conditions. On the assumption that the area of the SL-7 rudder was in accordance with good practice for such a large fast ship, it would appear that the anomalous results of the

SL-7 experiments may have arisen from the cross-coupling of heeling and yaw motions initiated by the extremely small levels of stability in the upright condition, illustrated by the excessive angles of heel and very long periods of roll of the model evident from the video. These low experimental GM values may have been acceptable in terms of the minima under the Load Line rules, but such small values would in practice lead to excessive angles of heel under beam winds or rudder action in a turn and while the experiments themselves are of great interest in demonstrating what might happen under abnormal combinations of low stability and high sea states, they cannot be regarded as realistic under prudent operations at sea, or provide a reliable guidance for use in new designs.

GENERAL DISCUSSION ON DAY ONE PAPERS

Mr T Haug (DNV) said that rules had been developed over many years based on experimental and full scale data. Now offshore we had units intended to stay on station for say 20 years without docking. The consequences of failure were great and the rules were stricter. DNV had a lot of data comparing bending moments measured in tankers with the traditional calculations. Their new rules were based on the 100 year wave. A FPSO could be meeting head seas continuously which was a harsh condition to have to meet. There could be a 20 to 60% increase in wave bending moment, based on linear theory with corrections for non-linearities.

Mr W Buckley (USA) in referring to the amidships bending moment, pointed out that the Webb Institute had carried out a study of an old dry cargo ship looking at the main hull girder in light and deep conditions. Still water bending moment and slamming loads were higher for the light ship with peak stress in light condition two and a half times that of the deep.

Dr E A Dahle (DNV) said captains were keen to maintain schedule. Did the author believe they should be allowed to do this if it caused risk by going into areas of extreme waves? Should we not set out acceptable routes and should not the ships be monitored?

Professor D Faulkner (UK) supported this but said there were pressures on masters. Masters and naval architects did sometimes err.

Mr W Buckley said that some masters tried to avoid the worst conditions.

Dr E A Dahle noted that there were there still 29 cases last year of structural damage incurred off south east Africa?

Professor D Faulkner suggested masters were very variable in their actions. Most were good.

Mr H Osborn ((WDC) showed vu-graphs of how waves built up against breakwaters. Civil engineers used stones at the base to reduce reflections. In dredgers reverse flare on the bulwark reduced the amount of water on deck. He suggested that a cutwater running from the bulbous bow aft might be useful. The Chairman said that a design from Vosper Thorneycroft used a reverse bow. This was for stealth but it would be interesting to see how this type of bow affected seakeeping.

SESSION IV - DESIGN OF OFFSHORE STRUCTURES

In the Chair: Mr E C Tupper, RINA

PAPER 10

SOME CURRENT PRACTICES AND REQUIREMENTS FOR EXTREME CONDITIONS FOR FIXED AND FLOATING PLATFORMS

Presented by S. Smith, Amerada Hess Ltd, UK

The Chairman noted the similarities and differences between problems facing the offshore engineer and ship designer. Each could learn from the other. He congratulated the offshore industry on their feedback and design improvements as a result.

Mr J A Sadden (Yarrows) said that a table for the hazard analysis for FPSOs would be interesting. They had a lot of top hamper which must affect stability and susceptibility to winds. The author said that the hazards for a FPSO were similar to those given in the paper. With topside equipment weighing 5,000 to 7,000 tonnes stability required study and could result in restrictions on the loading regimes.

Mr D Brown (Consultant) said 20 years was a long docking interval when loading/discharging cycles were likely to cause fatigue. The author said there were annual inspections. Cracks had been found and repaired with the experience fed back to new designs. Extra effort went into cathodic protection and coatings. Ten years experience with the semi-submersible shown gave confidence in the acceptability of long docking periods.

Mr D Hulse (Met Office) asked how these vessels responded to small amplitude waves of long period? The author did not think this would be a problem.

Professor D Faulkner (UK) Referred to equation 1. Comparing with ISSC limits the square root on the left hand side would be about 4 and 6 on the right. The left was of most interest as for extreme conditions it was the shorter waves which were of interest for shear loading forward, rolling, etc.

Dr E A Dahle (DNV) asked about drilling in extreme conditions. Normally one decouples and this could link in with dynamic positioning. The author said there were DP rigs although there were some concerns about reliability in operational terms of such systems in drifting off and then returning to station. He expected more such systems in future with more fail safe features.

PAPER 11

EMERALD FIELD FSU LONGITUDINAL STRENGTH ASSESSMENT

Presented by C A Singer, Midland and Scottish Resources, UK

Mr T Haug (DNV) noted that the ship in the paper had been shortened by 25 metres. This would make the scantlings stronger than required by standard bending moment calculation. This was one way of allowing an existing tanker to be used in these more onerous conditions. Fatigue induced by longitudinal stress should be greater than in a conventional tanker, but apparently most cracks were in the vicinity of the neutral axis. The author confirmed that they had been, that was 3 to 4 metres above the waterline. Mr Haug said this tallied with DNV experience.

Professor D Faulkner (UK) found some of the data confusing and submitted a written contribution:

Written Contribution

This is potentially one of the most important papers at this conference, but I regret that it is far from convincing. Moreover, it is spoiled by mixing mass and force units, by having results which appear to make no sense, and by its uncritical acceptance of the results. It does not reflect well on those involved, but we should all strive to improve and I offer my thoughts.

First, let me attempt to establish basic minimum requirements as specified in the IACS longitudinal strength standard (J. Mar.Str. Vol. 5, No. 1, 1992, pp 1-21). Assuming a block coefficient $C_b = 0.84$ for the vessel, as described in Section 2.1 and shortened by 25m we find:

$$\left. \begin{array}{l} \text{sagging } M_w = 7{,}209\text{MNm} \\ \text{hogging } M_w = 6{,}792\text{MNm} \end{array} \right\} \qquad \text{Eq (1)}$$

section modulus $W_{min} = 65.5\text{m}^3$ Eq (3) or (4)

And yet, from Tables 2.5.3 and 2.5.4 of the paper one deduces that the section modulus is only about 56.2m^3 which is only 86% of the minimum required for a trading tanker (reqt. 57). This hardly gives one confidence.

Conditions 1 and 2 are not specifically defined. I imagine condition 1 is for the case when the still water load causes the maximum still water bending moment. It is then difficult to understand why for monotonically increasing return periods and wave severities, condition 2 in Tables 2.5.2 to 2.5.4 has higher bending moments and stresses in condition 2 for the 10 year storm than in condition 1. In contrast, the conditions load 2 values for the 1 year, 50 year and 100 year storm appear to behave as one would expect.

The last sentence in section 2.5 infers from Table 2.5.5 that the maximum combined stresses "are within allowable limits". The maximum of these stresses is $237/\text{Nmm}^2$, which is just about the yield stress of mild steel. Moreover, the Green Seas loading is not included in Table 2.5.5. Although the paper does not state the hull material, one would expect in 1974 that most of it was Grade A mild steel. Leaving aside the proneness to buckling (see Section 2.6) all this would appear to be quite unacceptable even if one believed the wave induced bending moments. It should also be noted that the IACS unified standard, which I referred to earlier, in effect sets a limit on weather induced stresses of 110N/mm^2 irrespective of material.

Therein lies the biggest worry. It is noted that linear strip theory was used for the loading and response analyses. But, extreme storms which sink ships or overturn platforms are anything but linear, nor is the wave kinematics linear. As the Faulkner-Buckley paper shows, very steep, elevated waves are common enough that it is foolish to ignore them, especially if, as seems the case here, conventional loading leads to low safety. Moreover, even the 100 year wave is very notional, as is discussed elsewhere in this conference. Reference 6 of Paper 6 suggests that wave induced bending moments in abnormal sea conditions may reach as high as twice the IACS' standard for large ships. This requires confirmation, but there can be little doubt that present methods are quite inadequate for many applications.

In Section 2.4 reference is made to the importance of residual stresses on crack propagation rates, and this is hard to follow. First, the nature of these residual stresses is not stated, but their low value, no more than 20% of yield, suggests they are likely to be compressive. It would then be difficult to understand how these can then reduce fatigue strength. Tensile yield residual stresses are present in weld metal, and HAZ material, and these are much more damaging for crack propagation.

Secondly, the relative fatigue damage for 0.25 N/mm^2 and 50 N/mm^2 are said to be shown in Figs. 3, 4 and 5 respectively. There is very little difference between Figs. 3 and 5, that is 0 and 50 N/mm^2. But at the intermediate level of 25 N/mm^2 residual stress, there is much less damage with the tank empty. Even if one could conceive damage being so dependent on such low levels of residual stress, and I frankly admit this is quite beyond me, I find this non-monotonic behaviour to be quite unbelievable.

It would be helpful if the author could clarify and perhaps defend some of these points. This would add substantial value to the paper.

Author's Written Reply

Mr C A Singer: In response to the comments raised by **Professor D Faulkner:**

In general it should be remembered that this study was limited for commercial reasons and was also cut short after the longitudinal strength assessment due to the abandonment of the field, thus the fatigue and residual life expectancy assessment was cancelled. The study was limited to the linear analysis for two load cases in the first instance to be able to make an educated judgement on the future of the vessel and any further analysis required. This became unnecessary upon abandonment. The study was deliberately conservative, as seen in J.D. Clarke's paper, 'Advances In Marine Structures', ARE, 1986, the loads calculated using linear strip theory are generally conservative and therefore the loads calculated for the Emerald Field FSU were probably high.

Regarding the point of the minimum requirements for longitudinal strength as per IACS, 1992. This standard was not applicable to the vessel as it was built in 1974 to the rules prevalent at the time. I cannot confirm or otherwise the figure stated as minimum section modulus as I do not have further access to the necessary information. However the scantlings were checked against the then applicable Lloyd's Register of Shipping Rules and Regulations and found to be within the allowable limits. It should also be noted that the section moduli used for the analysis were for the most corroded scantlings as measured using ultrasonics and not the original scantlings.

Conditions 1 and 2 were, as stated in the paper, taken from the Loadmaster test conditions and represented conditions of maximum still water shear force and bending moment. The figures in tables 2.5.2 to 2.5.5. were wrong and have been revised in the final edition of the paper.

With regard to the maximum stresses, the figure changes slightly giving a new maximum of 217 N/mm^2. The vessel was built using high tensile steel in both deck and bottom structures and grade A for the rest. According to Lloyd's rules the allowable bending stress is 254 N/mm^2 for steel with a yield strength of 355 N/mm^2. The figure of 110 N/mm^2 is for weather induced stresses only and therefore does not allow for the still

water stresses presumably. Again, this standard was not applicable at the time of the vessel construction.

The residual stresses referred to in the paper are due to the welding process. The graph depicting the relative damage assuming a residual stress of 0 N/mm^2 is possibly not very clear. The relative damage for an empty tank is 0 over the height of the tank. This is due to the modelled detail being in compression at all times. Welding residual stresses and the loading effect from the tank contents result in an initial tensile stress on which the cyclic compressive stress is superimposed. Crack growth would be caused by the tensile part of the resulting stress time history. As the residual stress can only be estimated several analyses were carried out to obtain an indication of the sensitivity to this. The maximum residual stress was calculated as 51 N/mm^2, the likelihood is that the residual stress would be considerably less and therefore the calculations were performed for the three stresses.

PAPER 12

DESIGN OF MODERN LIGHTWEIGHT WELLHEAD PLATFORMS FOR ABNORMAL CONDITIONS UNDER THE NEW SAFETY CASE REGIME

Presented by P R Fish, Tecnomare (UK) Ltd, UK

The Chairman pointed out that in the paper the top graphs in figures 1 and 3 had been transposed.

Dr K Drake (UCL) referred to the novel frame arrangement in Fig. 9 and asked how it had originated. What methodology was used in designing the joints towards the base of the jacket where loads were transferred from leg to pile? There would be substantial crushing loads. The author said that the design had been developed from the 3LT concept pioneered by Tecnomare some ten years ago. The crushing loads were dealt with directly by the 20th edition of the API design code.

Asked if the effects of redundancy on residual strength had been studied, the author said reserve strength had been studied for extreme loading. Some members were not redundant. Members were not removed progressively as this was the older approach. The present method was to establish the hazard and then apply the design loads directly. For instance it was not possible physically to strike out one of the lower braces due to impact from a falling object. The designer assessed the dent in the tube and the ability of the structure to continue to take the loads.

Dr E A Dahle (DNV) said that DNV, as others, included ship impact in the design analysis. He was pleased to see that the 1981 curves for deflection and the assumption of a 5,000 tonne supply ship, moving at

2m/s, were used. There had been changes in the design and operation of supply vessels. They were now unlikely to subject the rig to repeated pounding. An ocean going ship would strike with much greater energy than 14MJ. He asked if it was worth carrying out the studies at stepped levels of impact.

The author said that since the analysis was a non-linear one, loads were incremented from a low level. The method presented was to deal with operational impacts. An unmanned platform could be designed for lower levels. 14MJ was close to the level that such structures could absorb. Asked about the relation between the impact energy assumed and the ability of a platform to withstand seas of varying severity, the author said he could only comment on the design presented in the paper. This had a base shear load due to a 14MJ impact almost identical with that due to the 100 year design wave. The situation could be different for each rig.

PAPER 13

THE GREEN WATER HAZARD TO MOORED FLOATING OFFSHORE UNITS

Presented by D Law Yuill, YARD Ltd, UK

Mr H Osborn (WDC) noted it was assumed green water would get on the deck. Could one design the bow to prevent this? The author said that the ALBA design was based on a conventional tanker. This assumed the vessel could change heading in waves if necessary. This was a design shortcoming. About 2 years ago ALBA took a wave over the bow that carried away some equipment fitted on the forward turret. The turret itself was not damaged.

Mr E Haig (YARD) asked if measures, other than fitting a bulwark, had been considered to reduce green water loading. The author said that the ALBA design was based on reducing motions to improve habitability. This increased the risk of green water forward. Little investigation had been carried out on alternatives.

Mr H Rathje (GL) asked if, in the relative motion calculations, the disturbances to the incident wave were considered. Mr Yuill said they had not been. He agreed this was a major limitation. Flow in way of the bow was three dimensional, whereas strip theory was two dimensional, and Mr Rathje asked if these effects were important. In the experience of Germanischer Lloyd they were. Mr Yuill thought they were not so significant based on comparisons of model tests and calculations, although bow flare was important in wetness forward.

Professor D Faulkner (UK) said he would like more detail on equations used. Referring to the flat plate analysis, he doubted the pressure coefficient used was high enough. It was about 2 and his work indicated a value like 4.5. He admitted it was an area of uncertainty. Fortunately not many deck areas were critical. Vents and hatch covers were.

SESSION V - SHIP OPERATIONS

In the Chair: **Mr D Brown**
                      Consultant Naval Architect, UK

PAPER 14

AN INTEGRATED APPROACH FOR A SHIP SAFETY ESTIMATION IN ABNORMAL CONDITIONS

Presented by Dr Eng M Gerigk, Technical University of Gdansk, Poland.

Mr A Bain (MoD) said he was interested to see the development of a method similar to that being developed in MoD. Were the library of application methods and criteria adequate yet for proper application of safety analysis? Dr Gerigk said the library of application methods covered stability, survivability, resistance, propulsion, seakeeping and manoeuvrability. Two methods were used in stability - cross curves and constant displacement. The second method was much faster and required less approximations. Deterministic and probabilistic methods were applied for survivability. IMO criteria were used. He used model tests for resistance. Manoeuvrability allowed for wind, current and wave impact. Coefficients could be used from model test, full scale or calculation.

Mr J. Edvardsson (Karlskronavarvet AB) queried the 1st, 2nd and 3rd level factors which may secure a ship at sea. The author said he had created the different levels because of the many inter-relationships that existed between the factors.

PAPER 15

ON THE USE OF FORMAL SAFETY ASSESSMENT WHEN ANALYSING THE RISK OF CARGO SHIFT IN ROUGH SEAS

Presented by J. Persson & A. Ericson, Royal Institute of Technology KTH, Sweden.

Mr H. Rathje (GL) doubted whether the strip method gave valid motion amplitudes as it neglected viscous effects. One method was to introduce non-linear damping coefficients into the equations. The authors agreed with this but pointed out that this was only a preliminary study. The models would be improved.

In response to a query the authors confirmed that in para 4.2.5 of the paper the radius of gyration for roll should be 0.35(breadth).

Dr M Gerigk (Poland) asked if liquid cargoes had been considered. In reply the authors said only unit cargoes, no bulk or liquid.

Dr K Spyrou (UCL) suggested that in studying roll, the shifting of cargo could usefully be taken into account. It would involve non-linearities.

SESSION VI - LOADING AND STRUCTURES

In the Chair: **Mr J A Sadden**
Yarrow Shipbuilders Ltd, UK.

PAPER 16

ELASTIC/VISCOPLASTIC RESPONSE OF HULL PLATING SUBJECTED TO ABNORMAL IMPACT LOADS

Presented by Dr P A Caradis, National Technical University of Athens, Greece.

The Chairman said that if we were to design structures to withstand the extremes of the elements, we must mobilise the full strength of the structure. With reference to Fig. 14 he asked for an explanation of what is happening at step 5 which shows a decrease in strain but a large increase in deflection. The author said the figures were possibly misleading. Measurements were not for the same point in the plate. The program selected the highest strain irrespective of position whereas deflections were at the centre of the plate. The large deflection change might be due the formation of a plastic hinge.

Professor D Faulkner (UK) said it was important, particularly for collisions, to validate any computer codes against model data and against each other. Variations between codes, even between standard finite element analyses, were considerable. For implosion damage in DERBYSHIRE he had looked at the criteria for plate element rupture. He found a defection of one eighth of the breadth between supporting longitudinal stiffeners was the critical one.

Mr E C Tupper (RINA) asked whether, bearing in mind we were dealing with extreme loading, initial deformation of the plate was likely to be significant. The author said that initial deformation would introduce

membrane stresses from the outset.   The study assumed a perfectly flat, uniform thickness, plate.

PAPER 17

ENHANCEMENT OF WAVE INDUCED LOAD EFFECTS FOR SHIPS IN ABNORMAL CONDITIONS

Presented by H. Rathje, Germanischer Lloyd, Germany.

The Chairman said there had been much debate within the UK on the adequacies of linear dynamics methods for calculating bending moments.   This paper showed they were not adequate. Large departures were shown for extreme wave heights.

Mr D L Yuill (YARD) asked why over 5,000 elements had been used in the FEM, and what was the effect of ignoring forward speed. He understood that including speed could make a big difference especially when talking about speeds of 25 knots. Mr Rathje said that the number of elements was to enable pressure distributions or relative motions to be deduced. Less elements could be accepted for global motions or bending moments. Ahead speed had been neglected to make the computational task manageable.   One frequency could take two days computation.   Speed was allowed for in the frequency shift as in strip theory. To get accurate results speed needed to be allowed for in higher speed ships and in twin hulled ships.

Professor D Faulkner (UK) asked if the bending moments obtained for higher waves had been compared with the IACS standard. The author said that he had not done this as this was not the design case. He confirmed that the units for Tables 4 and 5 of the paper were the same as those in Table 3.

The Chairman said he had long been aware that in slender ships there was a difference between hogging and sagging loads with sagging being higher than hogging. He had always thought that sagging moments would increase linearly and hogging at less than that. The present paper showed sagging growing more rapidly than linearly. He asked if calculations had been done for speeds other than 23 knots.   Was this a function of speed? Had model tests been conducted? The author replied that he had not considered other speeds. Model tests were to be carried out later.

GENERAL DISCUSSION ON DAY TWO PAPERS

Mr Vossnack (CERN Institute) gave an interesting presentation of conditions under which broaching might be expected in small ships including fishing vessels and lifeboats.

The Chairman read out a contribution to Paper 6 from **Mr Klaus of Berlin**. It was considered inevitable that to establish reliable wave loads, model tests were needed using tailored wave packets representing the most unfavourable superposition of all component waves. This would give similar maximum to significant wave height ratio and crest to wave height ratios close to those assumed in the paper.

Mr E Haig (YARD) remarked that the integrity of power systems was an important element in safety case analysis.

Professor D Faulkner (UK) said the 50/100 year wave should not be considered abnormal in design. It was important to allow for interaction between storms. There was a need to model what happened in shorter steeper seas. He was still concerned at differences between different codes. In 1992, when IACS finalised their code, the loading assumed was evaluated by some ten classification societies with the result that widely different bending moments and shear forces were obtained. Designers needed help in identifying critical conditions.

Mr S Smith (Amerada Hess), referring to collision damage, pointed out that the 14MJ figure was a case of prescription sitting within a goal orientated procedure.

In operations, action was taken to warn off approaching ships by stand-by vessels. Drifting vessels would be diverted if possible. If this could not be done the rig crew would be evacuated. The rigs were certainly very visible. If losses of bulk carriers were regarded as unacceptable the use of safety case analysis in design should help reduce losses.

Mr H Osborn (WDC) asked whether offshore structures could not be fendered against collision to absorb energy of collisions.

The Chairman noted that the MoD was now using the safety case approach. Had this led to any new design insights?

Mr A Bain (MoD) said that it had, particularly in relation to unusual conditions not covered by standard requirements.

Mr W Buckley, commenting on Paper 12, emphasised that the most severe wave conditions could result from the interaction of two or more storms. He mentioned that total forces on a column could be three times greater in a breaking wave than in a higher non-breaking wave. Hence we should be considering high breaking waves.

NAMES AND ADDRESSES OF AUTHORS

Mr A Gilfillan
YARD Ltd
1 Atlantic Quay
Broomielaw
Glasgow   G2 8JE

Fax: +44 141 221 8086

Mr D Brown
Consultant Naval Architect
'Glendale', Lochview Avenue
Gourock   PA19 1XN

Fax: +44 1475 635120

Dr D Cotton
Southampton Oceanography Centre
Empress Dock
Southampton   SO14 3ZH

Fax: +44 1703 596400

Dr K R Drake
University College London
Department of Mechanical
Engineering
Torrington Place
London WC1E 7JE

Mr E Aall Dahle
Det Norske Veritas AS
Veritasveien 1
N-1322 Høvik
NORWAY

Fax: +47 67 57 7474

Prof D Faulkner
4 Murdoch Drive
Fairways
Milngavie
Glasgow   G62 6QZ

Fax:+44 141 956 5071

Mr M Tsangiras
University of Strathclyde
Ship Stability Research Centre
8th floor, Colville Building
48 North Portland Street
Glasgow   G1 1XM

Fax: +44 141 548 4784

Dr K J Spyrou
Centre for Nonlinear Dynamics
Gower Street
London WC1E 6BT

Fax: +44 171 380 0986

William H Buckley
15308 Emory Lane
Rockville, MD 20853
USA

Fax: +1 301 929 9417

Mr S N Smith
Amerada Hess Ltd
Scott House
Hareness Road
Altens
Aberdeen   AB1 4LE

Fax: +44 1224 243 285

Mr A Singer
Midland and Scottish Resources PLC
Suite E, Stoneywood Office Complex
Stoneywood Park North
Dyce
Aberdeen   AB21 7EA

Fax: +44 1224 723300

Mr P R Fish
Tecnomare (UK) Ltd
Enichem House
111 Upper Richmond Road
Putney
London SW15 2TJ

Fax: +44 181 789 0017

Mr D Law-Yuill
YARD Ltd
1 Atlantic Quay
Broomielaw
Glasgow   G2 8JE

Fax: +44 141 221 6435

Mr P B Zahn
Advanced Marine Enterprises Inc
1725 Jefferson Davis Highway, Suite
1300
Arlington
Virginia 22202
USA

Fax: +1 703 413 9221

Dr Eng M Gerigk
Technial University of Gdansk
Narutowizcu Str 11/12
80-952 Gdansk
POLAND

Fax: +00 48 58 472 368

Prof O Rutgersson
Royal Institute of Technology
Osquars Backe 33
S-100 44 Stockholm
SWEDEN

Fax: +46 8 790 6684

Dr P A Caridis
National Technical University of
Athens
Dept of Naval Architecture & Marine
Engineering
9 Heroon Polytechniou Str
GR-157 73 Zografos
GREECE

Fax: +30 1 77 21 412

Mr H Rathje
Germanischer Lloyd
Vorsetzen 32
20459 Hamburg
GERMANY

Fax: +49 40 36 1492 00